MODERN ELECTRONICS

A Practical Guide for Scientists and Engineers

HENDRIK DE WAARD

Department of Physics, University of Groningen

DAVID LAZARUS

Department of Physics, University of Illinois

ADDISON-WESLEY PUBLISHING COMPANY

READING, MASSACHUSETTS · PALO ALTO · LONDON · DON MILLS, ONTARIO

621.38
W 111

This book is in the **Addison-Wesley Series in Physics**

PREFACE

Electronics can be many things to many people. It is a field of fundamental research in itself, replete with esoteric symbolism and profound concepts for a dedicated research scientist. It is a lifetime of creative technological development for the professional engineer, and a joyful and consuming hobby for the self-trained amateur. To the public, it is a marvelous and infinitely mysterious conglomeration of multicolored gadgets, wires, flashing lights, and glowing tubes that magically produce music and pictures from "nothing," compute faster than 100,000 mathematicians, or guide an airplane through the sky.

But to the professional physicist, engineer, chemist, or biologist who has never bothered to learn about electronics but who must rely on a large number of sophisticated circuits to conduct his research, electronics is a constant frustration.

This book is intended for use in a first course in electronics for advanced undergraduate students in science and engineering or for scientists whose prior formal training in electronics was minimal or lacking. It is presumed only that the reader is already familiar with elementary physics and with the behavior of simple passive dc- and ac-circuits.

The primary aim of this book is to give the reader an understanding of those basic electronic circuits into which even the most complicated electronic systems can be broken down. In large part, the operation of the basic circuits can be analyzed in terms of amplification, rectification, and feedback. A modest understanding of the physics of amplifying and rectifying circuit elements, like electron tubes and semiconductor devices, in addition to some knowledge of the ways in which they may be combined in circuits, offers an elementary insight into the operation of more complicated circuits.

Emphasis is on basic principles and limitations rather than on encyclopedic compilation of circuit variations. Thus, we have omitted many interesting and important topics like communication circuits, television circuits, and microwave components.

Rectifiers and amplifiers are never ideal, and the limitations on the utility of electronic circuits are inevitably traceable to nonideality in the behavior of the components. As we shall subsequently see, ideal behavior can be approximated only at the price of circuit complexity.

The inherent nonideality of electronic circuits, while it complicates the life of the scientist concerned with understanding basic properties of solids, actually simplifies the work of the technical person whose main concern is the use of practical circuits. The powerful network theorems, which are the pride of the professional engineer, are often too good for circuits that have some components whose behavior cannot be

iii

precisely specified in advance. It is like killing a gnat with an elephant gun. For electronic circuits, where the characteristics of the tubes and semiconductor devices are always subject to considerable *a priori* uncertainties, usually of ten or twenty percent or more, the mathematics needed to calculate the circuit response in advance often can be simplified enormously. Expressions accurate to five or ten percent usually suffice. If we want to know how the circuit will *really* behave, we must build it and find out. It may be tempting to the mathematically inclined to derive more-or-less complete differential equations for a circuit, and solve these, taking recourse, if necessary, to computers of great complexity. One should not forget, however, that by far the best computer available for this particular purpose is the circuit itself—and usually this takes less time to build and test than to program a computer to simulate the circuit behavior. So, happily, proficiency in electronics requires only simple mathematical skill. Most of what we want to do takes only a few straightforward calculations, plus a well-developed intuition.

Proficiency in electronics requires laboratory experience to supplement any formal text—the subject is as much tactile as intellectual. We specify no "optimal" set of experiments for use with the present text, for there is none. This depends on local variable interests, facilities, and budgets. Many of the circuits described are *real* circuits, employing realistic values for the components, and may be readily used as a basis for a coherent set of laboratory exercises. Quantitative study of the response of these circuits and of the effects of variation in the circuit parameters can provide essential practical experience.

Above all, this book is intended as a *practical* guide to the essentials of contemporary electronic circuit design. Both tube and semiconductor circuits are discussed with about equal emphasis, since this reflects existing technology. Similarly, the practical limitations of the basic circuits are also stressed, those limitations arising from the circuit configuration and from the nature of the active components. The problems have been selected with practical applications in mind and frequently suggest extrapolations from the basic circuits to other uses as well as practice in manipulation of the equations derived in the text.

In the modern research environment, a working knowledge of electronic circuits has become nearly as indispensable as a working knowledge of mathematics, even for the individual who never actually designs or constructs a circuit himself. He must understand his own equipment and its practical limitations, and must frequently provide or specify emergency servicing to avoid extensive delays in his experimental program. We earnestly hope that this book will provide the necessary background for all who require more than a superficial knowledge of modern electronics.

Groningen, The Netherlands   H. de W.
Urbana, Illinois   D.L.
March 1966

CONTENTS

Chapter 1

ELECTRONS AND ELECTRONICS

1.1 ELECTRONS IN CIRCUITS

In studying electronics, we are concerned chiefly with the motion of charges in circuits and with the response of different circuit elements to various electrical driving forces. In our study, the circuit elements are made of ordinary matter—solids, liquids, and gases—and the charged particles which move about under the action of electric and magnetic fields are most commonly electrons, but in a few devices we must concern ourselves with ions also.

The reader has probably learned long before this how charges move in a vacuum under the influence of fields. Of course, all of this is very important, but it does not suffice for understanding the behavior of circuits. The reason for this is that only a very small part of a circuit is much of a vacuum, generally only the spaces between electrodes in a vacuum tube, and even that is sometimes not a very good vacuum. In our circuits, the charged particles are seldom free but are confined to the inside of pieces of matter, where their detailed motion results not only from the external fields we apply but also from strong fields present inside the material. The exact paths followed by moving charges are therefore quite complex but, fortunately, are not of immediate interest. We need be concerned to some extent about the basic atomistic nature of electricity, but consideration of the following more-or-less obvious facts will suffice.

1. An electric current measures the *net* flow of charge per unit time past a point in a circuit.

2. Current will flow, in the steady state, only under the action of an external applied field (except in superconductors).

3. The basic effect of an electric field is to *accelerate* a charge, thereby increasing its kinetic energy. In a closed system, this increase in kinetic energy must be accompanied by an equal decrease in energy in another part of the system, since the total energy of the system must be conserved.

To this list, which applies equally to charges moving in vacuum or inside matter, we must add the following important facts, which are particularly relevant to the consideration of motion of charges within matter.

1

4. A moving charge interacts with its surroundings through its associated electric and magnetic fields.

5. Motion of charges obeys the laws of quantum mechanics; specifically, a charge can be accelerated inside a closed system only if there are electric fields *and if there are available energy states of the system corresponding to the change in motion of the charge.*

With charges in a vacuum, we are seldom concerned about points 4 and 5 since there is little for charges to interact with, and there is usually a continuum of available energy states. However, inside matter, the situation is quite different. Point 4 is related to the fact that there is always some *resistance* to the motion of charges, while point 5 gives us a hint that not all of the vast number of charges inside matter may be able to move even if there is an electric field present, since there may be no energy states available. Some knowledge of how these two additional facts apply is valuable for understanding what goes on inside real circuit elements, and we shall devote the remainder of this chapter to this subject.

1.2 A MATTER OF COUNTING

Any practical electronic circuit contains not a few moving charges but a vast number. Therefore, we are usually concerned only with the average, statistical behavior of the ensemble of charges. The moving charges are almost always electrons, which are much more alike than peas in a pod, and we shall first have to consider briefly how to go about counting the different states of a system comprised of these inherently indistinguishable elementary particles. This procedure is necessary for determining the state of minimum energy, or *ground state,* of the electrons inside a piece of material when there are no external fields applied. Electric current will flow, of course, only under the action of an external field, which can accelerate the electrons and thereby increase the energy of the system relative to the ground state.

Electrons, as well as all other elementary particles with half-integral spin, obey the *Pauli Exclusion Principle,* which requires that no two electrons in a single system can have identical values of all the quantized constants of their motion, such as the total energy and spin angular momentum. Thus, in a system of electrons there can be at most two electrons (and these must be of opposite spin) in any allowed energy state. To determine the ground-state energy of the whole system of electrons we fill the allowed energy levels one at a time, starting with the lowest level. The first two electrons will go in the lowest energy level, the next two in the second lowest, and so on, until we have added all the electrons in the material. The situation is not unlike filling a bucket with water—the first drops fall to the bottom, the next drops on top of these, and so on, until we have poured all the water into the bucket. We could logically talk about the maximum potential energy of the water at the top of the filled level relative to that at the bottom or the average energy of all the drops; similarly, in our system filled with electrons, we can consider the maximum energy of the most energetic electrons relative to those of lowest energy, or the average energy of the whole system. The only major differences are that with electrons, the energy differences are mainly in kinetic energy, rather than in gravitational potential energy, and that the energy levels are quantized, not continuous. In both cases, in finding the energy of the system, it makes no difference precisely which electrons, or which drops of water, are at any particular energy level since all the "elementary particles" are indistinguishable.

Thus, even at a temperature of absolute zero there must be a considerable spread in the energies of the electrons inside a piece of material. As the temperature is raised, the spread must, of course, increase. The actual form of this distribution is given by the *Fermi-Dirac distribution function* and, for this reason, all particles which obey the Pauli exclusion principle are called *fermions*.* Derivation of this law would take us far afield into quantum statistics, so we shall simply state the important result.† For particles which obey Fermi-Dirac statistics, the probability, $f(E)$, that a particular allowed state of energy E is occupied at an absolute temperature T is given by the function

$$f(E) = \frac{1}{\epsilon^{(E-E_F)/kT} + 1},\qquad(1.1)$$

where ϵ is the base of the system of natural logarithms, and k is Boltzmann's constant, 1.38×10^{-23} J/°K. The term E_F is generally called the *Fermi energy* of the system, and its physical meaning can be seen from a sketch of the function in Fig. 1.1. The solid line here shows that the value of f drops abruptly from

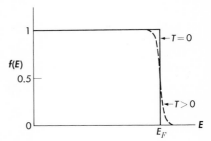

FIG. 1.1.   The Fermi-Dirac distribution function.   The solid line corresponds to absolute zero, and the dotted line to a finite temperature where $kT \ll E_F$.

---

* Just to keep the record complete, we should note that all elementary particles of zero or integral spin, such as photons, phonons, and some mesons, do not obey the Pauli exclusion principle, and hence are described by quite a different statistical distribution function, the Bose-Einstein distribution. Such particles are therefore called *bosons*. Since bosons are unconstrained by the Pauli principle, they can all reside in the same state of lowest energy at absolute zero, quite unlike fermions.

† This derivation can be found in standard texts in statistical mechanics or solid state physics, for example, C. Kittel, *Introduction to Solid State Physics*, Wiley, New York, 1953, pp. 224–228.

1 to 0 at absolute zero for $E > E_F$, so that there can be no occupied states at absolute zero of energy greater than the Fermi energy. The Fermi energy thus corresponds to the maximum energy which any particle in the system can have at absolute zero.

1.3   THE FREE-ELECTRON GAS

Many of the important electrical properties of metals can be treated by means of a simple model in which the metal is considered merely as a "gas" of free electrons contained in a box of volume equal to the actual volume of the solid. Each atom in the solid is assumed to "donate" one or more valence electrons to the gas, so that the solid as a whole remains electrically neutral. In this case, the ions themselves are assumed to play no special role in the electrical behavior of the metal. While this model has obvious deficiencies, at least it allows us to make a reasonable estimate of the value of the Fermi energy.

In an ideal gas, all of the energy of the particles is kinetic, so that the energy of any given particle is simply $E = \frac{1}{2}mv^2$. According to quantum statistical mechanics, the number of available states for a particle of momentum $p = mv$ in an interval dp is simply the volume of the spherical shell in momentum space, $4\pi p^2\, dp$, divided by the cube of Planck's constant h. With electrons, we can have two particles in each energy state if they have opposite spins, according to the Pauli exclusion principle; therefore, the number of allowed states in the interval dp at momentum p is $8\pi p^2\, dp/h^3$. Since $p^2/2m = E$, we may write for the number of allowed states with energy between E and $E + dE$,

$$g(E)\, dE = \frac{1}{2\pi^2} \left(\frac{2m}{\hbar^2}\right)^{3/2} E^{1/2}\, dE, \tag{1.2}$$

where $\hbar = h/2\pi$.

If the particles are electrons, as assumed, then in thermal equilibrium the number of electrons with energy between E and $E + dE$, $n(E)\, dE$, must be given simply by the product of Eq. (1.2) and the Fermi-Dirac distribution function (1.1):

$$n(E)\, dE = f(E)\, g(E)\, dE = \frac{1}{2\pi^2} \left(\frac{2m}{\hbar^2}\right)^{3/2} \frac{E^{1/2}\, dE}{\epsilon^{(E-E_F)/kT} + 1}. \tag{1.3}$$

If the solid contains exactly N free electrons and has a volume V, we can evaluate E_F by simply setting the integral of $n(E)\, dE$ equal to N/V. This is simplest to do at $T = 0$, since at that temperature there are no particles with energy greater than E_F. The exponential term is zero for $E < E_F$. Thus

$$\frac{N}{V} = \frac{1}{2\pi^2} \left(\frac{2m}{\hbar^2}\right)^{3/2} \int_0^{E_F} E^{1/2}\, dE = \frac{1}{3\pi^2} \left(\frac{2m}{\hbar^2}\right)^{3/2} (E_F)^{3/2}. \tag{1.4}$$

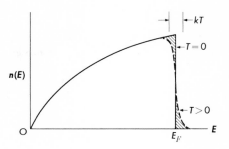

FIG. 1.2. The density of states for a free-electron gas as a function of energy. The solid line corresponds to absolute zero, and the dotted line, to a temperature $T \ll E_F/k$. Electrons of energy $E > E_F$ at $T > 0$ come from states with $E < E_F$; hence, the two shaded areas must be equal.

Then the value of the Fermi energy at absolute zero is

$$E_F = \frac{\hbar^2}{2m}\left(3\pi^2 \frac{N}{V}\right)^{2/3}. \tag{1.5}$$

If we assume that N is of the order of one electron per atom, and V is the atomic volume, so that a molar volume of the metal contains Avogadro's number of free electrons, we find that E_F is about 5 eV. The effective "temperature" of an electron at the maximum kinetic energy $E = E_F$ is

$$T_F = E_F/k \simeq 6 \times 10^4 \; {}^\circ\text{K}, \tag{1.6}$$

for $E_F = 5$ eV.

This value is important since it gives us a hint that at the temperatures at which we can use solids, generally below 2000°K, the actual energy distribution of the electrons will be only very slightly perturbed from its value at $T = 0$, as shown in Fig. 1.2. Thus, of the vast number of electrons in the solid, even at quite high temperatures, only a very tiny fraction will have energies much above the Fermi energy.

1.4 ELECTRONS IN SOLIDS; BONDS AND BANDS

Within a real solid, the electrons are not, of course, really "free" in the same sense as molecules in a gas. They interact strongly with the positive-ion cores of the parent atoms and, to a somewhat lesser extent, with one another. Therefore we can hardly expect that the previous treatment, where the basic energy distribution is assumed identical to that of a free-electron gas, as in Eqs. (1.2) and (1.3), will be exact.

The positively charged ion cores, as we know well from x-ray crystallographic studies, are actually arranged in a very regular lattice. The electrons therefore do not move "freely" in a vacuum, but in a region with a strong periodic potential. It is sometimes assumed that many of the electrons, far from being free, are localized in definite regions, called "bonds," between adjacent ion cores. These are illustrated in Fig. 1.3. Such "bond" models are extremely useful in calculating the crystal structures of different solids and the arrangements of

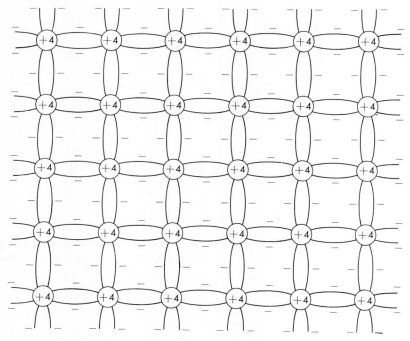

FIG. 1.3. Electron "bonds" in a tetravalent solid. Each of the four "valence" electrons is presumed to be shared with a neighboring ion in localized two-electron "bonds."

atoms in molecules. However, a model in which all the electrons are presumed to be locked into localized bonds is inconsistent with two important observations:

1. Metals are excellent electrical conductors, particularly at very low temperatures; hence, at least some of the electrons must be free to move rapidly in response to applied electric fields, and no extra energy is required to release these "conduction electrons" from bonds.

2. The actual specific heats of metals at temperatures near absolute zero are consistent with the free-electron gas model; therefore, the conduction electrons must have kinetic energies of the order of several electron volts.

Therefore, some of the electrons, the conduction electrons, cannot be localized into tiny regions of atomic dimensions but must really be free, in some sense, to move about over a range of several atoms.

The detailed calculation of the motion of partially free electrons, which interact with a not-quite-perfect lattice potential and with one another, is an exceedingly difficult problem that defies an exact solution. However, an extremely important new feature of the electron-energy distribution becomes apparent even in the simplest first-order approximation. In this model, we

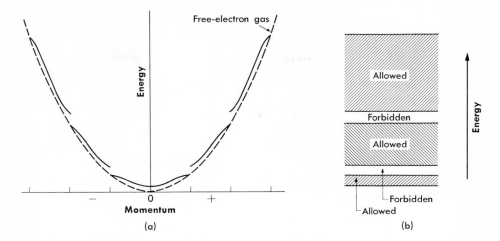

FIG. 1.4. (a) Energy-momentum relation for electrons in a solid. The dotted curve shows the relation $E = p^2/2m$ for a free-electron gas. (b) Cross section of energy states, showing allowed states separated by regions of forbidden energies.

consider that the electrons are essentially "free," as before, but their motion is also restricted by the fact that they are charged particles, which must interact with the periodic potential of the positively charged ion cores, arranged according to the crystal lattice of the solid. In the quantum-mechanical formulation, we deal with a "wave function" which describes the position of the particles. The "electron wave" interacts with the regularly spaced positive ions in a manner quite analogous to that of a light wave interacting with the regularly spaced obstacles in a diffraction grating. The "electron wave" is "diffracted" by the periodic lattice potential. When translated back into classical concepts such as the energy and momentum of the moving electron, this phenomenon leads to the following very important modifications of the results of the "free-electron gas" model, shown in Fig. 1.4.

1. The simple relationship between the momentum and kinetic energy, $E = p^2/2m$, is no longer valid for all values of the electron momentum. Certain values of the energy (corresponding to "electron wavelengths" which would be "reflected" by the "diffraction-grating" lattice) become *forbidden*. The only allowed energy states are those in certain *allowed bands*, which are in general separated by *forbidden bands*. The relative widths of the allowed bands and the forbidden bands depend on the distance between adjacent ions in the lattice, as shown in Fig. 1.5 for a simple case. In general, the allowed bands become broader and the forbidden bands narrower as the interatomic spacing decreases. As a consequence of the fact that the electrons are fermions, each allowed band must contain *exactly two energy states for each atom in the solid*.

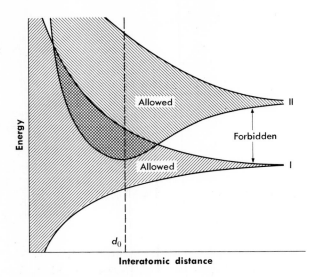

FIG. 1.5.   Relative width and spacing of allowed energy bands as a function of interatomic distance. For the case shown, the allowed bands I and II overlap at the equilibrium distance d_0.

2. In describing the motion of the electrons relative to the lattice, we must replace the actual mass m of the electrons by the *effective mass* m^*, defined by

$$m^* = (\partial^2 E/\partial p^2)^{-1}. \tag{1.7}$$

The effective mass of the electrons is therefore given by the reciprocal of the curvature of the energy-momentum function.   For the free-electron gas, $E = p^2/2m$, so that $m^* = [\partial^2(p^2/2m)/\partial p^2]^{-1} = m$ since the function has a constant curvature. For most of the electrons in the allowed bands in the periodic lattice, $m^* \approx m$, but for those near the top or bottom of the allowed bands, the curvature is larger, and the effective mass will be reduced. Moreover, for electrons which have kinetic energy *near the maximum permissible in an allowed band*, the curvature of the energy-momentum function is *negative* since it is bent toward the x-axis. Therefore, such electrons must behave as though they had a *negative mass*. What does this mean? How would an object with negative mass behave in the real world? By Newton's second law, $F = ma$, so that a positive force acting on a body of negative mass would produce a negative acceleration: if we push such a body toward the left, it would move to the right— it would fall up in a gravitational field! This analogy, absurd though it may sound, tells us what we must really mean when we talk about an electron having a negative effective mass. Under an applied electric field, an electron with a negative effective mass must move in the wrong direction; that is, it must move from plus to minus, instead of from minus to plus. Our "negative-mass" electron would thus behave as though it had a *positive charge*. To distinguish these strange negative-effective-mass electrons from ordinary positive-effective-mass electrons, we usually refer to the former as "holes," objects with a positive charge and a positive mass, while the latter are simply "electrons" with a negative charge and a positive mass.

The use of the concept of the effective mass replacing the actual electron mass does not mean that Newton's law, $F = ma$, fails for the solid. The effective mass applies only to the acceleration of electrons *relative to the lattice*. If we consider the motion of the whole solid, electrons plus lattice, and allow for momentum transfer between the accelerated electrons and the lattice, then Newton's law is perfectly valid when we use the actual masses of all the particles.

1.5   METALS, INSULATORS, AND SEMICONDUCTORS

The complications arising from the band structure of the allowed energies should become apparent only for solids which have an even number of electrons per atom (or per molecule, if the basic arrangement of the lattice is in terms of molecular units, rather than single atoms). If there is an odd number of electrons per atom, at least one of the allowed energy bands must be only partially filled, since each band includes two energy states per atom. The unfilled portion of the band provides available, unoccupied, states above those occupied by the conduction electrons at absolute zero, so that electrons in the partially filled band can be accelerated by an external electric field. Solids with partially filled bands, then, must clearly be good electrical conductors. They are metals. The partially filled band is frequently called the *conduction band*. If the conduction band is about half filled, as would be the case for monovalent metals such as the alkali metals, Li, Na, K, etc., the energy-momentum relation, as seen in Fig. 1.4, is very similar to that for a free-electron gas. Such metals, therefore, should exhibit electric and magnetic behavior similar to that calculated for the free-electron gas. Fortunately, for the sake of the band model, they do exhibit such behavior.

In free atoms larger than hydrogen, some electrons are always involved in closed "rare gas" shells. The atomic-energy states corresponding to these filled atomic levels must, by virtue of the Pauli exclusion principle, be broadened into energy bands as the atoms are brought together to form a solid. However, since the closed-shell electrons are always even in number, these "closed-shell bands" will almost always be completely filled in the solid, and the electrons in these bands cannot be accelerated since there are no available energy states above the filled levels. Thus, in solids, as in chemical reactions, we usually need be concerned only with electrons outside the filled bands; we call these "valence" electrons in chemistry, or "conduction" electrons in solids. Frequently, the number of valence electrons per free atom is the same as the number of conduction electrons per atom in the solid, as with the alkali metals. However, in a solid there are large forces acting on the electrons, due to many surrounding ion cores which may perturb the relative energies of the valence electrons, and these numbers may not be identical. Thus, for example, the noble metals, copper, silver, and gold, are practically ideal "one-electron" metals, like the alkalis, although free atoms of these metals frequently exhibit chemical valences different from one. Some confusion in terminology has resulted from these differences. It is common, for instance, to describe copper, silver, and gold as "monovalent metals." They are indeed "monovalent" as *metals* since they each have essentially one conduction electron per atom in the conduction band, but they could hardly all be described as monovalent atoms. Copper compounds, for example, are usually more stable when the copper atoms are doubly ionized.

The simple band picture therefore accounts very readily for the observed fact that all atoms with an odd number of electrons outside closed "rare-gas" shells form metals in the solid state. In some cases, for instance in solid iodine, the crystal structure is based on the diatomic iodine molecule I_2 rather than on the iodine atom. Such solids are known as *molecular crystals* and always have an even number of electrons outside closed shells. However, it is obvious that many good metals, for example the alkaline earths Be, Mg, Ca, Sr, etc., are comprised of atoms with an even number of "valence" electrons. This fact does not spell the demise of the simple band model. As we have seen in Fig. 1.5, the width of the forbidden band tends to decrease as atoms are brought closer together and, indeed, if the atoms are close enough, the forbidden bands may disappear and the allowed bands overlap, as in Fig. 1.6. To make matters worse for the theorist who tries to calculate such effects, the allowed bands may overlap only in some directions in the solid but be separated by forbidden bands in other directions. In such a case we may have some allowed bands which are nearly filled and others which are nearly empty. However, since clearly there are available energy states above those filled at absolute zero, if the allowed bands do overlap at all, the solid must behave like a metal, even if there is an even number of valence electrons per atom. In such cases the density of mobile charge carriers may be greater in the nearly filled band than in the nearly empty band, and the solid, while a good metal, will give evidence of the fact that the current behaves as though it is being carried predominantly by positive, rather than negative, charges and that the effective mass of the charge carrier may be quite different from the normal free-electron mass. One well-known phenomenon, the Hall effect (the details of which need not concern us here) does, in fact, measure the sign of the predominant charge carriers in an unambiguous fashion. Before the advent of the band theory, the fact that some metals, such as Be, Zn, and Cd, behaved as though they contained mobile positive charges was, to say the least, a disagreeable phenomenon to try to explain on the basis of a free-electron gas model. However, since these metals,

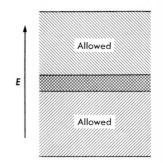

FIG. 1.6.   Overlapping allowed bands.

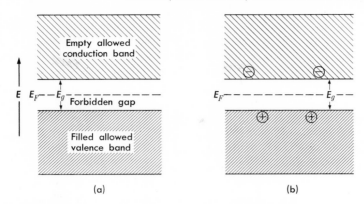

FIG. 1.7.   Band structure of insulator or intrinsic semiconductor. (a) At $T = 0°K$, there are no charges free to move. (b) With electrons "promoted" from valence to conduction band, both the electrons and positive "holes" are free to move. The Fermi energy, E_F, is in the forbidden gap.

and all others which apparently contain positive charge carriers, have an even number of electrons per atom, the observation of such effects becomes a triumph, rather than a trauma, for the band theory.

In analogy with the free-electron gas, the Fermi energy for a metal is obviously just the maximum kinetic energy of the electrons at absolute zero, and we may use this value for E_F in Eq. (1.1) in trying to calculate the properties of the metal. The energy distribution function, however, except for monovalent metals, would not be so simple as Eqs. (1.2) and (1.3).

An odd number of electrons per atom is thus a sufficient, but not a necessary, condition that a solid behave like a metal since solids with even numbers of electrons per atom can be metals, provided only that the allowed energy bands overlap. However, if the allowed bands do *not* overlap, then it follows from the model that if there is an even number of electrons per atom (or molecular unit), the solid *cannot* be a metal. Such solids must be *insulators*, or *semiconductors*, as shown in Fig. 1.7. If there is an even number of valence electrons per atom, and no overlap between allowed energy bands, the lowest available energy band must be *exactly filled* at absolute zero. Because no unoccupied energy states are available at small energies above the top of the filled levels, the electrons cannot be accelerated by an external field. Thus, there can be no electric current, and we have an insulator. The band theory thereby gives us a simple explanation for the fact that some solids are good electrical conductors and some are excellent insulators, even though they both must contain electrons.

The completely filled allowed band in insulators and semiconductors is usually called the *valence band*. The forbidden energy band separating it from the next higher allowed band is called the *band gap*, or *energy gap*, while the empty higher allowed band is referred to as the *conduction band*. Conduction can occur in insulators only if an electron is "promoted" from the valence band to the conduction band, as shown in Fig. 1.7(b). Such a "promotion" obviously requires an energy equal to that represented by the band gap, and might be provided by an incident quantum of radiation (photoconduction) or by thermal excitation at temperatures above absolute zero. The number of electrons which are thermally excited into the conduction band will depend, of course, on the temperature and width of the gap. We can easily find the general form of this relationship from the free-electron model by using Eqs. (1.1) and (1.3), even though these equations will not exactly describe the situation near the band edge. First, however, we must reconsider the definition of the Fermi energy E_F for this case. For ideal metals, the Fermi energy could be identified closely with the maximum kinetic energy of electrons in the conduction band at absolute zero of temperature. However, in an insulator or semiconductor, with a completely filled valence band at $T = 0°K$, the conduction band is completely empty, and there are simply no conduction electrons around, with or without kinetic energy. Thus, this sort of identification loses meaning. Actually, even for a metal, as shown in Fig. 1.2, the Fermi energy is defined by the requirement that the total number of electrons in the solid not vary with temperature, so that at finite temperatures there are as many electrons missing from levels below E_F as there are electrons thermally excited to levels above E_F. Promotion of a single electron from the top of the filled valence band to the bottom of the empty conduction band gives us a single hole at an energy corresponding to the top of the valence band and an electron at a higher energy separated by the gap energy E_g (Fig. 1.7). Clearly, then, E_F must lie somewhere in the gap. If we use this criterion, we find that the Fermi energy lies in the gap, above the top of the filled valence band, and has a value

$$E_F = \tfrac{1}{2}E_g + \tfrac{3}{4}kT \log (m_h^* / m_e^*), \tag{1.8}$$

where m_h^* and m_e^* are, respectively, the magnitudes of the effective masses of the hole and electron. If $m_h^* = m_e^*$, the temperature-dependent term in Eq. (1.8) vanishes, and

$$E_F = \tfrac{1}{2}E_g. \tag{1.9}$$

If $E_F \gg kT$, as is generally the case, the electron distribution function,

$$f(E) = 1/[\epsilon^{(E-E_F)/kT} + 1] \approx \epsilon^{-(E-E_F)/kT},$$

and, substituting this expression and (1.9) into (1.3) and integrating, we find that the number of electrons per unit volume in the conduction band, N_e, would then be approximately

$$N_e \simeq 2(2\pi mkT/h^2)^{3/2} \, \epsilon^{-E_g/2kT}. \tag{1.10}$$

For an insulator or semiconductor in which the electrons reach the conduction band by excitation from the valence band, the number of holes in the valence

TABLE 1.1

Characteristics of intrinsic semiconductors

Material	Energy gap, E_g, eV	Electron mobility, μ_e, cm^2/V sec	Hole mobility, μ_h, cm^2/V sec
Diamond	6	1800	1200
Silicon	1.1	1600	400
Germanium	0.7	3800	1800

band, N_h, must, of course, be identical with N_e. The actual electrical conductivity will result from the motion of both electrons and holes:

$$\sigma = N_e e \mu_e + N_h e \mu_h. \tag{1.11}$$

Here μ_e and μ_h are the magnitudes of the drift mobilities (drift velocity/electric-field strength) of the electrons and holes, respectively, and e is the electronic charge. From Eq. (1.10), the conductivity must increase exponentially with increasing temperature. Typical values for the energy gap and mobilities are given in Table 1.1.

This sort of conduction process, by equal numbers of electrons and holes, is usually called *intrinsic* conductivity. All pure insulators and semiconductors show such conductivity at sufficiently high temperatures. The distinction between insulators and semiconductors is simply a quantitative matter of the relative magnitude of the ratio of the gap energy to the absolute temperature. At very high temperatures all "insulators," which have large values of E_g, are to some extent or other "semiconductors," while at sufficiently low temperatures all "semiconductors" are effectively "insulators." Of the enormous number of pure materials found in nature that are ideal insulators at absolute zero, only a very few—graphite, silicon, germanium, a few intermetallic compounds such as InSb, and a few odd phases of some other materials—have sufficiently small energy gaps that they exhibit any electrical conductivity worth mentioning at ordinary temperatures. These are the "intrinsic semiconductors," and even these are rarely used in electronic devices in the intrinsic region.

Most of the more important intrinsic semiconductors, silicon and germanium in particular, have the same basic crystal lattice, a cubic arrangement in which each atom is surrounded by four nearest neighbors at equal distances. This structure, usually called the "diamond cubic" lattice, is shown in Fig. 1.8. According to the "bond" model of solids, the four valence electrons of each atom are paired in "covalent bonds" directed along lines joining the centers of adjacent atoms. According to the "band" model, at low temperatures the valence electrons are all in a filled band in energy-momentum space, and we do not ask where they are in the real space of the lattice since they are considered largely non-localized.

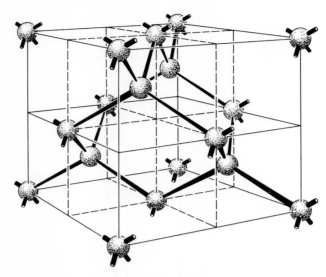

FIG. 1.8.   "Diamond cubic" crystal structure of silicon and germanium. Each atom is at the corner of a tetrahedron and has four nearest neighbors at equal distances.

Actually, most semiconductor devices employ slightly impure, rather than perfectly pure, materials. Then there are usually quite different numbers of mobile holes and electrons instead of the identical numbers characteristic of intrinsic semiconductors. Such semiconductors are usually called *extrinsic* and are further distinguished according to whether the majority of the charge carriers are negative electrons, in which case they are *n-type*, or positive holes (*p-type*). The two cases are shown in Fig. 1.9.

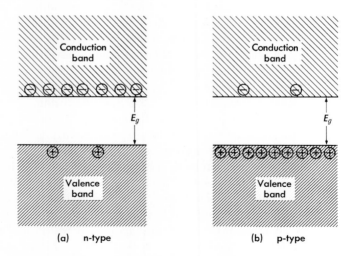

FIG. 1.9.   Extrinsic semiconductors: (a) n-type, (b) p-type.

The n-type semiconductors are formed by the addition, in the host semi-conductor lattice, of a small concentration of impurity atoms whose valence is one or more greater than that of the solvent, for example phosphorus, arsenic, or antimony in silicon or germanium. These impurity atoms occupy regular lattice sites, substituting for host atoms. Like the host atoms, they normally "lose" four valence electrons to the valence band on solution in the tetravalent host lattice, but are easily ionized to the +5 state with small additional thermal energy. The impurity atom thus can easily "donate" an electron to the con-duction band; hence the name *donor*.

In a completely analogous fashion, p-type semiconductors are formed by solution of an impurity whose valence is one or more less than that of the solvent, such as boron or indium in silicon or germanium. With additional thermal energy, these ions, nominally ionized to the +4 state on solution, can be "de-ionized" to the +3 state by capturing an electron from the filled valence band, thereby creating a mobile hole at the top of the valence band. The "deionized" impurity, since it "accepts" electrons from the valence band, is called an *acceptor*.

TABLE 1.2

Ionization energies of impurity atoms, eV

Host material	Donor			Acceptor		
	P	As	Sb	B	Al	In
Si	0.045	0.049	0.034	0.045	0.057	0.16
Ge	0.012	0.013	0.009	0.010	0.010	0.011

Very little energy is required to ionize donor atoms or deionize acceptor atoms when they are dissolved in the host lattice. The normal free-atom ionization energy of several electron volts is reduced by the factor $m_{\text{eff}}/m\varepsilon^2$, where m_{eff}/m is the relative effective mass of the electron or hole, usually about 0.1 to 0.3, and ε is the relative dielectric constant, 15.8 for Ge and 11.7 for Si. The impurity ionization energies are therefore reduced to only a few hundredths of an electron volt. Typical values for the ionization energies are given in Table 1.2. On an energy-band picture, the acceptor atoms occupy levels just a little above the top of the valence band, while the donor levels lie just below the bottom of the conduction band, as shown in Fig. 1.10. In an impure n-type material, the con-centration of excess conduction electrons, N_e', over that in the intrinsic material will be directly proportional to the concentration of donor atoms, N_d, and will vary approximately exponentially with temperature:

$$N_e' \simeq AT^{3/2}N_d\epsilon^{-(E_c-E_d)/kT}. \tag{1.12}$$

Similarly, in a p-type material, the excess number of holes, N_h', will vary with

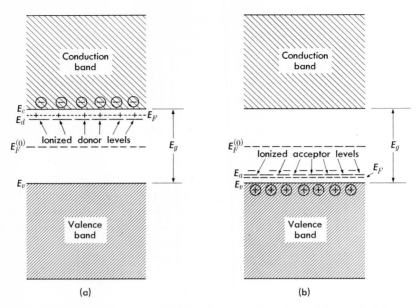

FIG. 1.10. Extrinsic semiconductors with (a) donor impurities and (b) acceptor impurities. As the impurities are ionized, the Fermi level (a) rises from $E_F^{(0)}$ to E_F in the n-type material and (b) falls from $E_F^{(0)}$ to E_F in the p-type material.

the concentration of acceptor atoms, N_a:

$$N_h' \simeq BT^{3/2}N_a\epsilon^{-(E_a-E_v)/kT}. \tag{1.13}$$

The energies (E_c-E_d) and (E_a-E_v) are, respectively, the ionization energies of donors and acceptors, as shown in Fig. 1.10. The coefficients A and B are approximately constant but depend to some extent on the number of "minority" acceptors in n-type material and donors in p-type. At very low temperatures, when the impurity levels are not ionized, the Fermi energy for extrinsic semiconductors lies near the center of the energy gap, at $E_F^{(0)}$, just as it does in intrinsic materials. However, at normal operating temperatures, many of the impurity levels are ionized, and the Fermi level shifts toward an energy between the top of the valence band and the acceptor levels in a p-type semiconductor and, similarly, between the donor levels and the bottom of the conduction band in an n-type material. As we shall see later, this fact is of considerable importance in understanding the behavior of practical semiconductor devices, which almost always contain both n-type and p-type regions in contact.

1.6 MOTION OF CHARGES IN SEMICONDUCTORS

Under normal conditions, semiconductors must, of course, be electrically neutral. The total number of positive charges (holes plus ionized donors) must equal the total number of negative charges (electrons plus ionized acceptors). In addition, since the number of electrons and holes depends only on the values of the Fermi energy, energy gap, and absolute temperature (Eqs. 1.8 through 1.10), the product of the number of electrons and the number of holes *must be a constant* at any given temperature and in any particular material. This condition is equally valid for both intrinsic and extrinsic semiconductors. Thus, in an n-type material, when the ionization of donors increases the concentration of electrons beyond the intrinsic value by some factor, the concentration of holes must be decreased below the intrinsic value by the same factor. The opposite situation applies for p-type semiconductors; enhancement of the hole concentration suppresses the electron concentration. Therefore, electric currents in extrinsic materials are carried mainly by the *majority carriers*—electrons in n-type material and holes in p-type. The suppressed *minority carriers*—holes in n-type material and electrons in p-type—will also contribute to the current, but to a smaller extent. However, the other charged particles that are present, the ionized impurities, are bound to the lattice, and hence do not take a direct part in charge transport.

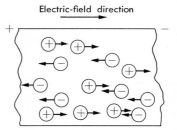

FIG. 1.11. Electrical conduction in a semi-conductor. Positive holes move from left to right and negative electrons from right to left. The total current is the sum of the individual hole and electron currents.

Since holes and electrons are of opposite signs and move in opposite directions under an applied field, both contribute in the same sense to the electric current, as shown in Fig. 1.11. From Eq. (1.11), we see that the magnitude of the electrical conductivity depends on the total number of electrons and holes combined. This is equally true for intrinsic semiconductors, where the numbers of holes and electrons are equal, as for extrinsic materials, where the numbers are different. In the latter, at normal temperatures many of the donor and acceptor impurity atoms are ionized, and the total number of majority carriers plus suppressed minority carriers is usually far greater than the combined number of holes and electrons in the intrinsic material. Therefore, the electrical conductivity increases in direct proportion to the concentration of donor or acceptor atoms if this concentration is appreciably larger than the number of intrinsic electrons and holes ($\approx 10^{12}/cm^3$ at room temperature), as shown in Fig. 1.12. This relationship holds for impurity concentrations of up to about 10^{18} impurity atoms/cm^3. If the number of impurity atoms becomes still larger, it is no longer a valid approximation to consider these atoms as "isolated" in the pure semiconductor matrix. The radii of the Bohr orbits for charges (electrons or holes) centered about the impurity atoms in the solid are increased, relative to

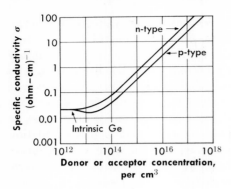

FIG. 1.12. Electrical conductivity of germanium as a function of the concentration of donor and acceptor atoms.

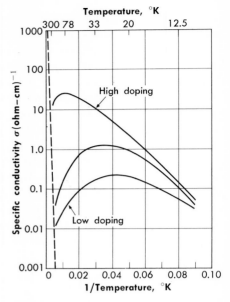

FIG. 1.13. Conductivity as a function of temperature for n-type germanium with various levels of arsenic doping. The dashed line represents the intrinsic conductivity of pure Ge.

those in the free atom, by a factor equal to the product of the relative dielectric constant times the reciprocal of the relative effective mass, a factor of about 47 for Si and 132 for Ge. In "highly doped" materials (containing large impurity concentrations) the charges can therefore move directly between ionized impurity atoms, even though these atoms are separated by relatively large distances. The electrical conductivity increases rapidly when this state is reached, and all of the impurity levels may be considered ionized. In this case, the effective Fermi energy lies above the bottom of the conduction band in n-type material and below the top of the valence band in p-type. While this condition is assiduously avoided by limitation of impurity concentrations in most semiconductor devices, it is prerequisite for at least one important device, the tunnel diode, which will be discussed later.

As already noted, the electrical conductivity of semiconductors will depend on temperature, through its effect on both the numbers of charge carriers and their mobilities (Eq. 1.11). In intrinsic semiconductors, the first effect is dominant since the number of carriers increases very rapidly with temperature when the energy required to create free-charge carriers is much greater than the thermal energy kT (Eq. 1.10). In extrinsic semiconductors at normal temperatures, on the other hand, the impurity ionization energy is smaller than or comparable to kT, so that the number of carriers changes only slowly with temperature. Then the main effect of a change in temperature on the conductivity is brought about by the change in mobility of the carriers, which varies approximately as $T^{-3/2}$. This effect tends to cause an increase in conductivity with decreasing temperature, offsetting the opposite effect that is due to the slow decrease in the number of charge carriers as the temperature is lowered. As a result, in extrinsic materials the conductivity can be fairly insensitive to temperature over a reasonably wide range, as shown in Fig. 1.13.

Even in extrinsic semiconductors, at sufficiently high temperatures there must always be some electron-hole pairs formed by the intrinsic process of direct ionization across the energy gap. When the number of intrinsic carriers becomes comparable to the number of extrinsic carriers, a further increase in temperature will cause the current to increase exponentially with temperature. The increasing current, in turn, heats the material, more charge carriers are formed, and the resulting chain-reaction process rapidly results in self-destruction of the semiconductor, unless the current is limited by the external circuit. This phenomenon obviously limits the maximum temperatures at which semiconductor devices can operate. For Ge, with an energy gap of only 0.7 eV, the maximum permissible operating temperature is about 85°C. In Si the energy gap is larger, about 1.1 eV, and silicon semiconductor devices can therefore be operated at higher temperatures, up to about 200°C. This process is usually called *thermal runaway*, and, as will be discussed later, special precautions must often be taken in the design of practical circuits using semiconducting devices to avoid accidentally permitting the devices to play this self-destructive role.

Direct ionization of electron-hole pairs can also be caused by sufficiently large electric fields, even when there is little previous current flowing to heat the material. The current will then increase exponentially with temperature, unless limited by the external circuit, and the device may be ruined. For this reason, there are natural limitations on the maximum allowable electric fields which may be applied to semiconductor devices without causing breakdown. As in thermal runaway, the onset of this phenomenon of *field breakdown* depends on the magnitude of the energy gap and will in general be less critical for Si than Ge devices.

In intrinsic semiconductors, or even in extrinsic materials in which the impurity ionization energy is large compared with kT, there are so few charge carriers present at room temperature that the material is a very poor electrical conductor. However, the conductivity can be increased enormously by absorption of light of energy greater than that required to create free charge carriers by direct ionization. Since the energy required is less than that of a quantum of visible light for Ge or Si, such semiconductors are frequently employed in practical *photoconductor* devices for use in the visible and infrared (e.g. "electric eyes" for cameras). Materials in which the ionization energy is much greater than the thermal energy also, as noted before, show a very rapid increase in electrical conductivity with increasing temperature. This fact is of great use in devising semiconductor temperature-sensing elements, usually called *thermistors*.

In intrinsic semiconductors the current is carried by electron-hole pairs, and in homogeneous extrinsic materials, almost entirely by the majority carriers.

However, most semiconductor devices used as *active* circuit elements (e.g. diodes, transistors) are neither entirely intrinsic nor homogeneous. Instead, they rely for their operation on junctions between metals and semiconductors, or between n- and p-type extrinsic materials. At such contacts, excess minority carriers can be *injected* into the extrinsic material, holes into n-type material, or electrons into p-type. Since the material must remain electrically neutral, an equal number of excess majority carriers must also be supplied from the external circuit. Of course, the injected carriers will move in response to an external electric field and will thus contribute to the conductivity. However, since initially they will be present on injection only in the small region near the junction, they will also move by ordinary *diffusional* motion, in such a way as to achieve a uniform concentration throughout the material, much the same way a drop of ink will spread through a glass of water. The rate of diffusional motion is measured by the *diffusion coefficient* D for the minority carriers, which is related to the drift mobility μ through the Einstein relation

$$D = \mu k T / e. \qquad (1.14)$$

Typically, for germanium at room temperature, the diffusion coefficient for electrons is 93 cm^2/sec, and for holes, 44 cm^2/sec.

The diffusional current of injected minority carriers in a semiconductor, unlike ink in water, will not persist until the excess carriers simply are spread out uniformly through the volume of the material. The presence of the excess carriers, in itself, disturbs the equilibrium charge distribution, and they must be completely removed before equilibrium is restored. This can occur, for instance, if they simply move through the material past another junction (a process called *drift*) or if the excess minority and majority carriers, which are of opposite sign, come together and annihilate each other (a process known as *recombination*). Normally, both drift and recombination will occur simultaneously. Recombination can result in emission of light (as in semiconductor *lasers*) or, by coupling to the lattice, in heat. Through recombination, the number of excess carriers will decrease exponentially with time, as exp $-t/\tau$, where τ is defined as the *lifetime*. If the only process involved were a direct radiative recombination, τ would have a value of the order of a second. However, observed lifetimes are about 0.01 sec in exceedingly pure materials, and about 100 μsec in those of commercial purity. In impure materials, particularly those with very small amounts of magnetic impurities, the lifetime is much shorter, as small as 0.1 μsec, and is usually different for holes and electrons. The chief recombination process is therefore clearly not due to direct radiative annihilation but apparently to an indirect process involving trapping of minority and majority carriers at impurity atoms, lattice imperfections, or surface states.

The values of the diffusion coefficient and the lifetime of the minority carriers are critical parameters in the design of practical devices, particularly transistors, which depend for their operation on the diffusional drift of injected minority carriers through one region of the device. The average distance a minority carrier can diffuse during its lifetime is called the *diffusion length L:*

$$L = (D\tau)^{1/2}. \tag{1.15}$$

For electrons in germanium at room temperature, L is about 0.2 cm if the lifetime is 1000 μsec, but 100 times smaller if the lifetime is 0.1 μsec. For effective operation, the thickness of the region in the device through which the minority carriers drift must be much less than L, if they are to survive the trip. Since L is usually less than 1 mm, commonly *much* less, transistor manufacturers have had to develop very special techniques for making useful devices, particularly for very-high-frequency operation when the dimensions must be further reduced to minimize transit time effects. Some of these will be discussed in Section 3.7.

1.7 ELECTRONS OUTSIDE SOLIDS

In some electronic devices such as vacuum tubes, charges flow part of the time through a vacuum, rather than inside solids. Therefore, the charges must somehow escape from the solid into the vacuum since nature does not provide electron-filled vacuums. It is clear that despite the fact that electrons have considerable kinetic energy inside solids (of the order of the Fermi energy, to be precise), the electrons do not spontaneously fly out of solids like gas molecules escaping into a vacuum from a hole in a bottle. To extract the electrons, we have to do more than poke holes in the solid; we must do some work on each charge. The minimum amount of work which must be done on an electron to free it from a solid is called the *work function* of that material.

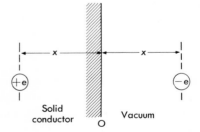

FIG. 1.14. Electron outside a solid. The electron, of charge $-e$, sees an equipotential 0 at a distance x, the same as would result if there were an "image" charge $+e$ at a distance $2x$.

Exact calculation of the work function of a solid, starting from the charges inside the material, can be difficult. However, if we take the opposite view, starting outside the solid, a fair estimate is simple. Looking from the outside of a solid, we are immediately aware that it has a *surface*, and it can easily be shown that an electron at rest outside the solid will be attracted toward the surface. The situation is represented schematically in Fig. 1.14, for a simple case. The electron, at a distance x from the surface of a conductor (all solids which emit electrons in practical circuits are generally conductors, even though not necessarily very good ones), sees a plane equipotential surface of potential zero (by definition) at the origin. If the surface of the solid were not there, but there was a charge $+e$ at a distance x to the left of the origin, then the electron would also see a plane equipotential surface of potential zero at the origin. Electrons, being unsophisticated, cannot tell the difference between the "real" zero equipotential surface of the conductor and the "imaginary" one resulting from the positive *image* charge. In either case, the electron is attracted toward the surface, with the same force that it would be attracted toward the image charge, namely the Coulomb force $-e^2/4\pi\varepsilon_0(2x)^2$. If the electron were initially at rest and "free" from the solid, it would have been at an infinite distance from the surface. Therefore, the work done on the electron in bringing it from infinity to the distance x from the origin must be simply

$$W_x = \int_x^\infty F\,dx = \int_x^\infty \frac{-e^2}{4\pi\varepsilon_0(2x)^2}\,dx = \frac{-e^2}{16\pi\varepsilon_0 x}. \tag{1.16}$$

The sign of W_x is negative, consistent with the fact that the charge would have done work on the restraining force as it approached the surface. Eventually, this simple picture must collapse, for the surface of a solid is not a nice, smooth, mathematical plane but is really an assembly of atoms spaced at some regular distance d_0 apart. Thus, when the electron comes very close to the surface, say within a distance d_0, it certainly cannot still experience the same Coulomb attractive force. Instead, we might guess, with some justification, that for very close distances the force might be constant, of the order of $-e^2/4\pi\varepsilon_0(2d_0)^2$. Then the total work done on the electron, bringing it from its free state at infinity to the surface at $x = 0$, would be

$$W = \int_0^{d_0} \frac{-e^2}{4\pi\varepsilon_0(2d_0)^2}\,dx + \int_{d_0}^\infty \frac{-e^2\,dx}{4\pi\varepsilon_0(2x)^2}, \tag{1.17}$$

$$W = \frac{-e^2}{16\pi\varepsilon_0 d_0} - \frac{e^2}{16\pi\varepsilon_0 d_0} = -\frac{e^2}{8\pi\varepsilon_0 d_0}. \tag{1.18}$$

Note that half the work done is involved in moving the small distance d_0 next to the surface. If we start with the electron at the surface and end up with the electron at rest "free" from the solid at infinity, we must add to the system the same amount of energy as the work done in moving from infinity to the origin. But this, in fact, is just the definition of the work function. Therefore, the work function must be about $e^2/8\pi\varepsilon_0 d_0$, in the approximation of our simple model. Since $d_0 \approx 3$ Å for typical solids, we may readily estimate the value for the work function as about 3 eV. We can verify this estimate by comparing it with the measured photoelectric thresholds for freeing electrons from solids by means of incident radiation. Since these vary from 1 to 5 eV, it seems that the simple model gives a fairly good result. In real solids the work function is extremely sensitive to the presence of impurities on the surface, even in extremely small

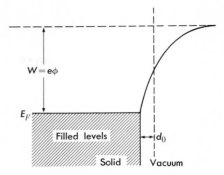

FIG. 1.15. Band structure of solid near surface. The work function $W = e\phi$ is the minimum energy required to remove an electron to infinity. Notice that roughly half the work is required to move the electron a distance d_0, the order of the interatomic distance.

concentrations. The presence of even a monatomic layer can cause appreciable increases or decreases in the work function, apparently by forming a dipole layer, which changes the effective electric field at the surface. A layer of electropositive ions tends to reduce the effective work function, while it is increased by electronegative ions. This phenomenon frequently causes important changes in the characteristics of vacuum tubes with time.

We may now construct a simple picture of a solid, including its surface and work function, as in Fig. 1.15. The work function $W = e\phi$ is just the energy which must be given to an electron of maximum energy inside the solid, E_F, to free it from the solid. Thus ϕ forms a potential barrier, sometimes called the *Richardson potential*. We can free electrons from the solid by supplying the extra energy $e\phi$ per electron by means of an incident photon, as in photoelectric cells, or the energy can come simply from the thermal energy of the whole solid. In this case, if the solid is at absolute temperature T, the relative number of electrons with energy $e\phi$ greater than E_F can be calculated from the distribution function. In the free-electron gas model, Eq. (1.3), the number of electrons in the interval dE at an energy $E_F + e\phi$ is

$$n(E_F + e\phi)\, dE = \frac{1}{2\pi^2}\left(\frac{2m}{\hbar^2}\right)\frac{(E_F + e\phi)^{1/2}}{\epsilon^{e\phi/kT} + 1}\, dE. \qquad (1.19)$$

But since $e\phi$ is of the order of 1 to 5 eV, $e\phi$ is much greater than kT, and

$$n(E_F + e\phi)\, dE \simeq \frac{1}{2\pi^2}\left(\frac{2m}{\hbar^2}\right)^{3/2}(E_F + e\phi)^{1/2}\epsilon^{-e\phi/kT}\, dE. \qquad (1.20)$$

From Eq. (1.20) we note that the number of electrons with sufficient energy to escape must increase approximately exponentially with increasing temperature. In the next chapter we shall see how this fact determines some of the important characteristics of vacuum tubes.

Before considering combinations of vacuum-filled and solid devices in circuits, we must resolve the problem of too many zeros of energy. When we considered

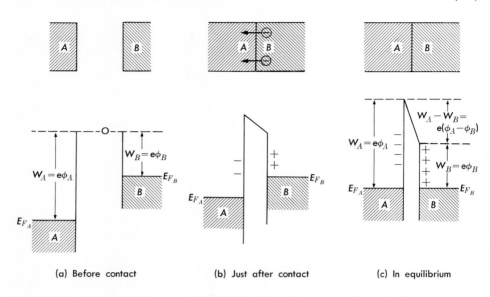

(a) Before contact   (b) Just after contact   (c) In equilibrium

FIG. 1.16.   Contact between two solids of different work function. (a) Before contact, the zeros of the work functions are at the same level. (b) Just after contact, electrons flow from the low work function material to the high work function material. (c) After equilibrium is established, the Fermi energies are at the same level, side A is negative with respect to B by the contact potential difference $(W_A - W_B)/e = \phi_A - \phi_B$.

the energies of "free" electrons *inside* solids, the only energy which had any physical meaning was the Fermi energy, so that our "zero" of energy was some arbitrary level at a value E_F *below* the Fermi level. For electrons outside solids, our "zero" of energy for the "free" electrons corresponded to the potential energy at an infinite distance from the surface of the solid, at an energy difference equal to the work function, $e\phi$, *above* the Fermi level. In a circuit where there are two or more different solids in contact with one another and also some vacuum as part of the circuit, as in Fig. 1.16, the energies of all the electrons in the circuit must come to equilibrium in the steady state. This situation occurs, for example, in a vacuum-tube circuit where the elements are made of different materials and are connected with wires. Just before the materials are connected, the only property they have in common is their "external zeros," so that on an energy scale the situation might look like Fig. 1.16(a), with all the "external zeros" at the same level. However, after they have been placed in contact for a time, the solids will have another important property in common, their temperature. Just as two gases brought into thermal contact with one another will eventually come to the same temperature, that is, to the same value of *kinetic energy* per molecule, the electrons in two solids which are placed in thermal contact must reach the same kinetic energy, that is the same *Fermi energy*. If the isolated solids have different work functions, then electrons must flow from the material of lower work function to the material of higher work function to bring the Fermi levels together, as shown in Fig. 1.16(c). The result of this flow of charge is that there will now be a potential difference measurable in the evacuated space between the two materials after they have been placed in contact, the material of higher work function becoming negative with respect to the lower-work-function material. This difference in potential, which is known as the *contact potential*, is just equal to the difference between the Richardson potentials of the two materials:

$$\text{contact potential} = \phi_A - \phi_B = \frac{W_A - W_B}{e}. \qquad (1.21)$$

Since the work functions are of the order of a few electron volts, the contact potential may be of the order of a volt; thus it is hardly negligible.

This situation must be true whenever there is no steady current flowing in the circuit, and must be taken into account in potentiometer circuits at balance as well as in vacuum-tube circuits. The actual amount of charge which must flow to establish the contact potential is not, however, enough to cause any appreciable perturbation of the "internal zeros" of energy of the two materials with respect to the Fermi energy. For example, if A and B are two metals with $\phi_A - \phi_B$ of about one volt, and if the capacity between the two parts separated by a vacuum is, typically, of the order of 10^{-11} F, then a charge, $Q = CV = 10^{-11}$ C, must flow from A to B to establish the contact potential difference. This tiny amount of charge, about 10^8 electrons, is a trivial perturbation to the total number of "free" electrons, about $10^{22}/\text{cm}^3$, available in the conduction band of each of the solids, so we would not expect any measurable changes in the internal-energy levels resulting from the charge exchange. In electronic circuits, the existence of a contact potential just gives us a slightly different zero to work from; it does not in itself introduce any physical problems. What does give trouble, on the other hand, is changes in the contact potential with time, resulting from changes in the work functions due to physicochemical effects at the surfaces of electrodes and due to changes in temperature. Such effects can cause shifts in bias points, cutoff characteristics, etc., with time, and can be annoying, even troublesome, unless proper account of these, as well as other "solid-state-type" variations, is taken in the design of the overall circuit.

PROBLEMS

1.1. Calculate the value of the Fermi energy at absolute zero for copper, according to the free-electron model. Copper has one free electron per atom and four atoms per unit cell arranged in a cubic lattice, where the unit cubic cell is 3.61 Å on a side.

1.2. The Fermi energy is not actually a constant, but it varies with temperature according to the relation $E_F(T) = E_F(0)[1 - (\pi^2/12)(kT/E_F(0))^2 + \cdots]$. At room temperature, $kT \approx 0.025$ eV.

(a) At what temperature would the Fermi energy be 10% different from its value at absolute zero?

(b) Copper melts at a temperature of 1093°C. How much is the Fermi energy of copper changed at this temperature from its value at $T = 0°K$?

1.3 For what value of the energy E above E_F is it a good approximation (within 10%) to take

$$n(E)\ dE \approx E^{1/2}\epsilon^{-(E-E_F)/kT}\ dE$$

as the value for the actual density of states of a free-electron gas at room temperature? From your answer, comment on the reasonableness of this approximation for calculating the densities of charge carriers in typical intrinsic and extrinsic semiconductors.

1.4 Consider an n-type semiconductor containing 5×10^{16} atoms/cm³ of arsenic donors dissolved in germanium.

(a) At what temperature are half the donors ionized?

(b) What fraction of the donors is ionized at room temperature (300°K)?

1.5 The drift mobility μ of charge carriers is defined as $\mu = v/E$, where v is the drift velocity and E is the electric field strength. In silicon

$$\mu = 1600 \text{ cm}^2/\text{Vsec} \quad \text{for electrons,}$$
$$400 \text{ cm}^2/\text{Vsec} \quad \text{for holes.}$$

One piece of p-type silicon contains a concentration of 2×10^{16} atoms/cm³ of indium acceptors; a second piece contains a concèntration c_0 of phosphorus donors.

(a) For what value of c_0 will the two semiconductors have the same conductivity at room temperature (300°K)?

(b) At what temperature would a piece of *pure* silicon have the same conductivity as one of the impure pieces at 300°K?

1.6 Two materials, A and B, with Richardson potentials ϕ_A and ϕ_B, are separated by a vacuum on one side and connected by a wire of material C on the other, as shown in Fig. 1.17.

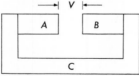

FIGURE 1.17

(a) Show that the potential difference V between A and B is $\phi_A - \phi_B$, independent of the material C.

(b) Given that A is Cu, with a Richardson potential of 3.9 V, and B is Pt, with a Richardson potential of 5.3 V, find the total charge which must flow from B to A to establish the contact potential difference, when the electrostatic capacity between A and B is 100 pF.

(c) Given that A and B each have a volume of 1 cm³, by what fraction is the free charge concentration perturbed by the charge calculated in (b)?

1.7 Calculate the relative number of electrons with energies equal to or greater than the work function at the melting temperature for each of the materials listed below.

Which of these materials would be the most efficient thermionic emitter? Which would be the least efficient?

Material	ϕ, V	Melting temperature, °K
Cu	3.9	1356
Ta	4.2	3123
W	4.5	3655
Ni	4.6	1725
Pt	5.3	2047

1.8 Show that the electrical resistivity $\rho = 1/Ne\mu$, where N is the number of electrons per unit volume, e is the electronic charge, and μ is the drift mobility. Determine values of N for each of the metals listed below.

Metal	μ, cm^2/V sec	ρ, $\mu\Omega$ cm
Ag	56	1.64
Al	10	2.70
Au	30	2.44
Cu	35	1.72

1.9 For each of the elements listed below, calculate the approximate value of the work function from the "image force" model, and compare it with the actual work function.

Element	Ag	Cu	Ni	Zn	Pt	Cr	Ta	W	Na	K	Cs
Interatomic distance d_0, Å	2.88	2.55	2.49	2.66	2.77	2.49	2.85	2.73	3.71	4.62	5.24
Work function, eV	4.8	3.9	4.6	4.3	5.3	4.6	4.2	4.5	2.3	2.2	1.8

1.10 A charge moving inside a solid with a momentum p has a kinetic energy $E_k = p^2/2m^*$, where m^* is the effective mass. Show that if the solid is placed in a magnetic field H, the charges, if otherwise unperturbed, will move normal to H in circular orbits with a frequency eH/m^*c. (This frequency, called the *cyclotron frequency*, defines the "cyclotron-resonance" technique for actual measurement of the effective mass.)

1.11 The intermetallic compound InSb has a gap energy of 0.18 eV and a relative dielectric constant of 17. The effective mass of electrons in InSb is 0.014 times the free electron mass. Find the ionization energy of a donor atom in InSb, given that the ionization energy of the atom in the free state is 5 eV.

1.12 A slab of n-type germanium contains 2×10^{17} atoms/cm^3 of phophorus. Acceptor atoms of indium are then diffused into the slab from the vapor to a final concentration of 2×10^{18}/cm^3.

(a) At what concentration of In will the material change from n-type to p-type?

(b) Find the final electrical conductivity of the slab at room temperature (300°K). [*Hint:* Recall that the *product* of the number of electrons and holes must remain constant, independent of composition; therefore, addition of holes suppresses the electron concentration. Use of a second type of impurity to change the sign of the charge carriers, called "compensation," is an important technique in the manufacture of semiconductor devices.]

1.13   A long slab of a conducting solid, which carries a current I_y in the y-direction because of a potential difference V_y across its ends, is placed in a perpendicular magnetic field H_z (Fig. 1.18). Show that there will be a potential difference V_x across opposite edges of the slab perpendicular to both y and z and that the ratio V_x/I_yH_z is proportional to $1/Ne$, where N is the density of mobile charge carriers and e is their unit charge. Show that the sign of the ratio depends only on the sign of the mobile charge carriers. This phenomenon is called the *Hall effect*. [*Hint:* Assume that the charges move with constant speed in the y-direction and that the combined effect of the electric field in the x-direction and H_z just causes the x-component of the force to vanish.]

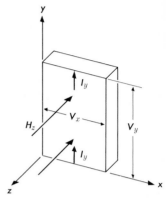

FIGURE 1.18

REFERENCES

Kittel, C., *Introduction to Solid State Physics*, Wiley, 1953.
Shockley, W., *Electrons and Holes in Semiconductors*, van Nostrand, 1950.

Chapter 2

ELECTRONIC TUBES

2.1 GENERAL REMARKS

This chapter is devoted mainly to *thermionic vacuum tubes,* i.e. tubes with an electrically heated cathode which emits electrons into a vacuum. This vacuum should be sufficiently good that only a very small fraction of the electrons traveling through it will ionize molecules of residual gas, so that the ion current should always be very much less than the electron current. For positive ions this ion current moves in a direction opposite to that of the electron current and therefore can be easily distinguished. The magnitude of the ion current gives a sensitive indication of the quality of the vacuum in the tube (a fact which is utilized to practical advantage in "ionization gauges" for measuring high vacuums). At some distance from the cathode there are one or more "cold" electrodes to which suitable voltages are externally applied. The positions and shapes of these electrodes and the magnitude of the voltages applied determine the distribution of the electron current between them. The primary aim of this chapter is to find out how these currents depend on the applied voltages.

One of the most important general properties of thermionic vacuum tubes is that they conduct current only in one direction, only when the combined action of the cold electrodes creates an electric field at the cathode that draws electrons away from it. If one or more of the electrodes becomes sufficiently negative with respect to the cathode, the direction of the field at the cathode will be reversed, and electrons will be pushed back to it. The tube current is then cut off. The transition between conduction and nonconduction is utilized in many circuits, where the tube acts as a switch operated by the voltages of one or more of the electrodes.

The simplest tube is a *diode.* In this tube there is, besides the cathode, only one other electrode, the plate or anode, which usually surrounds the cathode completely. A diode conducts current when the anode voltage is positive with respect to the cathode; at negative anode voltages it conducts hardly at all. A diode therefore acts in some respects like a valve—a tire can be pumped to a certain pressure through a valve; a capacitor can be charged to a certain dc-voltage through a diode which is connected to an ac-voltage. Valvelike action therefore implies rectification.

In normal operation, electrons are emitted by the cathode at a much higher rate than they are drawn away by the field of the other electrodes. Therefore, a cloud of electrons, the *space-charge cloud*, forms around the cathode. The existence of this space charge is of fundamental importance for the operation of thermionic vacuum tubes. The negative space charge tends to *shield* the cathode from the attractive field of the other electrodes; thus the electron current drawn from the cathode to a positive electrode will increase only gradually with the electrode voltage. The simplest amplifier tube is the *triode*, in which a grid of fine wires is placed between the anode and the cathode. Since it is kept negative with respect to the cathode, this grid can control the anode current without drawing current itself. The change in anode current for a particular change in control grid voltage is much larger than that obtained for the same change in the anode voltage. This is true not only because the control grid is much closer to the cathode, but mainly because the control grid shields the cathode from the anode, and only a small fraction of the field lines from the anode penetrates to the cathode through the grid wires. The control of the anode current by the grid voltage may be compared to the control of water flow by a tap. In both cases, practically no power is needed to control the current, while the current itself can deliver a large amount of power. If a reasonably large resistance is connected in series in the anode supply lead of a triode, an increase in grid voltage will be accompanied by a larger decrease in anode voltage. Thus voltage gain can be readily obtained. The maximum possible voltage gain is determined by the relative effectiveness of the control grid in shielding the cathode from the voltage changes at the anode; the more effective this shielding, the higher the maximum gain. For this reason, an extra grid, the *screen grid*, is often placed between the control grid and the anode. The presence of a second grid (or perhaps even more than two grids) also makes it possible to control the anode current by more than one voltage at the same time. Thus, multiple grid tubes can be used to mix two or more signals. In this chapter we shall review the chief characteristics of most common vacuum tubes, starting with the cathode itself, and then progressing through diodes, triodes, etc., to show how the successive electrodes influence the behavior of the device as a circuit element.

2.2 THERMIONIC EMISSION: CATHODES

In Chapter 1 we saw that according to the free-electron model, the number of electrons emitted by a solid varies exponentially with temperature, as $\epsilon^{-e\phi_k/kT}$, since the barrier to emission is simply the work function $e\phi_k$ of the solid. Thermionic cathodes are practical because of the existence of materials with Richardson potentials, ϕ_k, low enough to yield considerable emission currents at temperatures at which the material does not evaporate too rapidly. To see the fundamental role of the cathode in determining the magnitude of the tube current, we assume first that the other electrodes are sufficiently positive for all the electrons to be collected as fast as they are emitted by the cathode; then there will be no space charge. This condition is called *temperature limited operation*. To find the resulting current density, we must calculate the rate at which electrons inside the cathode with energies greater than $E_{Fk} + e\phi_k$ strike the cathode surface at right angles, so that when emitted, they will travel to the anode. This problem was first solved classically by Richardson, and later, through the Fermi-Dirac distribution function, by Dushman. Dushman's solution, usually called the Richardson-Dushman equation, shows that the thermionic current density is

$$J_{\text{th}} = 4\pi m e^2 h^{-3} T^2 \epsilon^{-e\phi_k/kT} = A_0 T^2 \epsilon^{-B\phi_k/T}. \qquad (2.1)$$

Calculation of this result is straightforward, but the detailed solution is of little concern here. The terms A_0 and B contain only universal constants and have the values

$$A_0 = 120 \text{ A}/(\text{cm}°\text{K})^2, \qquad B = 11{,}600°\text{K/V}. \qquad (2.2)$$

From the form of Eq. (2.1), the current varies essentially exponentially with temperature. The T^2-term in the pre-exponential has little effect in the ordinary case where $e\phi_k \gg kT$. Equation (2.1) has been derived for the free-electron gas model of a solid, but all real solids show the same exponential temperature-dependence of the thermionic current. The term A_0, however, is frequently quite different from the value given in (2.2) for the ideal case. Experimental values of A_0 and the Richardson potential ϕ_k are given for a few cases in Table 2.1. As seen from the table, ϕ_k varies from 1 to 4.5 V for typical cathode materials. Since the ratio ϕ_k/T determines the rate of emission, these cathodes must be operated at widely different temperatures to obtain comparable emission currents. In practice, temperatures between 1000 and 2700°K are used. The power needed for heating the cathode is chiefly dissipated at these temperatures by radiation. Although the radiated power increases as T^4, according to the Stefan-Boltzmann Law, the emission efficiency, defined as the emitted current per unit of heating power, still rises rapidly with temperature because the exponential increase of the emission current with temperature is much faster than the fourth-power increase of the thermal radiation. For cathodes with different values of ϕ_k, the emission efficiency is smallest for those with the highest Richardson potential since their operating temperature is also the highest. The following are the major characteristics of the commonly used cathode materials whose properties are summarized in Table 2.1.

A. Tungsten cathodes. Tungsten is the only pure metal commonly used as a cathode material, because its melting point is so high (3655°K) that even for its high Richardson potential (4.52 V), sufficient emission can be obtained at a temperature at which the life of the cathode is not appreciably shortened by evaporation. Even though the emission efficiency of tungsten cathodes is small compared with that of other cathodes, tungsten is frequently used, especially

TABLE 2.1

Characteristic properties of different cathode materials

Cathode material	Richardson potential, V	A_0, A/(cm°K)^2	Normal operating temperature, °K	Maximum useful emission, A/cm^2	Emission efficiency, mA/W	Principal use	Remarks
Tungsten	4.2	75	2600	1	2–10^d	Large transmitting tubes	Resistant against gas and fast ions
Thoriated tungsten	2.6	3	1800–2000	3	5–100^d	Medium large transmitting tubes	Not resistant against gas and fast ions
L-cathode	1.6–2.0	15	1200–1600	100	1–100^i	Special tubes	Poisoned by gas and damaged by fast ions, but can recover
Oxide cathode	1.0–1.5	0.01	1000–1200	100^p 2^c	10–200^i 200–1000^d	Normal tubes	Easily poisoned by gases (especially nitrogen and oxygen) and damaged by fast ions

p = pulse operation
c = continuous operation
i = indirectly heated
d = directly heated

in large transmitter tubes, where a very good vacuum cannot be maintained at all times. Tungsten is the only cathode material that can resist bombardment by the fast ions created by electron ionization of the residual gas.

B. Tungsten cathodes with a monoatomic surface layer. As noted in Chapter 1, the work function of a metal can be lowered considerably if it is covered with a monoatomic layer of suitable material. A frequently used cathode of this type is the thoriated tungsten cathode. A monolayer of thorium on a tungsten surface lowers the work function from 4.52 eV to 2.6 eV. For thoriated tungsten cathodes, therefore, the same emission current as for pure tungsten is obtained at a much lower temperature, and the emission efficiency is higher. A disadvantage of thoriated tungsten cathodes is that the thorium layer can easily be damaged by gas or by bombardment with fast ions. Thoriated cathodes must therefore be used only in tubes in which a good high vacuum is maintained. Cathodes of this type are frequently made of tungsten to which about 2% of thorium oxide has been added. During activation of the cathode, which is effected at a temperature well above that for normal operation, some thorium diffuses to the surface. At the normal operating temperature of about 1900°K, the diffusion of new thorium to the surface exceeds the evaporation of the monoatomic layer; thus this layer is kept active despite thorium loss.

L-cathode or replenishing cathode. A monoatomic layer of barium lowers the Richardson potential of tungsten to about 1.7 V. However, at the temperature required for appreciable emission, the barium layer will quickly evaporate. To make an efficient cathode, means must be found to replenish the barium layer rapidly, much more rapidly than was necessary in thoriated tungsten cathodes. Suitable cathode-construction techniques were developed by H. J. Lemmens in 1949. Some examples of the construction of this type of cathode (called the L-cathode in honor of its inventor) are given in Fig. 2.1. A mixture of barium

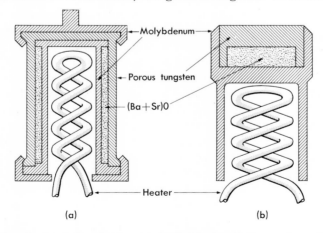

(a) (b)

FIG. 2.1. Two types of *L*-cathode. (a) Cylindrical emitting surface, (b) disc-shaped emitting surface.

and strontium carbonate is pressed into a cylinder or cap of porous tungsten, which is held by a molybdenum housing. The heater is mounted inside the molybdenum piece. The activation process of the older L-cathodes required considerable time; more recently, L-cathodes with good barium replenishment have been obtained by pressure-molding a mixture of tungsten powder alloyed with molybdenum and tribarium aluminate or by impregnating a porous tungsten carrier with molten barium calcium aluminate.

These cathodes are capable of providing high current densities: for $J = 10 \text{ A/cm}^2$, an average life of more than 10,000 hours is possible. Although L-cathodes can easily be damaged by ion bombardment or gases liberated during operation, they may often recover, so long as the barium layer can be replenished. Because the tungsten surface can be machined very precisely, the L-cathode is particularly suitable for tubes with very small tolerances in cathode dimensions, like very-high-frequency amplifier tubes where cathode-to-grid distances as small as $10\ \mu$ are required, or in precision electron guns.

C. Oxide cathodes. The principle of the oxide cathode was discovered in 1904 by Wehnelt, who observed that thin layers of the oxides of alkaline earth metals such as barium and calcium emit electrons abundantly when heated. The Richardson potential of such layers can be as low as 1 V. The desirable combination of low operating temperatures, large emission current, and long life expectancy have made oxide cathodes by far the most widely used. Oxide cathodes usually consist of a directly or indirectly heated metal base, most commonly nickel but sometimes tungsten, covered by a thick layer (10 to $100\ \mu$) of about equal quantities of activated barium and strontium oxides, in which a small quantity of barium and strontium metal is present. With increasing understanding of the physical processes involved in the oxide cathode, there have been some practical improvements in its properties. In normal use, there is an equilibrium between evaporation, diffusion, and formation of new free barium and strontium. If the temperature is increased, all these processes go faster and, because only a limited amount of free metal can be formed, the life span of the cathode decreases. If the temperature of the cathode is kept too low, the rate of poisoning of the cathode by gas increases. To obtain a maximum life, the cathode temperature must be maintained within rather narrow limits (1000–1050°K). For this reason, a narrow range for the heater voltage is sometimes specified for special long-life tubes, and a regulated heater supply may be required. In order to prevent liberation of gas inside the tube, the temperature of the "cold" electrodes should also be kept as low as possible. It is therefore advantageous to operate the tube with the lowest possible screen and anode voltages. Oxide cathodes are capable of delivering, during short pulses (duration of less than a few msec), a peak current considerably in excess of the expected saturation current. If we attempt to maintain this peak current for a longer period, the emission rapidly decreases, and sparking may occur inside the oxide, leading to permanent damage of the cathode. In continuous

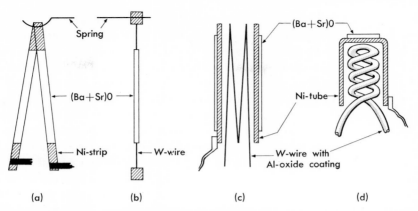

FIG. 2.2. Some common forms of the oxide cathode. (a) Directly heated, as used in power rectifiers, (b) directly heated, as used in battery-operated tubes (thickness of tungsten wire 5–50 μ), (c) indirectly heated (general use), (d) indirectly heated, as used in cathode-ray tubes.

operation, only a few percent of the saturation current may be drawn. A real temperature saturation of the cathode current, as is found for metal cathodes, does not occur in oxide cathodes. In the "saturation region," the current from an oxide cathode keeps increasing with voltage. This phenomenon apparently is connected with the resistance and the porous structure of the oxide layer. Both directly and indirectly heated oxide cathodes are widely used. Some common constructions are shown in Fig. 2.2.

Directly heated oxide cathodes have the highest emission efficiencies of all known types of cathodes. Therefore, they are particularly suitable if heating power is at a premium, for example when it must be supplied by small portable batteries. The voltage drop which occurs along a directly heated wire causes the interelectrode voltages in a tube with a directly heated cathode to vary from point to point along the cathode. This has an unfavorable influence on the characteristics of the tube when it is used as an amplifier or a rectifier. For this and other reasons, the heater voltage of battery-operated tubes with directly heated cathodes is kept as low as possible (about 1 V). When directly heated cathodes are fed from an ac-source, the anode current will show a ripple; hence, use of an ac-supply for the heaters of such tubes is unsuitable if small signals must be amplified.

Indirectly heated oxide cathodes have a smaller emission efficiency, but since the potential is now the same at each point on the cathode, the heaters may be fed from an ac-supply in most cases. As shown in Fig. 2.2(c) and (d) the heater filament is folded in such a way that wires with opposite currents lie close to each other. The magnetic fields around the wires therefore largely cancel, and their influence on the electron paths inside the tube is very small. Still, a very small ripple in the anode current may remain, so that it is sometimes necessary to use a dc heater supply in small signal amplifiers (signals $< 10 \mu V$).

Heater-to-cathode insulation is provided by a thin coat of aluminum oxide on the heater wire and sometimes also on the inside of the cathode cylinder. This layer can usually stand voltages of up to a few hundred volts for a short period. In continuous operation it is advisable to follow the specifications of the tube manufacturers since excessive heater-cathode voltage, if maintained for a long time, can lead to a marked reduction of the heater-cathode insulation.

Another feature of considerable importance in tubes with oxide cathodes is the increase of the effective electrical resistance between the metal base of the cathode and the oxide layer, which can occur when the tube is operated for long periods with the cathode heated but with the cathode current cut off by a large negative grid voltage. Under these conditions, a layer of low electrical conductivity may be formed on the surface of the metal by chemical reactions between the barium in the oxide and impurities in the base. This *cathode interface resistance* may become so large that the tube draws hardly any current when the grid voltage is finally made positive again (a phenomenon sometimes termed "sleeping sickness"). Such effects are most serious in circuits where a tube may be operated "cut off" for an extended period, as in the binary circuits involved in computers and nuclear counters. The effect can be prevented by use of very pure nickel as a base material.

2.3 FURTHER DETAILS OF TUBE CONSTRUCTION

Besides the cathode, an electronic tube contains grids, plates, and screens of widely different shapes. As already noted, the control grid, which is closest to the cathode, acts as a tap, controlling the current to the other electrodes. To make this current control most effective, the grid must be placed very close to the cathode; grid-to-cathode spacings of less than 0.1 mm are often found in modern tubes. To keep variation of the characteristic parameters of tubes with a narrow grid-to-cathode spacing within reasonable limits, differences in grid-to-cathode spacing must be maintained within a few microns. It is difficult to realize this tolerance limit with the normal grid construction shown in Fig. 2.3(a).

Better results have been obtained with the construction shown in Fig. 2.3(b) (frame grid). In this construction the grid wire is tightly wound on a rigid frame consisting of two cylindrical rods

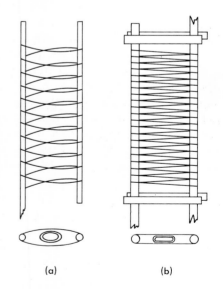

(a)   (b)

FIG. 2.3. Grid construction. (a) Normal grid, (b) frame grid.

held apart by welded strips. Here the space inside the grid, determined by the thickness of the rods, can be kept constant within a few microns.

Since the control grid is heated by radiation from the cathode, some barium may be deposited on the grid wires, and thermal emission from the grid may occur. This may have serious consequences when a large resistance is present in the grid circuit, because the grid voltage rises when the grid emits electrons, leading to an increase of tube current. A further increase of the grid temperature may then occur, and the tube current may "run away." Maximum permissible values, $R_{g\,max}$, of the resistance in the grid circuit are often given in tube manu-facturers' data. For small tubes these may vary from about 0.1 MΩ to many MΩ. Aside from the danger of runaway, these limits must be observed to keep grid-voltage variations caused by grid-current variations within certain limits. If the circuit requires a larger value of the grid resistance (in electrometer circuits, for example), a considerable improvement in stability may sometimes be obtained by use of a reduced heater voltage (4.5 V instead of 6.3 V, say). The anode current should be kept as small as possible in this case.

The *screen grid*, which is placed between the control grid and the anode, is usually connected to a positive voltage. A portion of the total cathode current is diverted to this grid. To keep this part of the current as small as possible, the screen grid is wound of thin wire. However, this makes the total heat-dissipating capability of the screen grid much smaller than that of the anode; in normal screen-grid tubes the maximum allowable screen-grid dissipation is only 20 to 30% that of the anode. Unless the screen-grid dissipation is limited to a safe value by use of a large screen-grid resistor, the anode circuit of a screen-grid tube must not be opened, or the screen grid would carry the whole cathode current. The maximum allowable dissipation of the screen may then be considerably exceeded, and the tube could be ruined.

In normal cases, the anode must dissipate the largest part of the total heat generated by the electron current. Measures taken to limit the anode tempera-ture include increasing the anode-radiating area by flanges, fins, etc., and by making the anode surface black. Nickel anodes should never be operated while red hot, because they would then give off gas. For most normal tubes the maximum anode dissipation in watts of black-nickel anodes is given approxi-mately by $W_a \approx 2 \times$ (anode area in cm^2). *Tantalum anodes* may be run at much higher temperatures (up to 1300°K) because this metal does not give off gases at a high temperature but, instead, actually absorbs them. The maximum anode dissipation per cm^2 of area for tantalum anodes is about a factor of 5 larger than for black-nickel anodes.

The electrodes of normal receiving and amplifying tubes are usually kept fixed with respect to each other by mica supports at the top and bottom of the electrode system (see Figs. 2.4 and 2.5). The electrodes or suitable extensions must fit tightly into these supports to prevent changes in their position which may lead to variations in the tube parameters, microphonics, or in the worst case, actual short circuits between electrodes. In most modern small tubes like

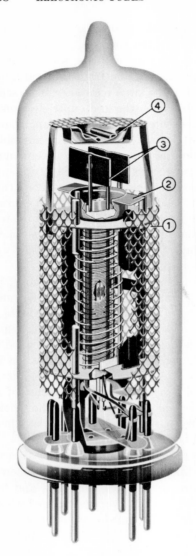

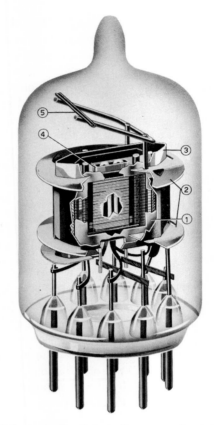

FIG. 2.5. Special quality pentode, with frame grid construction for control grid. 1. Suppressor grid, 2. mica supports (parts of the suppressor extend beyond these supports to provide extra shielding between control grid and anode), 3. anode, 4. cathode, 5. getter. (Courtesy Phillips, Inc.)

FIG. 2.4. Long-life pentode. 1. Outside shield screen, 2. shield between extended parts of control grid and anode, 3. control-grid cooling fins, 4. getter cap. (Courtesy Phillips, Inc.)

the ones shown in the figures, the electrode system is welded by very short leads to the tube pins which extend through the glass bottom. The very compact construction of these modern tubes contributes to their usefulness at high frequencies and makes them more resistant to shock and vibration.

After the electrode system is mounted, the bottom of the tube is sealed to the glass envelope. A glass tube is attached to the top of the envelope, through which the tube is pumped to a high vacuum. During pumping, cathode activation is started, and the electrode system is heated by means of an induction heater to drive out gases. After the tube is sealed off, a small vessel with some barium attached to one of the electrode pins is heated so that some barium evaporates onto the wall. The thin barium mirror thus formed is a *getter*, which absorbs the remaining gases and brings the vacuum to a final value well below 10^{-6} mm Hg. During normal operation the getter continues to absorb gases that may be driven out of the electrodes and therefore helps to prevent cathode poisoning.

2.4 SPACE CHARGE

In most thermionic vacuum tubes, under normal operating conditions the cathode is kept at such a high temperature that electrons are emitted more rapidly than they can be collected by the other electrodes. As a result, the evacuated space near the cathode becomes filled with electrons, which form a space charge. The relation between the applied voltages and the currents which flow between the cathode and the other electrodes is largely determined by the space charge. This relation, called the *space-charge law*, will be qualitatively derived for a general case. Consider a thermally emitting cathode k of arbitrary shape and an equipotential surface a, having a positive potential V with respect to k (Fig. 2.6). At each point P between k and a there is a definite space-charge density (space charge per unit volume). The product of this density ρ and the velocity v of the electrons at P gives the charge passing that point per unit area per unit time, i.e. *the current density $J = \rho v$*. We wish to determine the relation between this current density and the potential difference V. In order to derive the current-voltage relationship in its simplest form, two assumptions are made.

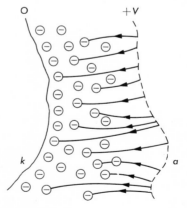

FIG. 2.6. Space charge. All lines of force from the surface a terminate on the space charge cloud.

1. The electrons leave the cathode with an initial velocity $v_0 = 0$. In this case the electrons derive all of their kinetic energy, $\frac{1}{2}mv^2$, from the field between k and a. On passing the surface a, they have gained an amount of energy $eV = \frac{1}{2}mv^2$, the speed varying as the square root of the potential, $v \propto \sqrt{V}$.

2. All field lines originating at any point in the surface a terminate on the space charge, i.e. the cathode is screened completely by the space charge (see Fig. 2.6). In this case the total space charge will be directly proportional to the potential V, as with the charge on the plates of a condenser. Under this condition the current is considered *space-charge limited*.

Since the distribution of the space charge is independent of V so long as condition 2 is fulfilled (this follows from general properties of the electrostatic field), the space-charge density at each point will also be proportional to V: $\rho \propto V$. Thus, $J = \rho v \propto V\sqrt{V}$, or

$$J = KV^{3/2}. \tag{2.3}$$

This is the familiar Child-Langmuir space-charge law. The constant K, which depends on the shape of the electrodes, can be calculated for several electrode shapes. The simplest configuration is that of a plane diode (Fig. 2.7). In this case

$$J = (K'/d^2)V_a^{3/2}, \tag{2.4}$$

where d is the cathode-anode distance and V_a is the potential difference between anode and cathode. The constant K' now contains only fundamental constants. A complete derivation of (2.4) yields $K' = 2.34 \times 10^{-6} \text{ A/V}^{3/2}$.

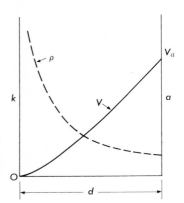

FIG. 2.7. Potential V and space charge density ρ in a plane diode, for zero initial velocity of the electrons.

The inverse proportionality of J with d^2 in Eq. (2.4) can be readily understood. As the distance d between the anode and cathode is varied, the potential V at any equipotential surface, and hence the total space charge between the cathode and the initial position of that equipotential, would change. Since the anode is an equipotential, and its potential V_a is kept constant (by an external battery connected between the cathode and anode) as d is varied, the *total* space charge between the anode and cathode must vary as $1/d$, as with the charge on a parallel-plate condenser. Since the volume available for the space charge also varies as $1/d$, the space-charge density, and hence the current density, will vary as $1/d^2$.

In a plane diode all equipotential planes are parallel to a and k. For each distance x from k we have the same current density

$$J = (K'/x^2)(V(x))^{3/2}.$$

Combining this with (2.4), we obtain

$$V(x) = V_a(x/d)^{4/3}. \tag{2.5}$$

This potential distribution is indicated in Fig. 2.7.

Another practical example is the cylindrical diode shown in Fig. 2.8. In analogy with the law for a flat diode, the space-charge law in this case may be written as

$$J = \gamma(K'/d^2)V_a^{3/2}. \tag{2.6}$$

Again, $d = r_a - r_k$ is the distance between anode and cathode, and γ is a function of r_a/r_k, as shown in Fig. 2.8. Its value differs from 1 (for a flat diode) by at most 20%.

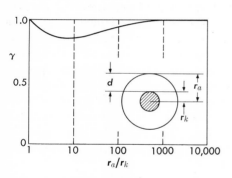

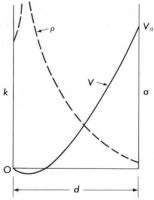

FIG. 2.8. Factor γ, which converts the space charge law for a plane diode to that for a cylindrical diode (from W. H. Aldous and E. Appleton, *Thermionic Vacuum Tubes*, Methuen, 1952).

FIG. 2.9. Potential and space charge density distributions in a plane diode, for finite initial velocity of the electrons.

So far, it was assumed that the electrons leave the cathode with zero initial velocity. In reality, they would have a velocity distribution with an average velocity corresponding to an energy of a few tenths of an electron volt, for the energy distribution of the emitted electrons actually obeys the Fermi-Dirac law (Eq. 1.3). This will cause the space charge to create a potential distribution with a minimum at a small distance from the cathode, making the potential gradient dV/dx negative closer to the cathode (see Fig. 2.9). The electrons leaving the cathode will therefore be pulled back. For normal tube voltages, only a small fraction of the total number of electrons emitted is able to traverse the potential minimum and reach the anode; the majority returns to the cathode. The potential minimum adjusts itself to such a value that the anode current closely follows the space-charge law. An exact derivation of the space-charge law, with the initial velocities of the electrons taken into account, has been given by Langmuir and Compton. Their theoretical treatment shows that the anode-cathode distance d in Eq. (2.4) should be replaced by the distance from the anode to the potential minimum, and that the voltage at the minimum should be added to the anode voltage V_a. The potential minimum acts as a *virtual cathode* at which there is no electric field. For a practical case, with $T = 1000°K$ and $J = 1\ mA/cm^2$, the potential minimum lies at a distance of 0.1 mm from the cathode and is 0.5 V deep.

2.5   EDISON CURRENT: RETARDED-FIELD REGION

Because the electrons leave the cathode with a finite average velocity, some anode current will flow even at a small negative anode voltage V_a. This current, the initial or Edison current, decreases very rapidly when the anode becomes more negative. If we disregard space charge, we can represent the potential distribution as in Fig. 2.10. We know that when two solids are placed in contact, the Fermi energies of the two come to the same level. When they are connected together through a battery with a potential difference V across its terminals, the two Fermi levels are displaced in energy by eV. Since we are drawing potential barriers for electrons, we conventionally draw negative potentials upward. From Fig. 2.10 it is apparent that if electrons emitted from the cathode are now to reach the anode, they must acquire a minimum thermal energy equal to the effective work function $W' = e(\phi_a - V_a)$, where ϕ_a is the Richardson potential of the *anode* if, as is usually the case, $\phi_a > \phi_k$. The number of such energetic electrons (compare with Eq. 2.1) will vary exponentially with the anode voltage as V_a is made negative, and the diode approaches cutoff as $\epsilon^{-e(\phi_a - V_a)/kT}$. Thus, for the current density as a function of V_a in this co-called *retarded-field* region,

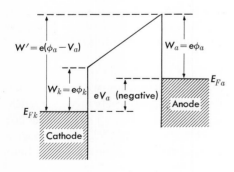

FIG. 2.10.   Potential distribution for retarded-field operation of a diode. The anode is V_a volts negative with respect to the cathode.

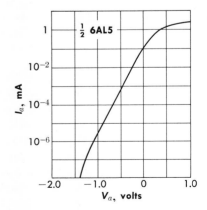

FIG. 2.11. Current-voltage characteristics of a diode in the retarded-field region.

we may write

$$J = J_0 \epsilon^{eV_a/kT},$$ (2.7)

where J_0 contains the factor $\epsilon^{-e\phi_a/kT}$. This expression is valid only when the influence of the space charge on the potential distribution in the tube is small, i.e. at low current densities. In practice the exponential dependence expressed by Eq. (2.7) is reasonably accurate in the range of $V_a = -0.1$ to -1.5 V. In this voltage range J varies by a factor larger than 10^6! Below -1.5 V, leakage currents generally dominate. The retarded-field region of a typical small diode is shown in Fig. 2.11. This region is sometimes utilized in logarithmic amplifiers, in which the output signal should be proportional to the logarithm of the input signal. Such a relation exists for a diode if V_a is taken as the output signal and J is proportional to the input signal $\left(V_a = (kT/e) \log (J/J_0)\right)$.

2.6 HIGH-FIELD OPERATION

Ordinarily, thermionic diodes are operated either at small positive anode voltages, under space-charge-limited conditions, or at relatively small negative anode voltages, in the retarded-field region or beyond, where the electron current is essentially zero. The circuit parameters are usually chosen deliberately to limit operation to this range, since the power rating of the device may be exceeded if the anode swings too far positive while the current continues to rise or so far negative that breakdown occurs. However, tubes may be forced into operating in these unusual regions either through a failure of some part of the circuit or through poor circuit design, and it is advisable to consider the characteristics of diodes in these atypical circumstances.

2.6.1 Temperature-limited operation

When the anode is made sufficiently positive that the electrons are collected as fast as they are emitted, there is no space charge, and the operation is designated temperature-limited. The potential diagram appropriate for this case is shown in Fig. 2.12. This was previously discussed in Section 2.2, and the current-voltage relationships were given in Eqs. (2.1) and (2.2).

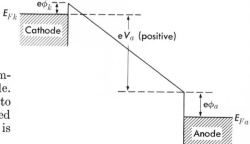

FIG. 2.12. Potential diagram for temperature-limited operation of a diode. The anode is very positive with respect to the cathode, hence electrons are collected as fast as they are emitted, and there is no space charge formed.

From Eq. (2.1) it is apparent that so long as the anode is sufficiently positive to collect the electrons, the current in the temperature-limited case is *independent of the anode voltage*. As the anode voltage is decreased, however, we must eventually reach a point where the electrons are emitted more rapidly than they can move to the anode, and the current will drop to zero following the space-charge law and the retarded-field law, as shown in Fig. 2.13.

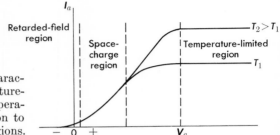

FIG. 2.13.   Current-voltage characteristics of a diode in temperature-limited operation, for two temperatures $T_1 < T_2$, showing transition to space-charge and retarded-field regions.

Since the effects of temperature limitation restrict the maximum current achievable, we usually take care to operate the cathode at sufficiently high temperatures that the over-all circuit performance is not limited by such effects, even when the heater voltage drops because of line fluctuations. However, when tubes age, the cathode work function may increase slightly due to loss or oxidation of the cathode surface, and temperature limitation may occur.

2.6.2   High positive-anode-voltage operation—Schottky effect

If the anode voltage is made very positive under temperature-limited operation, the current may begin to increase again because of a new effect. The electric field of the anode penetrates slightly inside the surface of the cathode, decreasing the effective work function of the cathode. This phenomenon is known as the Schottky effect.

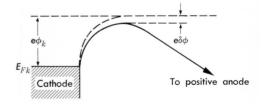

FIG. 2.14.   Schottky effect, showing decrease in the work function of the cathode when the anode is made very positive. The dashed curve shows the barrier for low anode voltages.

The potential at the surface of the cathode under these conditions is shown in Fig. 2.14. The presence of the electric field E between the cathode and anode causes a decrease in the work function, for the force acting on an electron at a distance x outside the cathode is no longer simply the image force $-e^2/4\pi\varepsilon_0(2x)^2$ but now includes a term $+eE$, tending to pull the electron away from the cathode. We can determine the effective work function, as before (see Eq. 1.16), by determining the work done in carrying a charge from the surface to infinity. The original Richardson potential of the cathode is reduced by an amount

$$\delta\phi = \sqrt{eE/4\pi\varepsilon_0}.\tag{2.8}$$

This effect causes an increase in J_{th} by a factor of exp $(e\delta\phi/kT)$. Ordinarily this is not a large correction. For example, for a field of 10^6 V/m and a temperature of 2500°K, this factor is only 1.2, so that the thermionic current is increased about 20%. Even for an oxide-coated cathode which normally operates at about 1000°K, the effect of this large field would cause only about a 60% increase in the current. Other effects in oxide-coated cathodes, such as the changing resistance of the oxide layer, may lead to a much larger increase in the saturation current at high positive anode voltages, quite overshadowing the Schottky effect.

2.6.3 High negative-anode-voltage operation—field emission

When the anode of a diode is made negative with respect to the cathode, the first effect, as we have seen, is simply that the cathode current drops to zero. However, if the anode is made very negative, as sometimes happens in rectifier circuits, we may reach a state where electrons are emitted from the *anode* by the quantum-mechanical process of *field emission*. Under these circumstances, the current will rise very rapidly with the electric field, as

$$J_{fe} \propto E^2 \epsilon^{-C(e\phi_a)^{3/2}/E}.\tag{2.9}$$

Here $e\phi_a$ is the work function of the anode and E is the electric field. The factor C contains only universal constants and has a value $6.8 \times 10^9 (\text{V/m})(eV)^{-3/2}$. This phenomenon, since it occurs only at very-high-field operation, almost always results in the destruction of the diode. All diodes, accordingly, have a maximum *peak inverse-voltage rating*, which must never be exceeded for safe operation. From Eq. (2.9) it is apparent that the maximum permissible field should increase exponentially with the $\frac{3}{2}$ power of the anode work function; hence, high work-function materials (for example, W, Ta, Ni) are mostly used for the anodes in rectifier diodes, to maximize the peak inverse-voltage rating. Note, however, that the same effect can occur if the cathode becomes very negative with respect to the anode *before the cathode is heated*. Since the cathode almost always is made of material of a much lower work function than the anode, we can easily damage the diodes by field emission from the cathode, even though the maximum voltage swing is well below the peak inverse rating of the tube. In high-voltage rectifiers it is therefore very important that the high voltage not be applied to the rectifier diodes before the cathodes have had time to reach their operating temperature. In some circuits, time-delay interlocks are used to avoid such catastrophic complications.

2.7 CURRENT CONTROL BY MORE THAN ONE ELECTRODE

The current drawn from the cathode of a tube with a number of electrodes (grids, anodes, etc.) will be influenced by the voltage of each of these to a different degree. In order to be able to formulate a simple space-charge law for this case, two important simplifying assumptions must be made.

1. *The influence of space charge on the potential distribution between the electrodes can be neglected.* Under this restriction, simple electrostatic laws relating charges and voltages can be applied. In particular, the induced charge on the cathode,

$$-Q_k = C_1 V_1 + C_2 V_2 + \cdots + C_n V_n,$$ (2.10)

is a sum of contributions from all the other electrodes; $C_1, \ldots, C_n$ are the capacities of these electrodes with respect to the cathode, and $V_1, \ldots, V_n$ are the voltages. The C_1 to C_n are different from the values given in tube handbooks, which include contributions of leads, shields, etc. The action of all the electrodes combined can be replaced by that of a single fictitious control electrode. We may think of an electrode constructed in such a way that its capacity, C_e, with respect to the cathode just equals the sum of the capacities of all the real electrodes,

$$C_e = C_1 + \cdots + C_n,$$ (2.11)

and apply to it a voltage

$$V_{ec} = -Q_k/C_e.$$ (2.12)

At the cathode *as a whole*, no change is felt; the average field at the cathode induced by the fictitious control electrode equals the *average* field from all real electrodes. Combining (2.10), (2.11), and (2.12), we find that the effective control voltage is

$$V_{ec} = \frac{V_1 + (C_2/C_1)V_2 + \cdots + (C_n/C_1)V_n}{1 + (C_2/C_1) + \cdots + (C_n/C_1)}.$$ (2.13)

The capacity ratio $D_x = C_x/C_1$ gives the ratio in which the field from electrode number x and electrode number 1 penetrates to the cathode. It is called the *penetration factor* of electrode x through electrode 1. The electrodes are usually numbered in such a way that D_x decreases with increasing x. In tubes with several grids, the values of D decrease by an order of magnitude for each following grid, which is effectively shielded by the grids closer to the cathode. Normally, D_2 is already small compared with 1, so that (2.13) may be approximated by

$$V_{ec} \approx V_1 + D_2 V_2 + \cdots + D_n V_n.$$ (2.14)

Because of the nonlinear current-voltage relationship expressed by the space-charge law, the cathode current in a tube is not uniquely determined by the value of V_{ec}. As noted, this voltage determines only the *average* field at the cathode. Different combinations of electrode voltages may produce the same average field but different field distributions along the cathode, leading to different cathode currents. We must therefore introduce the second restriction for formulation of a simple space-charge law.

2. *The field strength is the same for all points on the cathode.* Then the space-charge law (2.3) can be applied if we replace V with the effective control voltage V_{ec}:

$$J = KV_{ec}^{3/2} = K(V_1 + D_2V_2 + \cdots + D_nV_n)^{3/2}. \qquad (2.15)$$

The electron current from the cathode is distributed between all electrodes that carry a positive voltage with respect to the cathode. If conditions 1 and 2 are fulfilled, (2.15) is valid independent of the shape of the electrodes. The constant K can be evaluated, at least in principle, for any special shape of the electrodes.

In practical cases, deviations from conditions 1 and 2 often occur. Such deviations may lead to unwanted, as well as explicitly desired, changes in the tube characteristics. We shall see, for instance, how the useful properties of beam tetrodes (Section 2.9.2) depend to a large extent on the space charge between the screen grid and anode. Condition 1 is certainly not fulfilled here. On the other hand, in remote cutoff tubes the variation of the field along the cathode caused by a special construction of the control grid is utilized (Section 2.11). Condition 2 is violated here. Yet in many cases a major part of the useful tube characteristics follows the space-charge law rather well. We shall therefore continue with a discussion of some simple tubes, starting with Eq. (2.15).

2.8   TRIODES

A triode contains three electrodes: a cathode, an anode, and a control grid between the two. It normally operates with negative grid and positive anode voltages. In this case, current flows only from anode to cathode. The dependence of the anode current I_a on the grid voltage V_g and anode voltage V_a may be represented graphically in several ways. One of the most common is a plot of anode current as ordinate as a function of anode voltage as abscissa, usually called the *plate characteristic*. Another frequently used representation is a plot of anode current as ordinate against grid voltage as abscissa, called the *transfer characteristic*. Usually I_a vs. V_a plate characteristics are given for a number of values of V_g, or I_a vs. V_g transfer characteristics for a number of values of V_a (see Figs. 2.15 and 2.16). From such sets of curves, for any pair of given quantities the third can be found. Both I_a vs. V_a and I_a vs. V_g characteristics in principle give the same information; which of the representations is preferred depends on the particular application.

If the anode current is not too small, the characteristics given in Figs. 2.15 and 2.16 are in good agreement with the space-charge law:

$$I_a = K(V_g + D_aV_a)^{3/2}, \qquad (2.16)$$

which is a special case of (2.15).

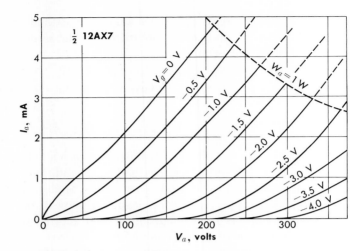

FIG. 2.15. I_a vs. V_a plate characteristics for one half of a double triode (12AX7). The dashed line $W_a = 1W$ indicates the limit above which the allowable anode dissipation is exceeded.

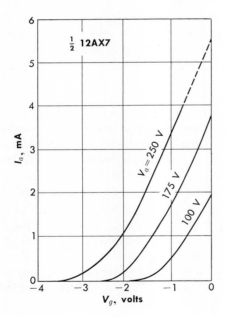

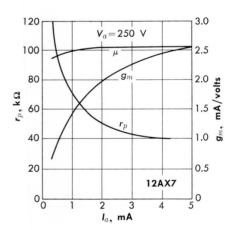

FIG. 2.16. I_a vs. V_g transfer characteristics for one half of a double triode (12AX7). The dashed line is for anode currents in excess of the allowable anode dissipation.

FIG. 2.17. Variation of mutual conductance g_m, plate resistance r_p, and amplification factor μ, with anode current for a triode.

For calculating circuit response or for evaluating which tube is most suitable for a certain application, it is often sufficient to have available the values of one or more of the following parameters, which may be derived from the characteristics by differentiation:

mutual conductance or transconductance: $g_m = \left(\dfrac{\partial I_a}{\partial V_g}\right)_{V_a}$,

plate resistance: $\qquad\qquad\qquad\qquad r_p = \left(\dfrac{\partial V_a}{\partial I_a}\right)_{V_g}$, $\qquad$ (2.17)

amplification factor: $\qquad\qquad\quad \mu = -\left(\dfrac{\partial V_a}{\partial V_g}\right)_{I_a}$.

A simple relation holds between these three quantities:

$$r_p g_m = \mu. \qquad (2.18)$$

This relation, attributed to Barkhausen, can easily be derived as follows: Small changes, dV_g and dV_a, in the grid and anode voltages cause a small change, dI_a, in the anode current, given by the total differential

$$dI_a = \left(\frac{\partial I_a}{\partial V_g}\right)_{V_a} dV_g + \left(\frac{\partial I_a}{\partial V_a}\right)_{V_g} dV_a$$

$$= g_m\, dV_g + (1/r_p)\, dV_a. \qquad (2.19)$$

For $dV_a/-dV_g = r_p g_m$, we see that $dI_a = 0$. But the ratio of dV_a and $-dV_g$ is the amplification factor μ, by definition.

From the space-charge law (2.16), we derive

$$g_m = \tfrac{3}{2}K^{2/3}I_a^{1/3}, \qquad (2.20)$$

$$r_p = \tfrac{2}{3}\mu K^{-2/3}I_a^{-1/3}, \qquad (2.21)$$

$$\mu = 1/D_a = \text{const.} \qquad (2.22)$$

The experimental dependence of these three quantities on I_a is shown in Fig. 2.17, for a particular case (one half of a 12AX7, a widely used high-μ double triode). Except for small I_a, where μ decreases, the curves of Fig. 2.17 are in good agreement with (2.20) through (2.22). Experimental values of g_m, r_p, and μ can also be found from the I_a vs. V_a and I_a vs. V_g characteristics. The slope of the tangent to an I_a vs. V_g characteristic, for instance, gives the mutual conductance at the point of contact. Similarly, tangents to an I_a vs. V_a characteristic yield values for $1/r_p$. The amplification factor is found from the shift ΔV_g of an I_a vs. V_g characteristic in the negative V_g-direction if the anode voltage is increased by an amount ΔV_a. The ratio $\Delta V_a/\Delta V_g$ is the amplification factor μ. Because μ is reasonably constant, the change ΔV_a need not be very small. The following values of the characteristic parameters of the 12AX7 were derived from Figs. 2.15 and 2.16 in this way:

$$g_m = 1.6 \text{ mA/V*}, \quad r_p = 58 \text{ k}\Omega,$$

and $\mu = 100$ at $V_a = 250$ V and $V_g = -2.0$ V $(I_a = 1.2 \text{ mA})$.

2.8.1 Amplification by a triode

In Fig. 2.18 a triode is schematically shown connected as a voltage amplifier in the *common cathode* circuit (i.e. cathode at a fixed voltage, input signal applied between grid and cathode, output signal derived between anode and cathode). The cathode heater, or "filament," must be connected to a voltage source if electrons are to be emitted at all from the cathode. However, since this fact is obvious, we frequently omit the heater circuit in the schematic diagram to avoid cluttering the picture. In most cases, the heater current is furnished at the rated voltage of the tube from the ac-line, either through a transformer or by connecting a number of heaters in series. Suppose that a very small signal voltage v_g is applied to the grid in series with the fixed negative grid bias V_{g0}. Replacing the differentials dV_a, dV_g, and dI_a in (2.19) with the small signal voltages v_g and v_a and the small signal current i_a, we have

$$i_a = g_m v_g + v_a/r_p, \qquad (2.23)$$

or, using Barkhausen's law (2.18),

$$i_a = g_m v_g + g_m v_a/\mu$$
$$= g_m(v_g + D_a v_a). \qquad (2.24)$$

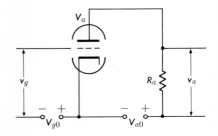

FIG. 2.18. Basic triode amplifier circuit. Capital letters V indicate dc-voltages, small letters v are small ac-voltages.

The anode signal voltage and current are related by Ohm's law, $v_a = -i_a R_a$ (minus sign because v_a decreases when i_a increases); therefore, we can write for (2.24)

$$v_a = -\frac{R_a r_p}{R_a + r_p} g_m v_g \qquad (2.25)$$

or

$$v_a = -\frac{R_a}{R_a + r_p} \mu v_g. \qquad (2.26)$$

---

* In some texts, transconductances are expressed in units of ohms^{-1} or *mhos*; 1 mA/V = 1 mmho or 1000 μmhos. This nomenclature tends to obscure the physical fact that g_m expresses the ratio of an increment in plate current to an increment in grid voltage and is not actually a conductance, although it has the dimension of conductance. To avoid confusion, we shall use units of mA/V for g_m.

The voltage *amplification* (or *gain*) of the amplifier, defined as $A = v_a/v_g$, is

$$A = -\frac{R_a r_p}{R_a + r_p} g_m \qquad (2.27)$$

or

$$A = -\frac{R_a}{R_a + r_p} \mu. \qquad (2.28)$$

Note that the gain A is a negative quantity, to account for the fact that the changes in grid voltage and anode voltage are of opposite sign. When V_g increases (grid becomes more positive), V_a decreases (anode becomes more negative). Expression (2.28) shows that the absolute value of the voltage amplification approaches μ if R_a is made much larger than r_p. If we attempt to realize this upper limit in practice, we must keep in mind that if R_a is increased at a constant supply voltage V_{a0}, the anode current is reduced, and therefore r_p becomes larger. For this reason, amplification close to μ can be realized only for a sufficiently high supply voltage. In Fig. 2.19 the amplification of one half of a 12AX7 is shown as a function of R_a for several values of V_{a0}. A supply voltage of at least 400 V is needed for the gain to approach μ within 10% for any value of R_a. For very large R_a, it is apparent that the gain actually decreases again; here the amplification factor μ itself becomes smaller because of the reduced anode current. This phenomenon, also apparent in Fig. 2.17, will be further discussed in Section 2.11.

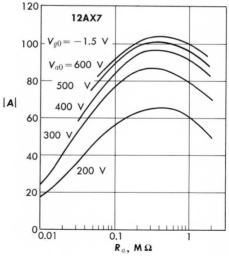

FIG. 2.19. Magnitude of voltage gain A for a 12AX7 triode in the circuit of Fig. 2.18, for various values of the anode resistor R_a and the anode supply voltage V_{a0}.

At values of I_a which are not too small, the value of the amplification factor μ is close to the ratio, C_{gk}/C_{ak}, of the electrostatic capacities of the grid and anode with respect to the cathode, according to the definition of D_a (Eq. 2.13). This ratio can be derived for various electrode configurations from electrostatic field theory. Results of such calculations are given in Fig. 2.20 for the case of a flat

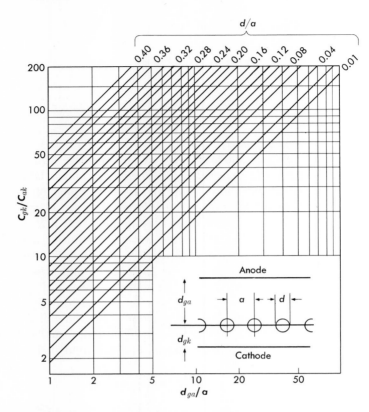

FIG. 2.20.   Theoretical capacity ratio of grid and anode with respect to the cathode (from K. R. Spangenberg, *Vacuum Tubes*, McGraw-Hill, 1948).

cathode and anode and a grid consisting of straight wires of equal spacing a and diameter d. Note that the values of the ratio C_{gk}/C_{ak} do *not* depend on the grid-cathode spacing d_{gk} but only on the ratios d/a and d_{ga}/a. The amplification factor μ thus depends sensitively on the spacing of the grid wires, and increases as the wires are brought closer together.

To illustrate the size and position of the electrodes in a typical commercial tube, a cross section through one half of a 12AX7 ($\mu = 100$) is shown in Fig. 2.21.

The anode voltage required to draw a certain amount of current through a tube at a fixed negative grid voltage increases with increasing μ; for this reason it is impractical to construct triodes with amplification factors larger than about 100. To achieve a higher voltage amplification, it is more convenient to use pentodes. Unlike the amplification factor, the mutual conductance is strongly influenced by the grid-cathode distance d_{gk}, but relatively little by the spacing a of the grid wires. By setting $K = K'/d_{gk}^2$ in Eq. (2.20) [as with the case of the flat cathode and anode of Eq. (2.4) for a diode], we see that the mutual conductance is inversely proportional to $d_{gk}^{4/3}$. Therefore, a large value of g_m requires a small grid-cathode spacing. The detailed construction of a triode, in particular the choice of the spacing of the grid wires and of the grid-cathode distance, determines whether the tube will have a high μ or a high g_m, or both. Every manufacturer makes a whole series of tubes, at various wattage ratings, to provide a number of different choices of μ and g_m in each size. The selection of the optimum tube for a given amplifier, as we shall see later, is dictated by the requirements of the whole circuit, and involves consideration of the available power supply voltages, the required input and output impedance levels, the amplitudes of input and output signals, and the required frequency bandwidth.

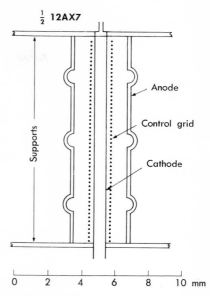

FIG. 2.21. Cross section of a high-μ triode ($\mu = 100$).

2.8.2 Grid current

Because of their initial velocity, some electrons may reach the grid even at negative grid voltages of a few tenths of a volt. This grid current causes a reduction of the apparent resistance in the grid circuit, which sometimes must be taken into account. In general, the grid current for the same electrode voltages will be larger if the grid wires are closer together (high μ) or if the grid is very close to the cathode (high g_m). If possible, a negative grid bias voltage of at least one volt is chosen in order to reduce this grid current to a sufficiently small value (for the 12AX7, for instance, $I_g < 0.3\,\mu\text{A}$ at $V_g = -1.3$ V).

In many applications, positive grid voltages occur. In oscillators, for example, the circuit is usually arranged so that the grid periodically becomes positive. In pulse circuits, grids are often held slightly positive most of the time. In such cases, the electrons emitted by the cathode are distributed between the control grid and the anode. The space-charge law, however, remains valid for the total cathode current:

$$I_k = I_g + I_a = K(V_g + D_a V_a)^{3/2}. \qquad (2.29)$$

But we are more interested in the current distribution between the grid and anode than in the total current. For this distribution, unfortunately, no simple law can be given. It is often greatly influenced by *secondary emission* from the grid, which starts for positive grid voltages of more than a few volts. Secondary electrons ejected from the grid will be drawn to the anode, thus increasing the anode current at the expense of the grid current. The latter may even change sign if, on the average, more than one secondary electron is created per incident primary electron. If the grid voltage should exceed the anode voltage, which in practice does not occur very often, the grid current would rise very rapidly because the secondary electrons from the anode are now accelerated toward the grid. Except for very low values of V_a, Eq. (2.29) remains valid all the time. Figure 2.22 is a qualitative representation of the behavior of I_a and I_g as a function of V_g.

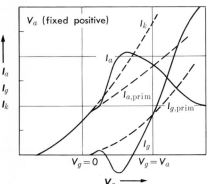

FIG. 2.22. I_a vs. V_g and I_g vs. V_g characteristics for a triode with positive control grid voltage. The dashed curves $I_{a\ \text{prim}}$ and $I_{g\ \text{prim}}$ indicate the shape of the characteristics in the absence of secondary emission. Note that $I_k = I_a + I_g$.

Secondary emission is strongly dependent on the condition of the surfaces of the electrodes. For instance, it may be increased considerably if barium, a common constituent of the cathode, is evaporated from the cathode onto the grid and the anode. The effect therefore varies from tube to tube and also changes with time during use. In Fig. 2.22 the behavior of the *primary* currents is also indicated. Their distribution will be considered in more detail in the next section.

2.9 SCREEN-GRID TUBES

We have just seen that voltage amplification in a triode is limited by the amplification factor, which is a measure of the relative effectiveness of the shielding of the anode from the cathode by the control grid. In a triode, this shielding could not be made arbitrarily great because, after all, some space must be left between the grid wires for current to flow. If, however, between the control grid and the anode, we place a second grid g_2, the *screen grid*, which is connected to a fixed *positive* voltage, the shielding of the anode from the cathode will be considerably improved while the anode current will be kept at a normal value determined largely by the screen-grid voltage. At normal operating voltages, the influence of the anode voltage on the cathode current will now be very small, which means that both the amplification factor μ and the plate resistance r_p will be quite high. In most cases, the anode load resistance R_a will be chosen much smaller than r_p, to keep the required anode supply voltage reasonable.

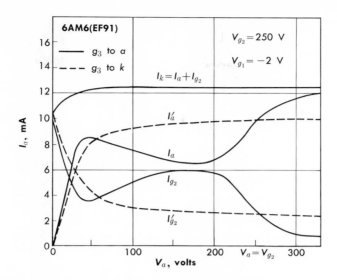

FIG. 2.23.   Solid lines: tetrode characteristics obtained by connection of suppressor grid of a pentode to the anode.   Broken lines: pentode characteristics, suppressor grid connected to cathode.

Hence, to a good approximation, the gain of the amplifier is simply

$$A = -R_a g_m. \tag{2.30}$$

This follows directly from (2.27), for $R_a \ll r_p$. The maximum possible amplification μ, which is much higher than that of a triode because of the smaller penetration of the anode field into the cathode space, will not often be realized in practice. The large values of R_a for which it could be obtained would necessitate impractically high supply voltages V_{a0} (voltages of up to a few thousand volts).

Historically, the screen grid was introduced to reduce the grid-anode capacity, which was likely to cause regeneration in the tuned-grid–tuned-plate amplifiers common in radio receivers. For a variety of present-day applications, both the capacitive and the electronic separation provided by the screen grid are still of great importance. For a negative control grid, the cathode current distributes itself between the screen grid and the anode. As in a triode with a positive grid, the anode-to-screen-grid current ratio in a screen-grid tube is strongly influenced by secondary emission; an extra current of secondary electrons goes to the most positive electrode, causing undesirable irregularities in the I_a vs. V_a characteristics (see Fig. 2.23). The secondary electron currents between the screen grid and the anode can be suppressed by a potential minimum between these electrodes. Since the initial velocities of the secondary electrons are small, this minimum need not be very deep; hence, the fast primary electrons are only

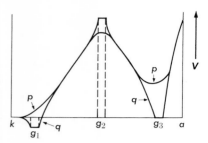

FIG. 2.24. Potential distribution between cathode (k) and anode (a) of a pentode; curve p is for a plane between the grid wires and curve q for a plane intersecting the grid wires; g_1 is the control grid, g_2 the screen, and g_3 the suppressor.

slightly affected. Such a potential minimum can be obtained in two ways:

1. By placing a grid with large spacing between a and g_2. This so-called *suppressor* grid (g_3) is usually connected to the cathode. The potential distribution in the *pentode* thus obtained is shown in Fig. 2.24.

2. By concentrating the electrons between g_2 and a in such a way that the resulting space-charge density leads to a lowering of the potential sufficient to suppress secondary electron emission. This is done in *beam tetrodes*. (Also in pentodes, especially at high currents, the space charge in the space between the screen grid and anode may influence the operation.) Both types of tube will now be considered in greater detail.

2.9.1 Pentodes

Because of the high voltage gain that can be obtained with pentodes, they are widely used in voltage amplifiers. Figure 2.25 shows the position of the electrodes in a medium-high mutual-conductance pentode.

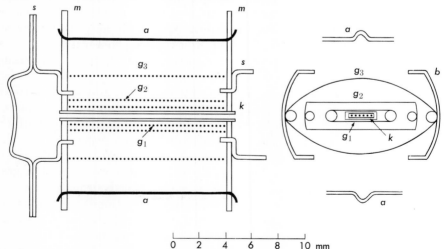

FIG. 2.25. Cross section of a high-frequency pentode: k, g_1, g_2, g_3, and a are the electrodes; s is a shield between the grid and anode support wires where they extend beyond the mica supports m; s is connected to g_3 and to the beam plates b that concentrate the electrons onto the anodes.

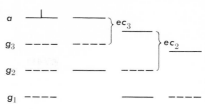

FIG. 2.26. Reduction of a pentode to an
equivalent triode with the aid of effective
control electrodes.

Two laws govern the current in a pentode: the space-charge law for the total
cathode current and a distribution law for the current between the screen grid
and anode (we consider only the common cases where g_1 and g_3 draw no current).
For this case the space-charge law can be written as

$$I_k = I_a + I_{g_2} = KV_{ec}^{3/2} = K(V_{g_1} + D_{g_2}V_{g_2} + D_{g_3}V_{g_3} + D_aV_a)^{3/2}.$$

$$(2.31)$$

The expression for the effective control voltage V_{ec} is a special case of (2.14).

The concept of the effective control voltage in a pentode can be clarified if
we replace the pentode with imaginary triode configurations, successively
combining electrodes, as indicated in Fig. 2.26. We may write, for the effective
control voltage in a triode consisting of anode a, grid g_3, and an imaginary
cathode replacing g_2 (Fig. 2.26b),

$$V_{ec_3} = V_{g_3} + D_{ag_3}V_a.$$

$$(2.32)$$

Let us consider ec_3 as an imaginary control electrode which combines the action
of a and g_3. This electrode can in turn be considered as the anode of the triode
indicated in Fig. 2.26(c) with an effective control voltage

$$V_{ec_2} = V_{g_2} + D_{ec_3g_2}V_{ec_3}.$$

$$(2.33)$$

Finally, the imaginary electrode ec_2 can be considered as the anode in a triode
that further consists of g_1 and c, having the effective control voltage

$$V_{ec} = V_{g_1} + D_{ec_2g_1}V_{ec_2}.$$

$$(2.34)$$

Eliminating V_{ec_2} and V_{ec_3} from (2.32) through (2.34), we find that

$$V_{ec} = V_{g_1} + D_{g_2}V_{g_2} + D_{g_3}V_{g_3} + D_aV_a,$$

$$(2.35)$$

with

$$D_{g_2} = D_{ec_2g_1}, \quad D_{g_3} = D_{ec_3g_2}D_{ec_2g_1}, \quad \text{and} \quad D_a = D_{ag_3}D_{ec_3g_2}D_{ec_2g_1}.$$

$$(2.36)$$

This relation shows that the contributions of the various electrodes to the effective control voltage are determined by *products* of the penetration factors. Since each of these factors may range from 0.01 to 0.2, the effect of the outer electrodes on the control voltage becomes very small. The I_k vs. V_a characteristics of a pentode are almost horizontal for a large range of V_a (see Fig. 2.23); this illustrates the weak penetration of the anode field to the cathode. For very low V_a, however, I_k decreases. This observation can be explained as an effect of the space charge created between g_1 and g_2 by electrons returning from the g_2-a space when V_a is much lower than V_{g_2}. This space charge causes a noticeable decrease of the effective control voltage. Clearly, condition 1 on p. 46 is now no longer fulfilled; therefore, a deviation from the simple space-charge law can be expected.

An accurate expression for the distribution of the cathode current between g_2 and a cannot easily be derived from simple arguments because this distribution depends on the individual paths of the electrons, which are determined by the precise arrangement of the grids and the anode and their voltages. One general statement can be made, however. When the voltages of all electrodes are changed by the same factor, the electron paths—aside from space-charge effects—remain the same, and hence the relative current distribution between g_2 and a, represented by the ratio of I_{g_2} to I_a, should be unchanged.

Neglecting the influence of the relatively small voltage of g_1 on the current paths in the neighborhood of g_2, and taking $V_{g_3} = 0$, the fraction of the cathode current which reaches the anode will be a function only of the ratio V_a/V_{g_2}:

$$I_a/I_k = \alpha(V_a/V_{g_2}). \tag{2.37}$$

For the function α, empirical expressions have been given; if V_a and V_{g_2} are not too different in magnitude, we may write $I_a/I_{g_2} \approx c(V_a/V_{g_2})^m$, where, depending on the geometrical arrangement of the electrodes, m may vary from 0.5 to 0.2 and c from 2 to 5. From Eqs. (2.31) and (2.37) we find for the characteristic quantities of a pentode:

$$g_m = \left(\frac{\partial I_a}{\partial V_{g_1}}\right)_{V_{g_2}, V_a} = \tfrac{3}{2}(K\alpha)^{2/3} I_a^{1/3}, \tag{2.38}$$

$$r_p = \frac{1}{(\partial I_a/\partial V_a)_{V_{g_1}, V_{g_2}}} = \frac{1}{[D_a g_m + (I_a/\alpha)(\partial \alpha/\partial V_a)]}, \tag{2.39}$$

$$\mu = r_p g_m = \frac{1}{[D_a + (I_a/\alpha g_m)(\partial \alpha/\partial V_a)]}. \tag{2.40}$$

These expressions differ from those for a triode (p. 49) by the terms in α and its derivative that result from the current distribution between a and g_2. The mutual conductance is reduced by a factor of $\alpha^{2/3}$; r_p and μ will be significantly smaller than the values $r_p = 1/D_a g_m$ and $\mu = 1/D_a$ because of the presence of terms in $\partial \alpha/\partial V_a$. Tube manufacturers try to find constructions for which

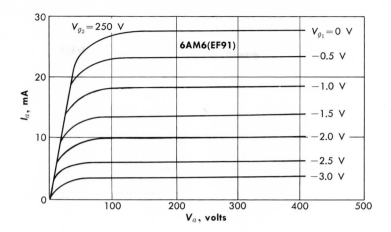

FIG. 2.27. I_a vs. V_a characteristics of a pentode.

α is as close as possible to 1 (small screen current) and varies as little as possible with V_a.

To allow for a large voltage swing at the anode (especially important in power amplifiers), it is further often desirable to keep α constant over a large range of anode voltage. Since the anode current must be zero for $V_a = 0$, the I_a vs. V_a characteristics will show a sharp "knee." This should occur at a low anode voltage (see Fig. 2.27), the lower the better for large-signal amplifiers. Depending on the construction of the tube, the sharpest bend occurs at an anode voltage between about 0.15 and 0.4 times V_{g_2}. For lower values of V_a, the screen-grid current rises rapidly at the expense of the anode current, their sum remaining almost constant. The sharp knee in the I_a vs. V_a characteristics is sometimes used for limiting or compressing a signal (see Chapter 9).

Favorable pentode characteristics are obtained by one or both of the following constructional features:

1. *Screen grid of thin wire wound at a small pitch.* This keeps the field homogeneous until the electrons are close to the screen grid. By a simultaneous reduction of the spacing and thickness of the screen-grid wires, the average deflection of the electrons by these wires is reduced; therefore, more reach the anode, especially at low anode voltages.

2. *Small g_3-a spacing.* Most electrons deflected by g_3 will still reach a; if the distance were larger, part of them could return to g_2.

Sometimes the knee of the I_a vs. V_a characteristics can be made sharper if g_3 is given a small positive voltage of 10 to 30 V.

Apart from the control that g_1 and g_2 can exert on the total current by virtue of the space-charge law, the anode current can also be controlled if g_3 is made negative. In this way, the distribution of the total current between g_2 and a

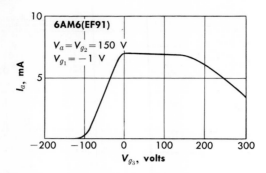

FIG. 2.28. I_a vs. V_{g_3} characteristic of a pentode.

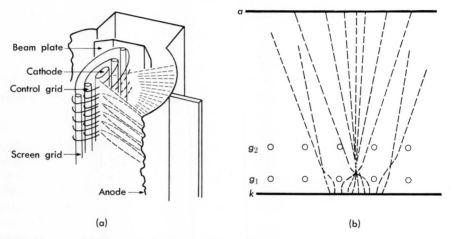

(a)   (b)

FIG. 2.29.   (a) Schematic diagram of a beam tetrode. (b) Electron paths in the beam tetrode. (From J. H. L. Jonker, *Wireless Engineer* **26**, 274, 1946.)

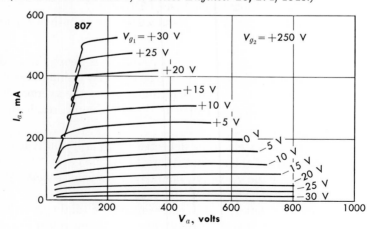

FIG. 2.30. I_a vs. V_a characteristics of a beam tetrode.

is affected. Two regions can be distinguished in the control action of g_3. When the voltage of g_3 becomes negative, at first more and more of the electrons that have penetrated into the space between g_2 and a, after deflection by the screen-grid wires, will be returned to g_2. At higher negative voltages on g_3, these returning electrons create so much space charge immediately in front of g_3 that a virtual cathode may be formed there (at zero potential). Now the suppressor grid acts in accordance with the space-charge law as applied to this virtual cathode. The effective control voltage is to a good approximation given by V_{ec_3} in Eq. (2.32). The I_a vs. V_{g_3} characteristic of Fig. 2.28 shows this behavior.

2.9.2 Beam tetrode

We have already noted that the role of the suppressor grid in a pentode is taken over in a beam tetrode by space charge accumulating between g_2 and a. To cause a potential drop sufficient to suppress the secondary electrons, the space-charge density, and therefore also the current density, must be sufficiently large.

Because of this requirement, beam tetrodes are used mainly in power ampli-fiers, where comparatively large currents are needed. A properly designed beam tetrode has a larger anode-to-screen current ratio than an equivalent pentode, and this ratio is constant over a larger range in V_a. These favorable charac-teristics are obtained by the use of principles of electron-optics in the construc-tion of the tube. In the first place, the control grid and the screen grid are *aligned* as shown in Fig. 2.29(b). The resulting field then forces the electrons to pass between the wires of the screen grid, reducing the screen current. Also, the electron paths in the screen-anode region diverge less than in normal pen-todes, leading to a higher space-charge density, further enhanced by the use of beam plates (Fig. 2.29a), which concentrate the electrons in a limited region between g_2 and a. Finally, the distance between g_2 and a is chosen rather large in order that a sufficient drop of the potential can occur. The ratio of anode to screen current is governed by the potential distribution between the anode and screen grid.

Some typical beam tetrode characteristics are given in Fig. 2.30. Note how the linear region of the I_a vs. V_a characteristics has been extended to much lower voltages than the pentode of Fig. 2.27.

2.10 MULTIPLE-CONTROL TUBES

In multiple-control tubes the anode current can in principle be controlled by the voltage on any one of a number of grids. As we have seen, the control and screen grids in a pentode largely influence the total cathode current, while the sup-pressor grid can be used to control the distribution of this current between the screen grid and the anode. In normal pentodes, only the control grid acts strongly on the anode current; the action of g_2 and g_3 is relatively weak. This is clearly shown in Fig. 2.28: in a normal pentode a negative g_3 voltage of about -100 V is needed to cut off the anode current. For some applications, however, tubes with two or more grids of about equal sensitivity are required. This has been achieved in the following tube types.

1. *Special pentode with narrow spacing of suppressor-grid wires (for example, 6AS6)*. These tubes are built like normal pentodes, but the suppressor grid is wound with a close spacing so that it controls the distribution of the current between anode and screen grid more sensitively. Such tubes are frequently used in switching circuits, the voltage on g_3 serving to "gate" the signal to the anode on or off.

2. *Hexode*. In the control region of g_3, the anode voltage of a pentode also has a rather large influence on the current distribution. To reduce this effect, one may use another screen grid (g_4) between g_3 and a, which also reduces the capacity between g_3 and a. Such a tube, with six elements, is called a *hexode*. Therefore, a larger amplification as well as a better separation between input and output circuits can be achieved with the hexode.

3. *Heptode*. Secondary-emission currents which may arise between g_4 and a may again be suppressed by a suppressor grid, g_5, placed between them. This type is called a *heptode* or *pentagrid* tube. A typical potential distribution of such a seven-element tube is shown in Fig. 2.31. Heptodes are widely used as mixing tubes in radio receivers. In such tubes, g_1 and g_3 each control the anode current, but in different ways. The first control grid, g_1, controls the cathode current in accordance with the space-charge law. The second control grid, g_3, on the other hand, controls the distribution of the cathode current between g_2 and $a + g_4$. Just as with the pentode, a virtual cathode can be formed between g_3 and g_2; the anode current as a function of V_{g_3} then also follows a space-charge law. For higher values of V_{g_3}, however, the virtual cathode disappears, and the current distribution is governed by the shape of the electron paths. If g_1 becomes positive, a substantial grid current will flow while I_a continues to rise. This situation is usually avoided by use of a sufficiently large negative bias voltage on g_1. But if g_3 becomes positive, it draws only very little current because the electrons pass g_2 at a high velocity and are repelled by the

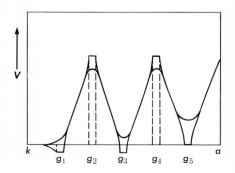

FIG. 2.31. Potential distribution between cathode and anode of a heptode, in a plane midway between the grid wires (upper curve) and intersecting the grid wires (lower curve).

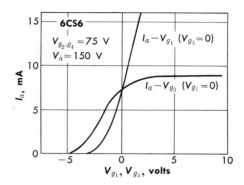

FIG. 2.32. I_a vs. V_{g_1} and I_a vs. V_{g_3} characteristics of a heptode.

wires of g_3 (I_{g_3} can even become negative because of secondary emission of g_3). The anode current hardly increases for positive values of V_{g_3}; the I_a vs. V_{g_3} characteristics therefore show a kind of saturation at positive V_{g_3}. This property is sometimes utilized in limiter circuits. The differences in the control action of g_1 and g_3 are illustrated in Fig. 2.32, in which the I_a vs. V_{g_1} and I_a vs. V_{g_3} characteristics of a typical heptode are given.

4. *Octode.* In this type of tube, the heptode configuration is supplemented by an extra electrode, a_1, that is between g_1 and g_2 and serves as the anode of a triode formed by k, g_1, and a_1. This type of tube has been used in the past as a mixer-oscillator for radio receivers. It is obsolete now and has been replaced by the triode-heptode, a combination of a completely separate triode and a heptode in one envelope, the triode serving as an oscillator.

5. *Ennode.* When it is desired to have two grids with the limiting properties of g_3 of a hexode in a single tube, one may use a system with seven grids, in which g_1 through g_4 have the same functions as in a hexode, g_5 and g_6 repeat the

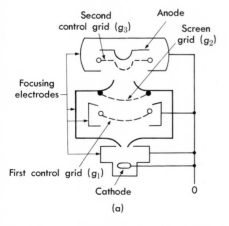

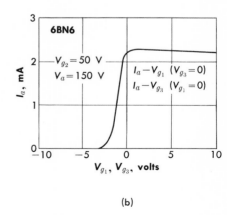

FIG. 2.33. (a) Cross section of gated beam tube 6BN6; (b) I_a vs. V_{g_1} and I_a vs. V_{g_3} characteristics of 6BN6 (coincident).

functions of g_3 and g_4, and finally g_7 is another suppressor grid. Such a tube has been developed by Philips (EQ80). With this tube, triple control of the anode current is possible: with V_{g_1}, V_{g_3}, and V_{g_5}.

6. *Gated beam tube (6BN6)*. Electron-optical methods may be used in a similar way as in beam tetrodes to obtain improved characteristics in multiple-control tubes. A very nice example of this is the 6BN6, whose construction, shown in Fig. 2.33(a), is markedly different from that of normal tubes. The cathode, placed at one side of the electrode system, emits electrons which are concentrated into a narrow beam by several focusing electrodes. This beam traverses the two grids at right angles. In this way a very sharp increase of the anode current with grid voltages is obtained. The I_a vs. V_{g_1} and I_a vs. V_{g_3} characteristics of this tube (Fig. 2.33b), which coincide, demonstrate the very steep rise of the anode current with grid voltage (compare with the characteristics of a normal heptode in Fig. 2.32). It should be noted that the anode-current cutoff is very sharp. This is achieved by shaping the control grids in such a way that electrons reflected by them are spread in all directions; thus the space-charge density in front of the grids remains small, so that no virtual cathode can be formed. This tube is well suited for use as a limiter or an electronic switch; signals of a few volts suffice to switch the anode current on or off.

2.11 ISLAND EFFECT; VARIABLE-μ TUBES

If the spacing a of the control-grid wires is made comparable to the distance d_{gk} between the grid and cathode, the field strength along the cathode will vary periodically; in this case condition 2 on page 47 is no longer approximately fulfilled, and we should expect marked deviations from the simple space-charge law (2.16). Such a case is illustrated in Fig. 2.34, which shows the field lines for

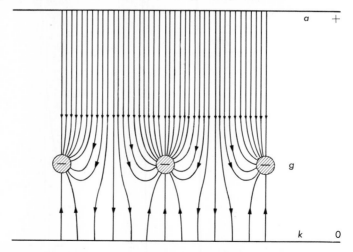

FIG. 2.34.   Lines of force in a triode, illustrating the island effect.

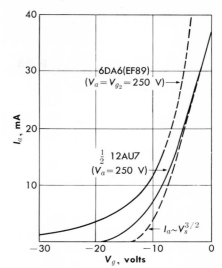

FIG. 2.35. Deviation of the I_a vs. V_g characteristic of a triode ($\frac{1}{2}$ 12AU7) and a remote cutoff pentode (6DA6) from the space-charge law ($I_a \propto V_s^{3/2}$) as a result of the island effect.

a triode whose grid and anode voltages have been chosen in such a way that the field at the cathode periodically changes its direction. In this case, the average field strength and, therefore, also the effective control voltage defined by Eq. (2.12) are zero (the numbers of lines of force pointing up and down are equal). Yet, an electron current will flow from the "islands" on the cathode between the grid wires, where the lines of force are pointing down (electrons are accelerated in a direction opposite to the direction of the lines of force because they have a negative charge). This so-called *island effect* causes the anode current to decrease less rapidly than the $\frac{3}{2}$ power law would allow, as shown in Fig. 2.35 for a practical case ($\frac{1}{2}$ 12AU7). The island effect therefore leads to a decrease of the amplification factor μ below the ratio, $\mu = C_{gk}/C_{ak}$, of the electrostatic capacities. One could also say that the influence of the anode voltage on the anode current increases compared with the influence of the control grid, because the anode field is stronger between the cathode wires than under them.

In Fig. 2.36 the influence of the anode current on the amplification factor is shown for three triodes (12AX7, 12AU7, and 12AT7) with decreasing ratios

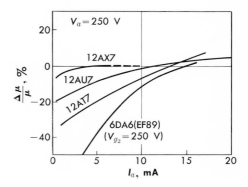

FIG. 2.36. Dependence of the amplification factor on the anode current for three different triodes (12AX7, 12AU7, 12AT7) and a variable-μ pentode (6DA6). The largest variation for the triodes is found for the 12AT7, which has the highest g_m and the smallest ratio d_{gk}/a.

d_{gk}/a. It is clear that the island effect becomes stronger as this ratio becomes smaller. It is often an undesired phenomenon, but can never be entirely avoided. In sharp-cutoff pentodes the effect has been minimized by using control grids wound of very thin wire with a close spacing (for example, 6AU6).

For some applications, tubes are needed which show a much more gradual decrease of the anode current than that characteristic of the space-charge law. Such characteristics can be obtained by use of a control grid with variable spacing between adjacent wires. This causes the field along the cathode to vary as in our previous discussion, but to a much larger extent. For an increasing negative control-grid voltage, an increasing part of the cathode becomes inoperative, while the influence of the voltages on the positive electrodes becomes relatively larger. Such tubes, for which the amplification factor μ varies markedly with the average control-grid voltage (see Fig. 2.36), are called variable-μ tubes or remote cutoff tubes. The magnitude of their small-signal amplification can effectively be controlled by the size of the negative grid-bias voltage. These tubes are widely used in radio receivers to provide automatic volume control.

2.12   COMBINATION TUBES

To conserve space and heater power, tubes can frequently be used in which two or more electrode systems are combined in one single envelope. If two systems of the same type are used, a better equality of the characteristics of both systems can often be achieved. This may be of importance in symmetrical circuits like difference amplifiers and flip-flops. In combination tubes, shielding screens are often used between the separate "tubes" to reduce capacitive coupling. In some practical cases it may be necessary to check whether such screening is sufficient. The most common combination tubes are the following.

1. *Double diodes.* When used for power rectifiers, such tubes almost invariably have internally connected cathodes; small double diodes often have completely separated halves.

2. *Double triodes.* These are widely used in pulse circuits. They are available with a large range of amplification factors and mutual conductances. Many of them have separate cathodes. In addition to symmetrical double triodes, the halves of which have been made as equal as possible, asymmetrical types are made for some special applications. An example of the latter type is the double triode used in cascode amplifiers, in which the halves of the tubes are used in series.

3. *Diode and duodiode triodes and pentodes.* These types are used mostly in radio receivers as combined detectors and audio-frequency amplifiers.

4. *Triode pentodes.* Especially when constructed with separate cathodes, these are very useful tubes which offer some economy of space. They are frequently used in audio-frequency amplifiers.

2.13   SECONDARY-EMISSION TUBES

The phenomenon of secondary emission, already encountered in screen-grid tubes as an *undesired* effect, can also be used to good advantage. A schematic cross section of a tube in which a very high mutual conductance has been realized by the use of secondary emission is given in Fig. 2.37 (Philips EFP60). Electrons emitted from a cathode (k) impinge on two secondary-emitting electrodes (the *dynodes d*) after passing through a control grid and a screen grid (g_1 and g_2) of a normal tetrode. The dynodes in the EFP60 are covered with a thin layer of a cesium-silver alloy which has a high secondary-emission coefficient δ (δ is the average number of secondary electrons per incident primary electron). At the normal working voltage ($V_d = 150$ V), $\delta \sim 6$. At lower values of the dynode voltage, δ decreases approximately linearly with voltage; at higher values, it first reaches a maximum ($\delta \sim 8$ for V_d about 400 V) and then decreases slowly again. In order to draw the secondary electrons away from the dynodes, the anode plates a must be connected to a voltage higher than V_d. The anode current is $I_a = \delta \alpha I_k$. The dynode current, $I_d = (1 - \delta)\alpha I_k$, is negative because there is a net flow of electrons away from the dynode. Thus, the sign of a signal across a resistor in series with the dynode is opposite that of a signal across the anode resistor. Because the mutual conductance at the anode of a secondary-emission tube is δ times the mutual conductance of the tetrode part, these tubes have a very high g_m. The EFP60, for instance, has $g_m = 25$ mA/V at $I_a = 20$ mA. Secondary-emission tubes may be used in wide-band amplifiers, but there may be some trouble in achieving sufficiently stable operation. They are also very useful for fast trigger circuits (see Chapter 9). During short pulses, very high currents (up to 1 A) can be drawn from the dynodes. The maximum allowable dissipation of the dynodes should, however, be watched carefully because the secondary emitting layer can easily be damaged by excessively high temperatures. Negative feedback methods may be used to protect the tube against overloading.

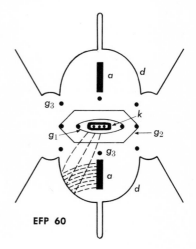

FIG. 2.37. Secondary-emission tube. There are six beam rods (g_3) internally connected, two dynodes (d), and two anodes (a).

2.14   GAS-FILLED TUBES

The characteristics of an electron tube are markedly changed by small quantities of gas. The main difference between gas-filled tubes and vacuum tubes is the occurrence of sudden jumps in the characteristics. A transition between nonconduction and conduction in a gas-filled tube is accompanied by the ignition of a gas discharge in which the gas suddenly becomes highly ionized. A distinction should be made between gas-filled tubes with a cold cathode and those with a hot cathode; operation and applications of these two types are quite different.

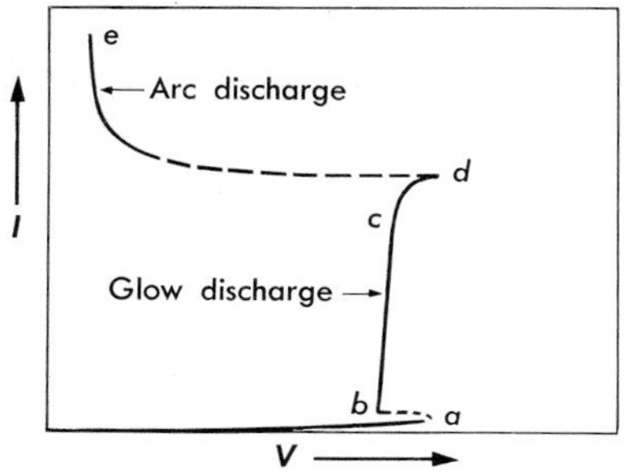

FIG. 2.38.   Current-voltage characteristic of a gas discharge.

The general behavior of a gas discharge between flat electrodes is indicated in Fig. 2.38. As the voltage between the electrodes increases from zero, initially only a very small current flows. This is caused by the few gas ions always present, due to radioactivity, cosmic rays, etc. As the velocity with which these gas ions bombard the cathode increases, they will knock out more secondary electrons. At a well-defined starting voltage, each secondary electron accelerated from the cathode toward the anode will produce so many new gas ions that on the average, one of these electrons produces another new secondary electron at the cathode. Now the condition for the formation of an avalanche of electrons is fulfilled, and the current will rise rapidly to a very high value if it is not limited by a resistor in series with the leads connecting the electrodes to the voltage source. The starting voltage depends on the constitution of the gas in the tube and the cathode material; it can lie anywhere between 80 and 200 V. The tube is now in its glow-discharge region (*bc* in Fig. 2.30). In this region, the current changes considerably with a very small change of voltage. The tube therefore has a low internal resistance. If the current is increased beyond the normal glow-discharge region, the voltage starts to rise again and then suddenly drops sharply. We have now reached the arc-discharge region, in which the cathode has been heated by ion bombardment to such a temperature that thermal emission prevails. In this region, the I vs. V curve shows a negative resistance, so that unless limited by an external resistance, the current would grow excessively large. In most cold-cathode tubes, such a high current would ruin the tube in a very short time; therefore, these tubes are always operated with a series resistor sufficiently large for the current never to reach the arc-discharge region.

In hot-cathode tubes, thermally emitted electrons are abundant from the start and these are particularly designed to operate in the arc-discharge region. To create an arc discharge the electrons have to be accelerated only by a small voltage, between 10 and 20 V, just enough to ionize the gas. This working voltage is therefore much lower than it is for cold-cathode tubes. Hot-cathode tubes must, of course, be capable of carrying a much larger current density than cold-cathode tubes. In the former, the electron space charge, which limits the current in vacuum tubes, is neutralized by the space charge of the positive ions. Because of this fact, the cathode can deliver its full temperature-limited saturation current at the low working voltage of the arc discharge.

Gas-discharge tubes must always be operated in series with an impedance large enough to limit the current to a safe value. In hot-cathode gas-filled tubes an overload of short duration will quickly ruin the cathode.

The following types of gas-discharge tubes are widely used.

1. *Cold-cathode diodes.* Most important of these are voltage-stabilization and reference tubes, which will be discussed at greater length in Section 7.6.

2. *Cold cathode triodes or trigger tubes.* In these, besides the cathode and anode, there is also a starting electrode. A gas discharge between the anode and cathode can be started if we apply a positive voltage to the starting electrode that is much lower than would be required on the anode. The starting electrode itself will draw little current. After a glow discharge is started, for instance by a positive pulse applied to the starting electrode, its voltage has hardly any influence on the current. To switch off the current, we must decrease the anode voltage to below the extinguishing voltage of the discharge between anode and cathode. While cold-cathode triodes are useless as amplifiers, they are frequently useful in switching and counting circuits. The main advantages of these tubes over vacuum tubes are their small size and small power consumption, because there is no heater. Also, the light emitted by the glow discharge gives a convenient visual indication of when the tube is conducting. A disadvantage is that these tubes have a relatively slow response due to the long de-ionization time of the gas. Because of this, counting frequencies are limited to a few tens of kcps.

3. *Gas-filled diodes with a hot cathode.* These are used mainly in medium- and high-power rectifiers. The low working voltage and the high maximum current of an arc discharge make them particularly suitable for this application. In these tubes oxide-coated cathodes are used, capable of delivering currents of the order of one or more amperes. The tubes are often filled with mercury vapor; sometimes they contain a noble gas or a mixture of noble gases. In the arc-discharge region, the anode voltage varies only slightly with the anode current, at least so long as the cathode emission is not saturated. This must never be allowed to happen in practice, because the voltage between anode and cathode would then start to rise, and the cathode would quickly be ruined by the gas ions bombarding it. Since the electron space charge is neutralized by the positive-ion space charge, the distance between cathode and anode need not be particularly small. This makes possible cathode constructions like the one

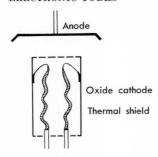

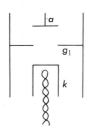

FIG. 2.39.   Cross section of a mercury
vapor rectifier with a thermally shielded
cathode.

FIG. 2.40.   Electrode configuration in a
triode thyratron.

indicated in Fig. 2.39. The cathode is surrounded here by a thermal shield which
reduces the loss of heat by radiation and therefore improves the thermal
efficiency of the cathode. Some precautions necessary in rectifiers with gas-filled
tubes are mentioned in Chapter 7.

4. *Hot-cathode triodes and tetrodes (thyratrons)*. The electrode configuration in
a typical triode thyratron is shown in Fig. 2.40. A control electrode (g_1) has
been placed between the anode and the cathode, shielding the anode electro-
statically from the cathode. The penetration of the anode field to the cathode
is determined by the diameter of the hole in g_1. The anode and control-electrode
voltage together determine an effective control voltage V_{ec} in the plane of this
hole. As soon as V_{ec} becomes larger than zero, electrons can penetrate into the
anode space and ionize the gas. The positive ions cover the control electrode
and neutralize its field. Thus an arc discharge is started between anode and
cathode. With a sufficiently high impedance in the anode circuit, the anode
voltage rapidly drops to 10 to 20 V above that of the cathode. The control
electrode has now lost its influence on the anode current, and the tube behaves
just like a gas-filled diode. We can stop the discharge by decreasing the anode
voltage to below the extinguishing voltage (10 to 20 V). Important information
about the operation of a particular thyratron is offered by its starting characteristic, which gives the relation between anode and grid voltages for which the

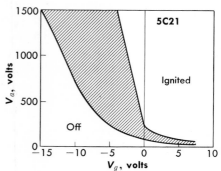

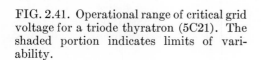

FIG. 2.41. Operational range of critical grid
voltage for a triode thyratron (5C21). The
shaded portion indicates limits of vari-
ability.

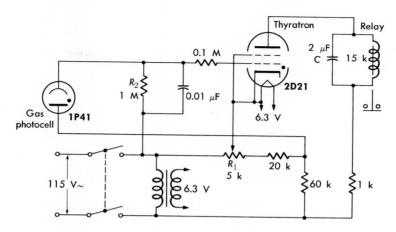

FIG. 2.42.   Photoelectric relay circuit.

tube fires. Since the exact position of this characteristic depends on the temperature and age of the tube, the manufacturer usually gives a tolerance region for
the anode and control-electrode voltages for which the tube fires (Fig. 2.41).
Usually the grid is constructed in such a way that the useful part of the characteristic occurs at negative control-grid voltages.

In a tetrode thyratron a screen grid, placed between the control electrode and
the anode, can be used to influence the position of the starting characteristic.
Usually this screen grid is connected to the cathode and serves to shield the
anode from the control grid, reducing the chance of spurious ignition by sudden
voltage jumps at the anode. Also, the input impedance is much higher at the
control grid of a tetrode thyratron than in a triode thyratron, making it possible
to drive this grid directly from a source with a very high internal resistance
(for instance a photocell). Small thyratrons are very useful for switching
electromagnetic relays. Relay circuits with thyratrons may be energized directly
from the ac-line, the thyratron serving at the same time as a rectifier for the
relay current. An example of a simple photoelectric relay is given in Fig. 2.42.
So long as no light falls on the photocell, the thyratron in this circuit will not
fire, because the cathode has been made sufficiently positive with respect to
the control grid by the voltage divider R_1. If light falls on the photocell, a
positive voltage is developed across R_2, which causes the starting voltage to be
exceeded each time the anode becomes positive. The buffer condenser C is now
charged by the current pulses passing through the thyratron at the line
frequency, and the relay is energized.

Large thyratrons, capable of delivering currents of many amperes, are often
used as variable power rectifiers, for instance for control of electric motors and
light installations. We control the average dc-power delivered by such rectifiers
by varying the magnitude or phase of the control-grid voltage, which determines
the instant at which the thyratron fires.

PROBLEMS

2.1   The cathode of a thermionic diode is heated at constant power. Explain why the cathode temperature must be higher when the anode is negative with respect to the cathode than when the anode is positive. Using reasonable values for the parameters involved, estimate the magnitude of this temperature difference for an oxide cathode operating at 1000°K and furnishing an electron current of 100 mA/cm² to the anode when it is positive. Is this effect a serious limitation in practical rectifiers?

2.2   A diode consists of a plane anode and plane cathode, separated by a distance of 1 cm. The anode is 5 V negative with respect to the cathode.

(a) With what initial velocity must electrons be ejected from the cathode in order to reach the anode?

(b) What fraction of the electrons in the cathode have sufficient thermal energy to reach the anode for an oxide cathode at 1000°K? For a pure tungsten cathode at 2500°K? (Assume that, in each case, the anode is tungsten.)

2.3   Suppose that the diode of Problem 2.2 is operated under temperature-limited conditions (no space charge), with the anode 20 V positive with respect to the cathode.

(a) How long does it take an electron emitted from the cathode with zero initial velocity to reach the anode?

(b) Show that it takes 1.5 times as long if the diode is operated under space-charge-limited conditions.

2.4   When the temperature of a cathode is raised from 1000°K to 2000°K, the saturation current increases by a factor of 10^6. What is the work function of the cathode material?

2.5   A diode has a cathode with a Richardson potential of 1.5 V and an anode with a Richardson potential of 4.5 V. What fraction of the cathode current will reach the anode for zero applied volts between the electrodes at a cathode temperature of 1200°K?

2.6   The anode voltage of a diode is increased from +50 V to +200 V. By what factor does the power dissipated in the anode increase

(a) when the tube is operated, throughout the range, under temperature-limited conditions,

(b) when the tube is operated, throughout the range, under space-charge-limited conditions?

2.7   (a) What positive-anode voltage must be applied across a plane diode, with 2-mm spacing between anode and cathode, to increase the saturation current by a factor of two when both cathode and anode are of pure tungsten and the cathode is heated to 2500°K?

(b) How large a reverse voltage must be applied to the anode of the same tube to produce the same current as in (a) when the anode is at room temperature (300°K)? How large a reverse voltage is required when the anode is heated under forward operation so that it is red hot (1000°K)?

2.8   The anode current of an ideal triode is given by the relation

$$I_a = K(V_a + 50V_g)^{1.5}.$$

Suppose that $I_a = 2$ mA for $V_g = -2$ V and $V_a = +200$ V.

(a) Find the values of μ, g_m, and r_p at this operating point.

(b) For what value of V_g would I_a be reduced by a factor of 2?

(c) By how much will the values of μ, g_m, and r_p change under the conditions of (b)?

2.9   The triode of Problem 2.8 is connected as an amplifier in the circuit shown in Fig. 2.18, with $R_a = 20$ kΩ, $I_a = 2$ mA, and $V_{g0} = -2$ V.   Find

(a) the value of the anode supply voltage V_{a0},

(b) the voltage gain of the amplifier.

(c) Suppose that R_a is increased to 200 kΩ and V_{g0} and V_{a0} remain fixed; find the new value for I_a and for the voltage gain.

2.10   The I_a vs. V_a plate characteristics of an ideal triode are given by the relation $I_a = K(V_a + \mu V_g)^{3/2}$. Starting with the actual plate characteristics of a real triode, e.g. the 12AX7 triode shown in Fig. 2.15, show that $I_a = K(V_a + \mu V_g)^n$. Find the values of K, μ, and n.

2.11   The bridge circuit shown in Fig. 2.43 can be used to measure the effective transconductance of the tube. Find an expression for g_m in terms of the values of R_1, R_2, and R_3 when no current flows through the detector.

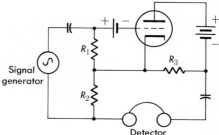

FIGURE 2.43

2.12   The cathode heater of a triode is operated by means of a stepdown transformer from a 115-V ac line. Assume that the triode has an oxide cathode operating at a temperature of 1000°K for a line voltage of 115 V and that the grid and anode are made of nickel. When the line voltage is subject to fluctuations of ±10%, what *qualitative* effect would this change have on

(a) the emission current,

(b) the small-signal tube parameters μ, g_m, and r_p,

(c) the control-grid cutoff-bias voltage,

(d) the gain of an amplifier connected as in Fig. 2.18, with fixed values of V_{a0} and V_{g0}?

(Do not attempt an *exact* solution to this problem; only a semiquantitative treatment is expected.)

2.13   (a) We can make an "ionization gauge" for measurement of a high vacuum by connecting a triode to a vacuum system with a glass tube, so that the pressure around the tube elements is the same as in the system. The triode is operated with the control grid 200 V *positive* with respect to the cathode, and with the anode about 25 V *negative*. Show that the anode current, at constant grid current, should be directly proportional to the pressure of gas in the tube and that a pressure of 10^{-4} mm Hg should give an anode current of about 1 μA, for a grid current of 10 mA and a cylindrical anode of 4 cm^2 area surrounding the grid and cathode.

(b) Usually special triodes are used for ionization gauges, with very rugged grid structures and pure tungsten cathodes. Why are such features desirable?

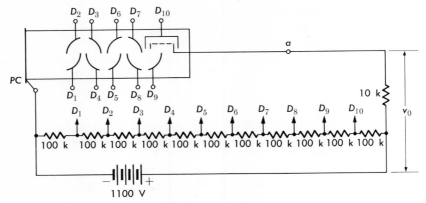

FIGURE 2.44

2.14 We make a *photomultiplier* tube by using a semitransparent photoemissive photocathode, *PC*, followed by a ten-stage electron multiplier consisting of the dynodes $D_1, \ldots, D_{10}$ (Fig. 2.44). Each dynode is made of a material which emits an average of four secondary electrons for each incident electron when the dynodes are connected as shown. Find the total current amplification of the tube. What voltage v_o will appear across the output when the photocathode has an emission efficiency (ratio of electrons emitted to photons absorbed) of 10% and is struck by a light flux of 10^4 photons/sec?

REFERENCES

Aldous, W. H., and E. Appleton, *Thermionic Vacuum Tubes*, Methuen, 1952.
Millman, J., *Vacuum Tube and Semiconductor Electronics*, McGraw-Hill, 1958.
Millman, J., and S. Seely, *Electronics*, McGraw-Hill, 1951.
Spangenberg, K. R., *Vacuum Tubes*, McGraw-Hill, 1948.

Chapter 3

SEMICONDUCTOR DEVICES

3.1 THE ROOTS OF MODERN ELECTRONICS

In a little more than ten years, the invention of the transistor and other semiconductor devices has radically changed design concepts in electronics. New methods of packaging and construction of electronic circuits, introducing "solid-state" components, have resulted in a degree of miniaturization and power reduction that would have seemed impossible two decades ago. A complete radio transmitter-receiver, which a few years back would have been as large as a refrigerator, can now be compressed to the size of a pack of cigarettes. In a box only as large as a refrigerator, instead of in a whole building full of vacuum-tube circuitry, a complete electronic digital computer that performs a bewildering number of arithmetic operations in fractions of microseconds can now be constructed. Moreover, the compaction has not been achieved at the expense of cost and reliability. "Solid-state" circuits, properly designed, are cheaper and more reliable than their vacuum-tube counterparts. Nor is the end of this revolution yet in sight. Still newer "solid-state" techniques, employing "integrated circuits" now under development (see Section 3.8.7), appear likely to effect another order-of-magnitude reduction in circuit size within the next decade.

Yet the essence of "solid-state" electronics was already there in the "crystal set" of the early days around the time of the first world war, in the fundamental electronic processes taking place inside the piece of Rochelle salt or Galena (lead sulphide) which, with its metal base and "cat's whisker" probe, comprised the heart of the crystal set. However, these interactions were not well understood (quantum mechanics had not yet been invented), and crystal sets, at best unreliable devices, were rapidly replaced by vacuum-tube receivers.

By the 1930's, the mysterious rectifying properties of the "crystal" diode could finally be understood in terms of the essential nonohmic nature of a metal-semiconductor contact (see Section 3.2.2), but not until the second world war was there any serious technical interest in semiconductor devices. With the development of ultrahigh frequency and microwave radar, a critical requirement suddenly arose for reliable detectors, since vacuum-tube diodes proved inadequate at these high frequencies due to transit-time and capacitive limitations.

The search for new detectors quickly centered, ironically, on the discarded crystal set. With the substitution of pure germanium or silicon for the Galena and a short point contact for the cat's whisker, the new detector worked admirably.

After the war, some physicists, intrigued by strange physical phenomena encountered during the detector-development program, continued studying the basic physics of semiconductors. In 1948, Bardeen and Brattain at the Bell Telephone Laboratory tried to probe the electric-field distribution near a forward-biased metal-semiconductor contact with a second reverse-biased contact. Surprisingly, the reverse-biased contact, which should have drawn a negligible current, drew a current about as large as the forward-biased contact when the two were close together. Moreover, since the reverse-biased *collector* contact could be maintained at a much higher voltage relative to the semiconductor *base* than the forward-biased *emitter* contact, the device was obviously producing a power gain. It was an amplifier! This device was christened a *transistor*, and this particular type, now seldom used, is currently called a *point-contact transistor*.

In studying the properties of this new device, Bardeen and Brattain were joined by Shockley, who showed that they could obtain a similar effect by making a "sandwich" of alternate junctions between p-type and n-type semiconductors. This *junction transistor* proved even better than the original and provided the basis for most modern "solid-state" devices.*

With semiconductor devices capable of amplifying as well as rectifying, the applications to practical circuits were immediately obvious. The electronics industry responded as rapidly as possible, producing ever newer and better semiconductor devices of higher power, higher frequency capability, greater reliability, and lower cost, while developing ever-improving circuits for their use. Thus, by a circular route, with semiconductors replacing vacuum tubes, which had previously replaced semiconductors, modern "solid-state" electronics emerged.

In this chapter we shall consider the physical behavior of semiconductor devices, their salient properties and their limitations. In later chapters we shall see how they can be used in a wide variety of circuits.

3.2. SEMICONDUCTOR DIODES

3.2.1 The pn-junction

Most active semiconductor devices contain regions where p-type material is joined to n-type material at one or more places. The region of contact is called a *pn-junction,* and almost all of the important characteristics of the elements are

---

* For the invention of the transistor and the elucidation of its properties, Bardeen, Brattain, and Shockley were awarded the Nobel Prize in physics in 1956.

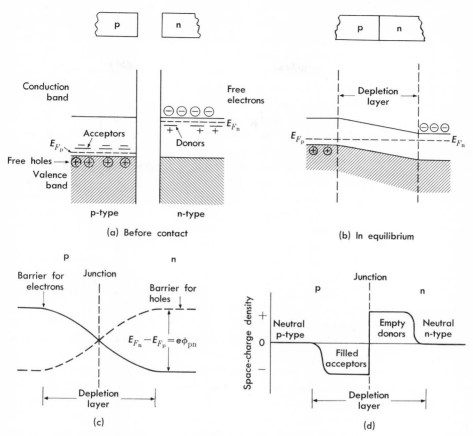

FIG. 3.1.   The pn-junction. (a) Before contact, the Fermi levels are unequal. (b) After contact, holes flow to n-side, electrons to p-side, bringing Fermi levels together and forming depletion layer at junction. (c) Energy barriers for electrons and holes at junction. (d) Charge distribution at junction; p-side is negative, n-side positive.

derived from the electrical behavior of the region just around the junction. The junctions may be formed in a variety of ways, which will be discussed in Section 3.7; at the moment we shall be concerned only with the basic electrical properties of the junction since these are common to all active devices.

When p- and n-type materials are joined, they will, of course, come to thermal equilibrium. As we saw in Section 1.7, this means that the Fermi energies of the two materials must come to a common level. In Fig. 1.10, the Fermi level of the p-type material was originally below the center of the gap, while that of the n-type material was above the center of the gap. Before the two regions are joined, the potential distribution must be as represented in Fig. 3.1(a). After the regions are brought into electrical and thermal contact, some charge must flow to bring the Fermi levels together as shown in Fig. 3.1(b), just as is required to establish the contact potential difference between two dissimilar metals. Positive holes will diffuse from the p-type material into the n-type material while electrons will diffuse in the opposite direction until the Fermi levels reach the same value on either side of the junction. However, the holes which move into the n-side of the junction will recombine with the electrons there, causing a decrease in the concentration of electrons on the n-side of the junction. Similarly, electrons which have crossed into the p-side will cause a decrease in hole concentration there. Thus, on *both* sides of the junction there will be a *decrease* in the number of *free charge carriers*. This layer about the junction is called the *depletion layer*. The p-material, having lost positive holes and gained electrons in the transfer process (while the opposite was occurring on the n-side of the junction) will now have a net negative charge, while the n-type material will be charged positively. The potential difference across the junction, once equilibrium is reached, must be equal to the original difference between the Fermi levels of the p- and n-materials before they were joined, as shown in Fig. 3.1(c). The equilibrium charge distribution around the junction will be in the form of a dipole layer, as shown in Fig. 3.1(d). The thickness of this layer, which depends on the conductivities of the p- and n-regions, may vary from a few hundred angstroms (Å) to a few microns.

Of course, in equilibrium there is no net hole or electron current flowing across the junction. For each electron which flows from right to left across the junction, "uphill" against the potential gradient, another electron originally present in the p-material as a minority carrier must flow "downhill" in the opposite direction. A similar situation must hold for hole flow, except that uphill for holes is the opposite direction, from left to right. The uphill and downhill currents of both holes and electrons exactly cancel when there is no external driving force, so that with no emf in the circuit, the net current will vanish, as in Fig. 3.2(a).

In order for a hole to move uphill from left to right, or an electron from right to left, it must first acquire an additional energy, $e\phi_{\mathrm{pn}}$, equal to the barrier height, which is of the order of a few tenths of an electron volt, considerably larger than the average thermal energy ($\frac{1}{40}$ eV at room temperature). Naturally, no additional energy is required for the reverse (downhill) trip. Since there are no space-charge effects to be considered here (the free-carrier concentration is small in the depletion layer at the junction), the situation for the reverse current is very similar to that for a thermionic diode under temperature-limited operation. The "forward" current I_f, which is the sum of the hole current from left to right and the electron current from right to left, with no applied external voltage, is given by

$$I_{f0} = I_0 \epsilon^{-e\phi_{\mathrm{pn}}/kT}. \tag{3.1}$$

The reverse current I_{r0}, the sum of the right-to-left hole current and the left-to-right electron current, must be equal in magnitude to I_{f0} but opposite in direction, so that the total current $I = I_{f0} + I_{r0} = 0$. The magnitude of

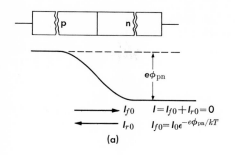

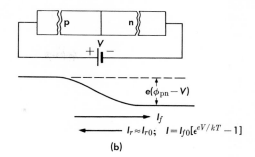

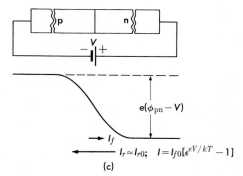

FIG. 3.2. Potential energy barriers and positive current for electrons in a pn-junction. (a) Zero bias ($V = 0$), (b) forward bias ($V > 0$), (c) reverse bias ($V < 0$). Identical diagrams would apply to flow of holes in the opposite direction, except that "uphill" for holes is from left to right.

I_0 depends on the concentrations of free *minority* carriers around the junction—holes on the n-side, and electrons on the p-side—and on their mobilities and diffusion lengths. The increase of I_0 is directly proportional to the minority-carrier concentration and mobility, and inversely to the diffusion length. For a small I_0, the junction should be made of pure n- and p-materials, with as sharp a concentration gradient as possible at the junction.

If the junction is now biased in the forward direction, that is, if the p-side is made positive with respect to the n-side by a potential difference V, as in Fig. 3.2(b), the situation is quite different. The potential barrier at the junction is now reduced by an amount V for both holes and electrons, and the forward current must increase as

$$I_f = I_0 \epsilon^{-e(\phi_{pn} - V)/kT} = I_{f0}\epsilon^{eV/kT}. \tag{3.2}$$

The reverse current I_r will be unaffected by the change; the minority carriers will not fall quite so far downhill now, but this has little effect. Therefore $I_r \approx I_{r0}$, and the total current will be simply

$$I = I_f + I_r = I_{f0}\epsilon^{eV/kT} - I_{f0} = I_{f0}(\epsilon^{eV/kT} - 1). \tag{3.3}$$

For $V > 0$, the current will increase very rapidly with voltage; according to Eq. (3.3), it should increase exponentially with the applied voltage. This will be true for small positive values of V, but for larger values the potential drop across the junction will be less than the applied voltage because of the ohmic voltage drop in the body of the semiconductor, and the actual increase will be less rapid. When $V < 0$, as shown in Fig. 3.2(c), the total current rapidly drops to the value $-I_{f0}$, the *reverse saturation current*, and is independent of the magnitude of V. The pn-junction thus forms a rectifier; typical current-voltage characteristics are as shown in Fig. 3.3, which closely approximate Eq. (3.3), with $I_{f0} = 0.3\ \mu\text{A}$.

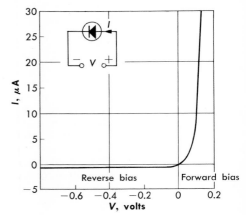

FIG. 3.3. I vs. V characteristic of a small junction diode.

The sharpness of the "knee" in the current-voltage characteristic depends on the magnitude of the Boltzmann factor $\epsilon^{eV/kT}$. The transition from *forward* to *reverse* characteristics occurs over a voltage range of the order of kT/e, about $\frac{1}{40}$ V at room temperature. It is useful to define a *differential resistance*, $r_i = dV/dI$, for a junction diode. This parameter varies strongly with the applied voltage since, from differentiation of (3.3), we obtain

$$r_i = \frac{kT/e}{I + I_{f0}},\tag{3.4}$$

and I is a rapidly varying function of V. For the diode shown in Fig. 3.3, at room temperature, $kT/e \approx 0.025$ V, so that $r_i = 2.5$ ohms for $V = +0.25$ V ($I = 10$ mA), and $r_i = 2.5$ MΩ for $V = -0.1$ V ($I = -0.29\ \mu\text{A}$). According to (3.4), since $I \rightarrow -I_{f0}$, r_i would tend to infinity for increasing negative values of V. Effects such as surface conduction, however, limit the maximum values of r_i. Such effects are usually dominant for negative values of V larger than a few tenths of a volt. In practice, values of r_i are usually less than a few megohms for germanium diodes, but may be as large as 100 MΩ for silicon devices.

The value of r_i, from (3.4), varies inversely as I_{f0}. If I_{f0} increases, the reverse resistance of the diode at a given value of V will decrease. From Eq. (3.1), we see that I_{f0} increases exponentially with temperature, so that if we want to maintain constant junction characteristics, the temperature of the junction must be kept constant. In addition, we must be careful that no thermal "runaway" can occur, which would lead to rapid destruction of the diode. This is more critical for germanium than for silicon, for silicon has a larger energy gap and hence a larger value of ϕ_{pn} and a much smaller I_{f0}.

When the diode is reverse-biased, the magnitude of the reverse current can also be increased if ionizing radiation falls on the junction, creating new hole-electron pairs which can travel downhill across the junction. This excess current will persist only so long as the radiation is present. Because of this effect, back-biased pn-junctions can be used as efficient photoelectric and charged-particle detectors.

The reverse-biased junction has another useful property, particularly if it is made so that I_{f0} is very small. In this case the junction acts like a condenser, since charge must be supplied to the diode if the reverse voltage is increased. Moreover, as the reverse voltage increases, the width of the depletion layer increases, and the effective capacitance decreases. Because of this property, reverse-biased junctions can be used as voltage-tunable condensers. Such devices, usually specially designed to optimize this property, are called *varactors*.

3.2.2 Point-contact diodes; the semiconductor-metal junction

The basic physical interaction which occurs at the junction between a metal and a semiconductor in a point-contact diode is completely analogous to that in a pn-junction, but the potential distribution is more complex. The metal of the point contact, like the p-material in a pn-junction, has a higher work function than the semiconductor, and must become charged negatively with respect to the semiconductor to bring the two Fermi levels together, as shown in Fig. 3.4. The metal thus assumes the role of the p-side of a pn-junction, and the diode draws a large current when the metal is made positive with respect to the semiconductor.

Unlike the semiconductor, the metal contains a vast number of free-charge carriers; hence, there can be no depletion layer formed on the metal side of the

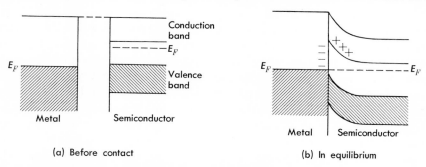

(a) Before contact   (b) In equilibrium

FIG. 3.4. Formation of rectifying metal-semiconductor contact. (a) Energy levels before contact, (b) in equilibrium after contact.

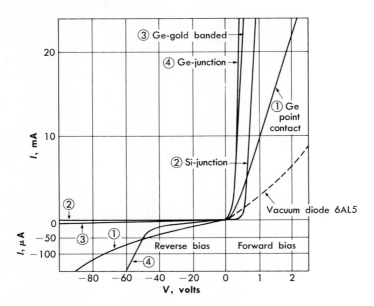

FIG. 3.5. *I* vs. *V* characteristics of typical diodes. Note the much smaller increase of current with forward voltage in the vacuum diode and the difference in characteristics between the point contact and junction diodes. (Note scale change for forward and reverse currents and voltages.)

junction. The free electrons in the metal, just like the electrons near the cathode in a vacuum tube under space-charge-limited operation, tend to screen the potential difference around the junction. As a result, the full applied voltage does not appear across the junction, and the point-contact diode shows a much slower rate of increase of current with voltage, and hence a larger forward resistance, than a junction diode. When reverse-biased, the point contact diode shows little tendency to reach a saturation current but, instead, usually shows a simple ohmic relationship with a large back resistance. Typical point-contact diode characteristics are shown in Fig. 3.5.

Not all semiconductor-metal contacts are rectifying, as is the point junction of the point-contact diode. Indeed, if all contacts had such nonohmic behavior, there would be a major circuit complication every time a lead had to be connected to a semiconductor. The rectifying properties of a pn-junction or of a semiconductor-metal contact are due to the sharp discontinuity in the composition at the junction. If the materials, instead of being brought together carefully to preserve the sharp discontinuity, are simply fused together at high temperature, the resulting interdiffusion can cause a gradual rather than an abrupt change in characteristic, and the contact may behave simply like an ohmic resistance. For the same reason, a device such as a diode or transistor, which depends on the presence of a sharp boundary between the p- and n-regions, may be irreparably ruined if the junction is overheated to the point where interdiffusion can occur. This can happen in use if the device is operated above its rated power level or even when the circuit is assembled, if care is not taken to ensure that the heat from the soldering iron does not reach the junctions.

3.2.3 Barrier rectifiers

Long before the invention of the pn-junction diode, quite different types of solid-state rectifiers had been developed. These are of two types and are generally known as *barrier rectifiers*, because rectification takes place in a narrow barrier region. One type is a metal-semiconductor-metal "sandwich," with one of the metal-to-semiconductor interfaces formed, by proper heat treatment, as a rectifying junction, effectively a two-dimensional extension of the point-contact junction just discussed. The second metal-to-semiconductor interface is formed as a simple ohmic contact. Thus, rectification occurs only at the first interface. A typical example is the copper-copper–oxide-copper rectifier with I vs. V characteristics as shown in Fig. 3.6. The second class of barrier rectifiers is made from two plates of dissimilar metals separated by a very thin layer of leaky insulator. The rectifying action can be seen from Fig. 3.7. In equilibrium, the metal plate A, of higher work function, will be charged negatively, relative to the plate B. In this case, the Fermi levels are brought together by charges leaking through the "insulating" boundary layer. The charge exchange will actually be effected by electrons flowing through the empty conduction band of the insulator. Note that the bottom of the conduction band is closer to the Fermi level of the low-work-function metal B than to that of metal A. The potential distribution is shown in Fig. 3.7. When a potential difference is applied between the plates so that metal B becomes negative with respect to metal A, the Fermi level of B is raised closer to the bottom of the conduction band of the insulator, and the current will increase as $\epsilon^{eV/kT}$; when B is made positive, the current quickly decreases to a small reverse-saturation value since the barrier height, as seen from the A-side, changes only slightly with the applied voltage.

Practical *metallic* barrier rectifiers are usually made from sandwiches of copper, copper oxide, and nickel ($\phi_{Cu} < \phi_{Ni}$) or aluminum, selenium, and

FIG. 3.6. I vs. V characteristic of a typical copper oxide rectifier. Note the much higher reverse currents than for the pn-junction diodes of Fig. 3.5. (Also note scale change for forward and reverse currents.)

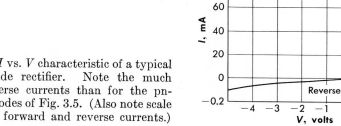

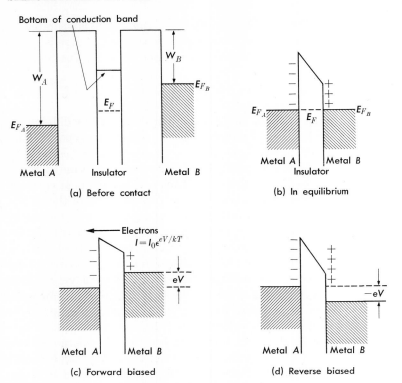

FIG. 3.7. Formation of rectifying contact between two dissimilar metals separated by a thin layer of leaky insulator. (a) Energy levels before contact. (b) In equilibrium after contact, metal A, of higher work function, is negative with respect to metal B. (c) Forward-biased, (d) reverse-biased.

cadmium ($\phi_{Al} < \phi_{Cd}$). Characteristics of these rectifiers are compared with those of typical germanium and silicon pn-junction rectifiers in Table 3.1. In all respects, the barrier rectifiers are distinctly inferior. However, the cost of the rectifiers listed in the table increases from left to right; that is why barrier rectifiers still find a steady market in inexpensive circuits.

TABLE 3.1

Characteristic	Copper oxide	Selenium	Germanium	Silicon
Maximum current density, A/cm^2	0.05	0.06	60	3000
Maximum operating temperature, °C	60	100	65	150
Maximum reverse voltage per cell, V	5	36	200	1000

3.3 PRACTICAL LIMITATIONS OF SEMICONDUCTOR DIODES

Semiconductor diodes usually operate with much smaller voltages and higher currents than vacuum tubes. Since the current tends to vary exponentially with the junction temperature and with the applied voltage, careful control of the thermal and electrical environment, as well as of other factors which influence the electrical behavior of the device, is essential. In this section we shall review the most important limitations on the use of semiconductor diodes; many of these apply with equal fervor to transistors and other more complex devices. While some of these limitations have been noted earlier, it may be useful for future reference to collect the pertinent criteria into a single section. Typical parameters for a variety of diodes are given in Table 3.2.

3.3.1 Forward-operation limits

Current and power limits for operation under forward-bias condition, usually specified by the manufacturer for any particular device, must be carefully observed with all semiconductor components. First, and most important, there is the fundamental problem of maintaining the junction temperature within bounds when there is a large forward current. As we have seen, heating of the junction causes an increase in thermally excited minority carriers, with a corresponding decrease in both forward and back resistances. The current increase may result in further heating of the junction and more current flow. If this occurs, the device will eventually reach such a temperature that rapid interdiffusion can occur at the junction, permanently and radically altering the electrical characteristics. Under such circumstances, the device can become so hot that the soldered leads or even the semiconductor itself can melt, although the junction itself will usually be ruined by diffusional effects long before physical melting occurs.

Since semiconductor devices are frequently quite small and have a small heat capacity, the temperature can rise very rapidly unless the device is in good thermal contact with a *heat sink*. The maximum allowable power that can be dissipated therefore depends to a considerable extent on the thermal contact of the device with the chassis or other cooling surfaces, as well as on the ambient air temperature. Sometimes different values of maximum permissible power dissipation ($W_{0\max}$) are given in specification tables, depending on the way the device is mounted. The value of $W_{0\max}$ sets the maximum value of the root-mean-square forward current which can be safely passed through the diode. However, the values for the maximum continuous current, $I_{d\max}$, and the maximum peak current, $I_{dp\max}$, may be different. If the peak current flows for only a very short time, so that the safe operating temperature is not exceeded, $I_{dp\max}$ can be much greater than $I_{d\max}$. For reasons to be discussed in the next section, the maximum current carried under steady dc-conditions, $I_{d\max}$, can be somewhat greater than the maximum rms current permissible when the diode is used as a rectifier.

TABLE 3.2

Typical Semiconductor Diode Characteristics

Diode type	Type number	Material	PIV, V	Minimum forward characteristic		Maximum reverse characteristic			Absolute maximum ratings				Storage delay, nsec
				I_f, mA	at V_f, V	I_r, μA	at V_r, V	at T, °C	W_{0max}, mW	$I_{d\,max}$, A	$I_{dp\,max}$, A	T_{max}, °C	
General purpose (point contact)	1N34A	Ge	60	5.0	1.0	500	50	25	100	0.05	0.50	90	—
	1N55B	Ge	180	5.0	1.0	500	150	25	130	0.03	0.25	90	—
	1N485A	Si	180	100	1.0	0.03	150	25	250	0.2	2.0	200	—
Rectifier (junction)	1N340	Si	100	400	2.0	100	100	150	—	0.3	5.0	175	—
	1N343	Si	300	800	2.0	500	300	150	—	0.6	10	175	—
	1N1105	Si	600	200	1.5	300	600	150	—	1.2	15	175	—
Switching (point contact)	1N192	Ge	70	5.0	1.0	250	50	25	—	0.03	—	90	500
	1N914A	Si	100	20	1.0	0.03	20	25	—	0.08	—	150	4
Voltage reference (Zener)	1N2046	Si	12.8*	—	—	—	—	—	10,000	—	—	150	—
	1N4071	Si	62*	—	—	—	—	—	2,000	—	—	100	—
	1N742	Si	150*	—	—	—	—	—	250	—	—	175	—

* Zener breakdown voltage.

3.3.2   Reverse-operation limits; Zener diodes

Another critical parameter in the use of semiconductor devices is the value of the maximum reverse voltage, or *peak inverse voltage* (PIV), which can be applied across a junction. If the rated value of PIV is exceeded for even a very short time, the junction may be permanently damaged. From Eq. (3.3), we note that the diode current should be simply $-I_{f0}$ for not too small a reverse bias, due to the presence of residual minority carriers. However, if the voltage is made excessively negative, the reverse current will not remain constant at its saturation value but will, in fact, increase.

There are two separate physical processes which can cause an increase in reverse current. First, if V is sufficiently large, the minority carriers, while traveling through the depletion layer, may be sufficiently accelerated that they can attain kinetic energies comparable to the gap energy, and so can create new hole-electron pairs by impact. This process, called *impact ionization*, is similar to the phenomenon of ionization by collision in a gas, which results in ignition of a gas discharge. Impact ionization in semiconductors will cause an increase in the reverse current by the creation of additional secondary free carriers. If V is made even larger, the secondary carriers may also achieve enough energy to create new carriers, and the multiplication factor can become infinitely large, resulting in extremely rapid growth of the diode current.

The second process which can cause rapid current growth in a diode under reverse-bias conditions is analogous to field emission in vacuum diodes and arises from direct tunneling of charge carriers from the valence band on the n-side to the conduction band on the p-side. As we shall see in Section 3.4, this may occur only when the bottom of the p conduction band falls below the top of the n valence band, as the reverse voltage is increased. This phenomenon, which can cause a sudden enormous increase in reverse current when a critical voltage is reached, is usually called *avalanche breakdown* or *Zener breakdown*, and the voltage at which it occurs is termed the Zener voltage, after the theoretical physicist who first predicted the possibility of such an effect, many years before junction diodes were a practical reality.*

Depending on the composition of the materials in the diode, one or the other of these processes may dominate. Typically, in germanium diodes, which have small energy gaps and hence rather large reverse saturation currents, the limit is set by the onset of impact ionization; in silicon diodes, with large gaps and small reverse saturation currents, operation is more often limited by Zener

---

* The term "Zener breakdown" was actually introduced by Dr. William Shockley in 1951; he attributed the recently discovered effect to a process previously hypothesized by Dr. Clarence Zener. Further study of the effect, however, showed that the actual process involved was not that described by Zener but was a physically distinct process termed *avalanche breakdown*, suggested by Dr. Frederick Seitz. But the use of the terms Zener breakdown and Zener diode continues to be widespread. In some publications this usage is gradually being changed to avalanche breakdown and *reference diode*.

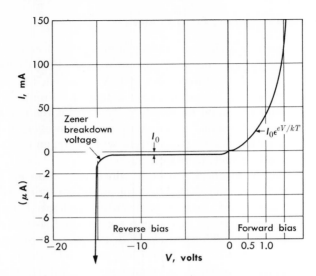

FIG. 3.8.   *I* vs. *V* characteristic of a typical Zener diode.   (Note scale change for forward and reverse voltages and currents.)

breakdown at voltages where the width of the barrier is not too great.   Some typical reverse-bias characteristics are shown in Fig. 3.8.

Zener breakdown sets in at a very reproducible voltage, dependent only on the composition of the junction materials.   The temperature coefficient of the Zener voltage is quite small (of the order of $10^{-4}/°C$).   These features make such devices very well suited for use as voltage-reference sources; some examples will be discussed in Chapter 7.   Zener diodes are available with breakdown voltages ranging from 0.4 V to over 500 V and with power ratings as high as 250 W.

Point-contact diodes, unlike pn-junctions, generally show a gradual, rather than a sudden, increase in current as the reverse voltage is raised.   Both impact ionization and field-emission breakdown can occur in such diodes if the voltage is increased very rapidly to a high value.   Since there is a continuum of available energy states on the metal side of the junction for tunnel currents, there is no well-defined Zener-breakdown voltage.

The ultimate deterioration of the diode under reverse-bias conditions results from excessive heating of the junction, just as it does under forward-bias conditions.   Since diffusion cannot occur instantaneously, some time is required at excessive temperatures before permanent damage results.   However, there is a significant difference in the amounts of power dissipated when excessive currents flow under forward and reverse operation.   Under forward bias, the current increases exponentially with voltage and is already very large, perhaps at its maximum value, when *V* is of the order of a few tenths of a volt.   Under reverse-bias conditions, the current is at first very small and relatively constant as *V* increases in magnitude, but it may then suddenly increase even more rapidly than exponentially to a very large value when breakdown occurs, unless limited by external resistors. This sudden growth of current can occur when V is already large, of the order of tens or even hundreds of volts. Thus the power dissipated when breakdown occurs may be thousands of times greater under reverse-voltage operation than under forward operation, and heating may occur so rapidly that the excess heat cannot be conducted to a heat sink fast enough to prevent destruction of the junction, which can occur within microseconds after breakdown.

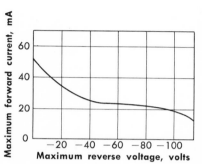

FIG. 3.9. Derating curve for a point-contact diode, showing decrease in maximum allowable reverse voltage with increasing forward current. This characteristic is of particular importance when the diodes are operated under ac-conditions.

The situation is worse for impact-ionization breakdown if the diode is already heated because of its normal forward operation. For this reason, the maximum allowable reverse voltage for cases other than Zener breakdown depends on the average forward current through the diode, as illustrated for a point-contact diode in Fig. 3.9. For a similar reason, since some heating can occur under reverse bias, the maximum permissible forward dc-current may be larger than the rms-current allowable under ac-conditions.

3.3.3 Frequency limitations

All electronic devices have inherent limitations in the maximum frequency at which they will operate efficiently. In vacuum diodes or triodes, for example, nothing significant can occur in a time much less than that required for an electron to be emitted and to cross over to the anode. No matter how vigorously we may change a grid voltage, virtually no change in anode current occurs until an electron has traversed the grid. In ordinary tubes this takes only a small fraction of a microsecond; therefore, this particular transit-time effect, while it clearly limits the operation of vacuum tubes, becomes serious only for frequencies of 100 Mcps or higher. Such transit time effects introduce a natural minimum delay in the time required to turn any vacuum tube circuit "on." As for semiconductor diodes, there is quite a different sort of physical frequency limitation. It can be turned on as rapidly as minority charge carriers can be injected across the very narrow junction; hence, only a negligible delay is usually introduced. However, turning the diode "off" is quite another matter. In order for the diode current, once started, to fall back to its reverse saturation value when the voltage

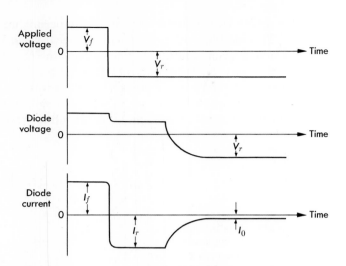

FIG. 3.10. Storage delay in a junction diode driven through a series resistance. When the applied input voltage is reversed, the diode current does not immediately fall to zero but first reverses until the excess minority carriers are swept back across the junction and then finally decays to the reverse saturation value.

changes from positive to negative, all the excess minority carriers which have been injected across the junction under forward operating conditions must be removed—either by recombination or by being swept back to their own side of the junction. So long as "stored" carriers remain on the other side of the junction, a large reverse current will flow. This behavior, illustrated in Fig. 3.10, is sometimes called *storage delay*. It is much worse in pn-junction diodes than in point-contact diodes. In junction diodes the materials are generally

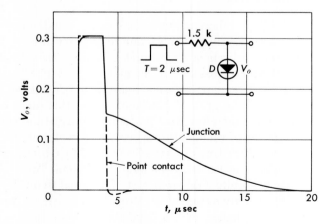

FIG. 3.11. Comparison of storage delay effects in junction and point contact diodes. The rectangular input pulse starts from 0 V at $t = 2\,\mu$sec and lasts for $2\,\mu$sec.

quite pure, and the recombination lifetime is long, whereas the opposite is true for point-contact devices. (Some typical results are shown in Fig. 3.11.) For this reason, point-contact diodes are widely used for fast-switching applications, although for low-frequency use, particularly as rectifiers in power supplies, they are much inferior to junction diodes, which have far higher power ratings per unit volume and far lower forward resistance. Special junction diodes can be made for very-high-frequency operation if we deliberately add impurities that aid recombination and shorten the minority-carrier lifetime. However, since these have a higher resistance than conventional high-purity diodes, they are less efficient at lower frequencies.

3.3.4   Environmental limitations

A properly designed semiconductor device is a precisely balanced physico-chemical system which has been made optimal for a particular use. Care has been taken to optimize the chemical purity for good, long-lived operation, to maximize the power rating, and to minimize the size and cost. For different circuit applications, different chemical compositions, sizes, and construction methods have been carefully selected. All of this can be spoiled if the device is not properly isolated from external disturbing influences. One of the worst of these is oxygen, which can diffuse from the surrounding air into the semi-conductor, upsetting the delicate pn-balance and also forming electronic surface trapping levels which limit minority-carrier lifetime. For this reason, semi-conductor devices are always "potted" in a chemically inert resin or, in par-ticularly critical applications, actually sealed off in a tiny glass vacuum jacket.

Another serious limitation can be caused by intense high-energy radiation, such as may be encountered near x-ray machines or nuclear reactors. Such radiation can knock atoms out of their normal lattice sites or transform their nuclei to another species (in the case of slow neutrons), permanently upsetting the perfection of the crystal structure. The atoms that are displaced now act as multivalent donors, while the "vacancies" left behind act as acceptors. If the number of displaced atoms becomes comparable to the normal donor and acceptor concentration, the electrical behavior of the device will be radically altered.

3.4   TUNNEL DIODES

The phenomenon of quantum-mechanical tunneling, which was responsible for field-emission breakdown in vacuum tubes and Zener breakdown in pn-junctions, has at least one beneficial effect in a special class of junction diodes, which are called *tunnel diodes* or *Esaki diodes*, after their discoverer. In tunnel diodes, the p- and n-materials forming the junctions are very heavily doped. Indeed, the impurity concentrations are so high ($> 10^{19}/cm^3$) that tunnel diodes are quite useless as normal junction rectifiers. With such large impurity concentrations,

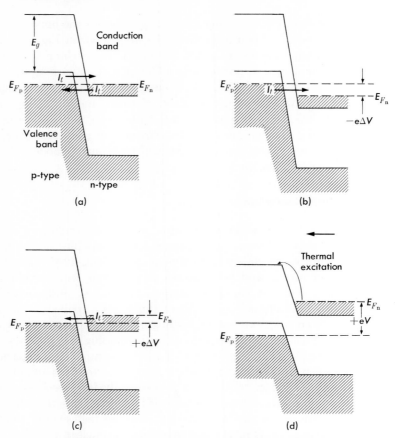

FIG. 3.12.   Energy levels in a tunnel diode.   (a) With no bias, forward and reverse tunnel currents cancel; (b) with small reverse bias, there is a large reverse tunnel current; (c) with small forward bias, there is a large forward tunnel current; (d) with larger forward bias, there is no tunnel current, only the normal, forward, thermally activated current.

the Fermi level of the n-material is slightly above the bottom of the conduction band, while that of the p-material is slightly below the top of the valence band. With no external voltage across the junction, the equilibrium potential distribution is therefore as shown in Fig. 3.12(a) (note that the barriers are shown for electrons, not positive charges).   Because the barrier height is about equal to the full gap width, there will be very few carriers thermally excited over the barrier.   However, if the transition from p to n is very sharp, the width of the junction will be very small, and if empty energy states are available, current can flow by charges tunneling through the barrier.   (Because of the very high charge concentrations, the depletion layer will be very thin, for example, 100 Å.)   In the tunnel diode the positions of the Fermi levels are such that there are indeed empty electron states in the conduction band on the n-side immediately opposite the filled electron states in the valence band on the p-side, so that tunneling is possible. If $V = 0$, the tunnel currents in the two directions will exactly cancel, after the two Fermi levels have come to equilibrium, and the total current will vanish. As in ordinary junction diodes, the p-side will now be negative relative to the n-side.

If a small reverse voltage $-\Delta V$ is applied across the junction, as in Fig. 3.12(b), a large reverse tunnel current will flow, for there are now many additional empty energy states in the conduction band on the n-side opposite the filled states on the p-side. (Therefore, this device is hardly a good rectifier!) Similarly, if there is a small forward bias $+\Delta V$, a forward tunnel current can flow from the filled states in the conduction band on the n-side to the empty states in the valence band on the p-side, as shown in Fig. 3.12(c). But now if V is made slightly more positive, the situation shown in Fig. 3.12(d) occurs: the filled conduction-band levels have now been "pushed" above the top of the valence band; there are no longer any adjacent unfilled energy levels, and so there can be no tunnel current. Thus, between (c) and (d) the forward tunnel current will rise to a maximum and then fall to zero. As V is made still larger, the effective barrier height is decreased, and normal forward-bias operation of the junction occurs, with minority carriers thermally excited uphill over the barrier.

The result of this rather strange sort of operation is a current-voltage characteristic such as is shown in Fig. 3.13. In the region ACB, the forward tunnel current is decreasing faster than the forward thermal current increases; hence, *I decreases as V increases.* This sort of characteristic is physically equivalent to a *negative resistance;* as we shall see later, a circuit element with an equivalent negative resistance can be employed as a basic component in an amplifier or oscillator circuit. Some typical tunnel-diode characteristics are given in Table 3.3. The maximum negative resistance corresponds to the inflection point C in Fig. 3.13.

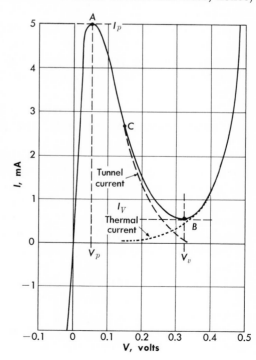

FIG. 3.13. *I* vs. *V* characteristic of a tunnel diode.

TABLE 3.3

Typical Tunnel Diode Characteristics

Type number	Material	Peak current, I_p, ma	Peak/valley current ratio, I_p/I_v	Voltage at I_p, V_p, mV	Voltage at I_v, V_v, mV	Maximum negative resistance, Ω	Cutoff frequency, kMcps
1N3713	Ge	1.0	7.0	65	355	—118	3.2
D4961C	Ge	2.0	6.0	70	350	— 65	32
MS1530	GaAs	5.0	12	130	500	— 15	8.0
1N2931	Si	10.0	3.5	75	450	— 22	0.15
MA4608A	Ge	30	6.0	55	350	— 4	10
D5066C	Ge	100	6.0	120	350	— 1.3	14

The most important characteristic of the tunnel diode is *not* shown in Fig. 3.13, and it is this feature which makes it a unique device. In the tunnel diode, the forward and reverse currents for voltages $V < V_v$ result from *tunneling of majority carriers*, not from the normal process of injection of minority carriers. Therefore, no recombination or minority-carrier return is necessary before the state can be reversed; there is negligible storage delay. The tunnel current can exactly follow the applied voltage up to the highest frequencies that can be imposed, limited only by the very small self-inductance and capacitance of the semiconductor itself. If the semiconductor and leads are kept small, the tunnel diode can be made to operate at frequencies as high as 10^{10} cps, much higher than those attainable with any "normal" semiconductor device. However, as is evident from the voltage scale in Fig. 3.13, only small voltage swings are possible within the tunnel region, so that this is essentially a very small signal device.

3.5 SEMICONDUCTOR TRIODES: THE JUNCTION TRANSISTOR

A semiconductor diode, like its vacuum-tube counterpart, is basically a rectifier, not an amplifying device. The transistor is the analog of the vacuum triode and, like the triode, can be used in circuits to provide a voltage, current, or power gain. Although the original transistor was of the point-contact variety, most modern transistors employ only pn-junctions instead of rectifying metal-semiconductor contacts. Moreover, since the operation of the junction transistor is far easier to understand, we shall restrict our attention to junction devices in this section.

The basic junction transistor, as shown schematically in Fig. 3.14, consists of a three-layer sandwich of p- and n-type semiconductors: either a thin layer of n-type between two layers of p-type, called a pnp-transistor, or its opposite, a thin layer of p between two layers of n, called an npn-transistor. Except for the sign of the majority charge carriers, positive holes in pnp-devices and negative electrons in npn, the basic electrical interactions which take place

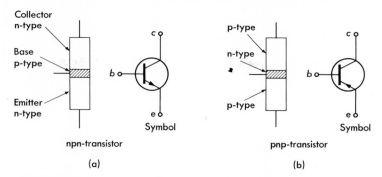

FIG. 3.14.   Schematic representation of npn- and pnp-transistors.

within both types of transistors are identical. We shall concentrate here on the physics of the pnp-transistor, if only to emphasize the fundamental difference between transistors and vacuum triodes, in which only electron flow is important. It should be understood, however, that we can utilize the same basic equations for npn-transistors, merely by reversing the sign of the currents and voltages.

3.5.1   Basic operation of a pnp-transistor

In a junction diode, the "heart" of the device was the pn-junction itself; the rest of the semiconductor was really needed only to support the junction physically, and we paid little attention to what was happening in a region much beyond the depletion layer.   The heart of a pnp-transistor consists of the thin base region and the two pn-junctions on either side, as shown in Fig. 3.15.   Conventionally, the emitter junction is on the left and the collector junction on the right.   (As we shall see later, for optimal operation the emitter and collector junctions often have somewhat different compositions and areas, but we shall ignore these differences for the moment and simply assume that the device is symmetrical.)   Therefore, when equilibrium has been reached and the Fermi energies of the emitter, base, and collector have reached the same level, the potential distribution will be as represented in Fig. 3.15(a).   (Note that the valence band is shown above the conduction band, so that the barriers are upward for holes.) In order for the device to operate as an amplifier, the emitter-base junction must be forward-biased and the collector-base junction reverse-biased.   Accordingly, the potential diagram for the transistor, under operating bias conditions, is as shown in Fig. 3.15(b), where the emitter is now at a positive voltage, V_{eb}, with respect to the base, while the collector is at a negative voltage, V_{cb}, with respect to the base (the collector is also obviously at a negative voltage, $V_{ce} = V_{cb} - V_{eb}$, with respect to the emitter).

The emitter-base junction is a forward-biased diode operating in normal fashion; thus, the emitter current I_e, carried by holes flowing from emitter to

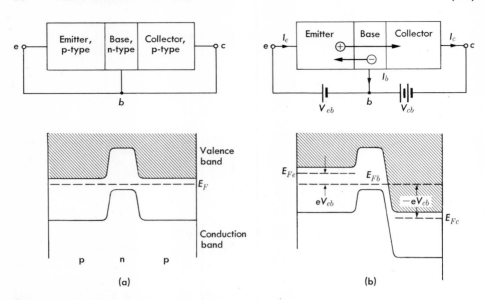

FIG. 3.15.   Energy levels in a pnp-transistor under (a) no bias, (b) normal bias conditions with emitter forward-biased and collector reverse-biased. Most of the emitter
current drifts through the base to the collector. (Note that the valence band here is
shown *above* the conduction band, since the barriers are indicated for holes rather than
electrons.)

base and electrons flowing from base to emitter, must be, from Eq. (3.3),

$$I_e = I_{e0}(\epsilon^{eV_{eb}/kT} - 1).\tag{3.5}$$

If the base region were very wide, so that the collector junction was far removed
from the emitter junction, then the collector current I_c would simply be the
reverse saturation current I_{c0}, typical of a reverse-biased diode, arising from
residual minority carriers in the base and collector. Under these conditions,
we would simply have two diodes in series, not a transistor. In fact, the "secret
ingredient" of a transistor is that the width of the base region is *much smaller
than the diffusion length of the minority carriers in the base* (see Section 1.6).
Therefore, most of that fraction of I_e which consisted of holes injected into the
n-region of the base will simply drift across the base region to the collector where
the holes will be accelerated downhill at the collector junction. In the p-material
of the collector, these injected holes are *majority carriers*, simply adding to the
collector current; they will not be removed by recombination. If we designate
by αI_e the fraction of the emitter current which crosses into the collector, then
the total collector current will be simply

$$I_c = I_{c0} + \alpha I_e.\tag{3.6}$$

The fraction of the emitter current which does not reach the collector must, in order to conserve charge, flow out of the base into the external circuit. This current is called the *base current* I_b and, clearly, $I_b = (1 - \alpha)I_e - I_{c0}$ since we require that $I_e = I_c + I_b$.

For a properly designed transistor, the fraction α is very nearly unity, so that $I_c \approx I_e$; in normal operation, some base current will flow, and I_c will therefore be a little less than I_e. It is immediately apparent that as a result of this behavior, the transistor operates primarily as a *power amplifier*. The power input to the emitter will be simply $V_{eb}I_e$, while the power output will be $V_{cb}I_c$. Since $I_c \approx I_e$ but V_{cb} can be much greater in magnitude than V_{eb}, the power output can be much greater than the power input. Obviously, if optimal operation is to be achieved, I_c should be as nearly equal to $|I_e|$ as possible. From (3.6), to maximize $|I_c|$ the magnitude of I_{c0} must be as small as possible and the magnitude of α as large as possible. The materials actually used in the emitter, base, and collector regions can be selected with these requirements in mind. The following points warrant special emphasis.

1. In order to make α as large as possible, almost the whole of I_e should result from holes injected from emitter to base; only a negligible fraction should be from electrons injected in the opposite direction since they will not contribute to I_c. Therefore, the emitter region should be much more heavily doped than the base region. In addition, in order that the injected holes not be lost by recombination in the base before they can reach the collector, the width of the base must be much smaller than the diffusion length of the holes. Hence, the base region should be as thin as possible, and the lifetime of the minority carriers in the base should be as *long* as possible (see Eq. 1.15). To maximize the hole lifetime in the base, the concentration of donor impurities and other trapping levels there must be as small as possible. Fortunately, the realization of this criterion is consistent with the requirement for a small electron contribution to I_e.

2. To keep I_{c0} as small as possible, the equilibrium concentration of minority carriers should be kept as small as possible around the base-collector junction— few holes on the base side and few electrons on the collector side. To achieve this, the collector, as well as the base, should not contain too high a concentration of impurities; the collector must, however, contain enough acceptors so that it is strongly p-type with respect to the n-type base and can withstand the reverse-bias voltage without breaking down. For this reason, the collector region of a transistor is sometimes made somewhat more pure and less heavily doped than the emitter region.

In addition, since there is usually much more power dissipated at the collector junction than at the emitter junction, transistors, particularly for high-power use, are frequently made with much larger collector junctions than emitter junctions and with the collector junctions close to a heat sink. We shall discuss the ways in which transistors can be fabricated to achieve this result, as well as other desirable features, in Section 3.7.

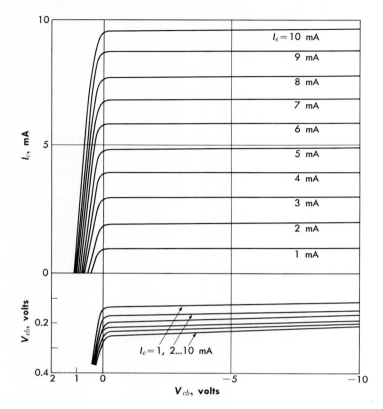

FIG. 3.16.   Common-base characteristics of a pnp-transistor, showing collector current as a function of collector-base voltage for various values of the emitter current. The V_{eb} vs. V_{cb} characteristics are also shown.

3.5.2   Current-voltage characteristics of a pnp-transistor

If the collector is biased sufficiently negative with respect to the base, the collector current is as given by Eq. (3.6), and is essentially independent of the collector-to-base voltage V_{cb}. However, if V_{cb} is small or positive, Eq. (3.6) will not be appropriate. Instead, we must consider the contribution to I_c from the unsaturated base-collector junction, so that we must write

$$I_c = \alpha I_e + I_{c0}(1 - \epsilon^{eV_{cb}/kT}). \tag{3.7}$$

Equation (3.7) reduces to (3.6) for V_{cb} negative and eV_{cb} large compared with kT. The current-voltage characteristics of a typical pnp-transistor are shown in Fig. 3.16. The measured characteristics are in good agreement with Eq. (3.7). For V_{cb} large and negative, I_c is essentially a constant and depends only on I_e. The lower part of the figure shows another effect, which we have not previously considered but which can be important in transistor-circuit applications.   The magnitude of V_{cb} influences the *emitter* current in the following way: the net emitter current consists of the current of carriers injected by the emitter into the base less the fraction that diffuses back to the emitter after having traveled some distance in the base. As V_{cb} increases, the collector field penetrates farther into the base toward the emitter junction, and it therefore captures an increasing portion of those carriers which would otherwise diffuse back to the emitter.

This leads to an increase of the emitter current with increasing negative collector voltage at constant V_{eb}. To keep I_e constant, V_{eb} must be reduced, as shown in the lower part of Fig. 3.16. If V_{cb} becomes positive, the reverse collector current tends to cancel the forward emitter current, and V_{eb} must become very large to keep I_e constant. In practice, transistors are seldom used in this region.

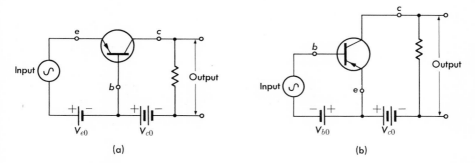

FIG. 3.17.   Simplified transistor amplifier circuits: (a) common-base connection, with input connected between emitter and base and output between collector and base, (b) common emitter connection, with input between base and emitter and output between collector and emitter.

In Fig. 3.16, voltages are measured with respect to the base, and the emitter current is taken as a parameter. These characteristics are known as the *common-base characteristics* of the transistor, and would correspond to a circuit arrangement such as that shown schematically in Fig. 3.17(a), where the input signal is connected between the emitter and base and the output signal taken between collector and base. This circuit, while sometimes employed in practical amplifiers, is about as common as a vacuum-tube circuit, in which the input signal is connected between cathode and grid and the output signal taken between anode and grid (the so-called "grounded grid" amplifier). It is much more common in vacuum-tube amplifiers, as discussed in the examples of the previous chapter, to connect the input signal between grid and cathode, and take the output signal between anode and *cathode*. Similarly, in the most commonly used transistor amplifier circuit, the *common emitter* circuit shown in Fig. 3.17(b), the input signal is connected between the base and emitter and the output signal taken between the collector and emitter. For this circuit, it is more

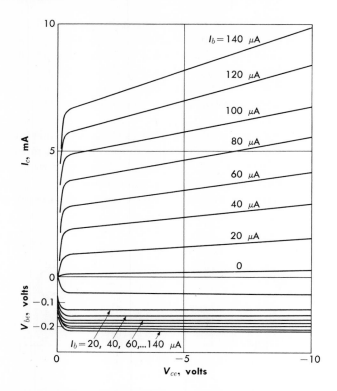

FIG. 3.18.   Common emitter characteristics of a pnp-transistor, showing collector current as a function of collector-emitter voltage for various values of the base current. The V_{be} vs. V_{ce} characteristics are also shown.

convenient to plot the *common emitter characteristics* of the transistor, as shown in Fig. 3.18.   Here the collector voltage is measured with respect to the emitter, and the base current I_b is taken as the parameter.   Since I_b is simply the difference between I_e and I_c, and since $V_{ce} = V_{cb} - V_{eb}$, Fig. 3.18 contains no more information than Fig. 3.16, but the parameters are merely rearranged in somewhat more useful form.   The characteristics of Fig. 3.18 are strikingly similar to those of a vacuum pentode, except that the base *current* now plays the role of the control-grid *voltage*.   In analogy with the vacuum-tube parameters g_m, r_p, and μ, which permit simple analysis of small-signal amplifier circuits, it is convenient to define small-signal parameters for transistors.   In transistor amplifier circuits, we have currents flowing in both base-emitter and collector-emitter circuits, so that we require two equations to describe the interrelationships between I_c, V_{ce}, I_b, and V_{be}.   For convenience, let us choose I_b and V_{ce} as the independent variables, with the other two as dependent variables, so that

$$V_{be} = f(I_b, V_{ce}) \qquad \text{and} \qquad I_c = g(I_b, V_{ce}). \tag{3.8}$$

We can now define the small-signal parameters in terms of the partial derivatives:

$$\text{input resistance:} \quad h_{ie} = (\partial V_{be}/\partial I_b)_{V_{ce}}, \qquad (3.9)$$

$$\text{reverse voltage ratio:} \quad h_{re} = (\partial V_{be}/\partial V_{ce})_{I_b}, \qquad (3.10)$$

$$\text{forward current transfer ratio:} \quad h_{fe} = (\partial I_c/\partial I_b)_{V_{ce}}, \qquad (3.11)$$

$$\text{output admittance:} \quad h_{oe} = (\partial I_c/\partial V_{ce})_{I_b}. \qquad (3.12)$$

The subscript e denotes that the parameters are evaluated for the common-emitter characteristics. Similarly, one can define other small-signal characteristics for other representations, such as the common-base characteristics.

The choice of dependent and independent variables in Eq. (3.8) was quite arbitrary, and it is possible to make other choices and to define other whole sets of small-signal parameters. Many of these can be found in current literature. Since, physically, only two currents and two voltages are actually involved, any set of parameters can be transformed into any other set by a suitable linear transformation. (See Problem 3.10.)

It would be pleasant if the same definitions of small-signal parameters were used in all the literature on transistors, just as g_m, r_p, and μ are universally used for vacuum tubes. However, a universally accepted standard notation has not been adopted at the time this book is written. The h or *hybrid* parameters, defined in Eqs. (3.9) through (3.12), seem to be nearer current universal acceptance than previous symbols and will be used exclusively in this text. Some typical values of h-parameters for a number of transistors are given in Table 3.4. These parameters, as well as other small-signal parameters still in use, represent transistor properties that are of primary importance for designing transistor circuits, like input and output impedances and current and voltage transfer ratios. How these parameters are related to the basic physical phenomena in a transistor is of great interest. To facilitate a discussion of this problem we introduce the *equivalent circuit* shown in Fig. 3.19, which represents a tran-

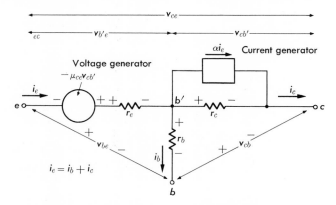

FIG. 3.19.   Equivalent circuit of a transistor at low frequencies.

TABLE 3.4

Some Typical Transistor Parameters

Type	Type number	Typical parameters at 25°C								Absolute maximum ratings at 25°C						
		P_e, mW	I_{c0}, μA	Bias V_{ce}, V	Bias I_e, mA	h_{fe}	h_{oe}, MΩ⁻¹	h_{ie}, ohms	h_{re}, ×10⁻⁴	T_{max}, °C	BV_{cb}, V	BV_{ce}, V	BC_{eb}, V	I_{cmax}, V	$f_{\alpha b}$, Mcps	Structure
Ge, pnp	2N519A	150	25	0.25	20	35	30	1100	3	85–100	25	–	10	–	0.5	alloy
	2N1094	150	5	6	4	50	100	500	11	85–100	30	15	1	40	645	drift
	2N464	170	15	6	1	26	17	900	3	85–100	45	40	12	100	1	alloy
	2N417	170	5	6	1	140	100	3600	11	85–100	30	10	20	200	20	alloy
	2N296	20k	1k	2	1000	20	–	–	–	85–100	30	60	15	2k	.08	alloy
	2N1147	90k	4k	2	5000	60	–	–	–	85–100	60	45	30	15k	.24	alloy
Ge, npn	2N438A	150	10	1	50	25	25	600	4	85–100	25	–	25	300	3.7	alloy
Si, pnp	2N1025	250	0.03	6	1	15	20	500	10	170–200	40	35	40	100	1	alloy
	2N2801	800	0.1	10	150	75	–	–	–	170–200	50	35	5	–	120	epitaxial
Si, npn	2N929	300	10	5	1	60	160	1800	6	170–200	45	45	5	30	30	planar
	2N1564	600	10	5	5	35	25	450	1	170–200	80	60	5	100	120	mesa
	2N1711	800	0.01	10	150	130	24	4400	7	170–200	75	50	7	–	160	planar
	2N1483	25k	15	4	750	40	–	–	–	170–200	60	60	12	3.5k	1.3	mesa
	2N1016	150k	10k	4	5000	10	–	–	–	140	60	60	25	7.5k	0.3	fused

sistor operating at small low-frequency signal currents (i_e, i_b, i_c) and voltages (v_{be}, v_{cb}, v_{ce}). The elements of this circuit correspond directly to physical concepts already encountered.

The point indicated by b' represents a physical point somewhere in the transistor base between the emitter and the collector. To this point three resistances are connected.

1. *The emitter resistance r_e.* This is the differential resistance of the forward-biased emitter-base diode. In alloy transistors the ohmic resistance of the emitter part is very small, so that for not too large currents ($I_e \lesssim 5$ mA), r_e is given to a good approximation by $r_e = kT/eI_e$ [compare with Eq. (3.4)]. At room temperature, for instance, $r_e \approx 25\ \Omega$ at $I_e = 1$ mA. It is obvious that r_e depends strongly on the emitter current.

2. *The base resistance r_b.* This is mainly the ohmic resistance between the external base connection and the point b'. This resistance depends a little on emitter current and on collector voltage. For various transistor types, r_b may vary from 30 to 1000 Ω.

3. *The collector resistance r_c.* This is the internal resistance of the reverse-biased base-collector junction. As already remarked, this resistance becomes very large for junction diodes at reverse biases above about 1 V. For transistors, however, we must take into account the effect of the penetration of the collector field into the base, which causes the emitter current and therefore also the collector current to increase with negative collector voltage. Besides being affected this way, the value of r_c is strongly influenced by surface conduction between the collector and base. Manufacturers' data for r_c give values varying from a few hundred kΩ to many MΩ.

In addition to the resistances, we find in Fig. 3.19 the following.

4. *A current source αi_e,* signifying that the emitter passes a signal current αi_e into the collector circuit. The quantity α has already been discussed in Section 3.5.1. The total collector current i_c is obtained by the addition to αi_e of a current $v_{cb'}/r_c$, caused by the reverse conduction of the base-collector junction.

5. Finally, a *voltage source,* $-\mu_{ce}v_{cb'}$, has been inserted in the emitter circuit. This represents the feedback effect of the collector already mentioned in the discussion of Fig. 3.16. The value of μ_{ce} usually lies between 10^{-4} and 10^{-3}. Its influence on the values of input and output impedance and of current gain can usually be neglected.

The five quantities just discussed are actually more directly related to physical processes in the transistor than parameters denoting input and output impedances and voltage or current transfer ratios, such as the h-parameters. They cannot be measured directly, but are closely related to the other parameters. A conscientious application of Ohm's law to the equivalent circuit of Fig. 3.19 yields expressions for any of the parameters in current use for common-emitter, common-base, or common-collector connections.

We shall derive such expressions only for the h-parameters defined by Eqs. (3.9) through (3.12) for a transistor in the common-emitter configuration. In terms of the symbols used in Fig. 3.19, we can rewrite the input resistance as

$$h_{ie} = v_{be}/i_b, \quad \text{for} \quad v_{ce} = 0. \tag{3.13}$$

Neglecting the loading of point b' by the large resistance r_c ($r_c \gg r_b$ and r_e), we derive from the figure

$$v_{be} = -\mu_{ce}v_{cb'} + i_e r_e + i_b r_b. \tag{3.14}$$

The condition $v_{ce} = 0$ in (3.13) implies that $v_{cb'} = -v_{b'e} = \mu_{ce}v_{cb'} - i_e r_e$, so that

$$v_{cb'} = -i_e r_e/(1 - \mu_{ce}).$$

Since μ_{ce} is always much smaller than 1, we may write $v_{cb'} \approx -i_e r_e$. To eliminate i_e, we need

$$i_e = i_b + i_c = i_b + v_{cb'}/r_c + \alpha i_e$$

or

$$i_e = \frac{i_b}{1 - \alpha - r_e/r_c} \approx \frac{i_b}{1 - \alpha}. \tag{3.15}$$

Inserting this value into (3.14), we readily find that

$$h_{ie} = v_{be}/i_b \approx r_b + r_e/(1 - \alpha), \quad \text{for} \quad v_{ce} = 0. \tag{3.16}$$

We see from this expression that the input resistance is not simply the base resistance, but that a resistance $r_e/(1 - \alpha)$ appears in series with it. Since $1/(1 - \alpha)$ is often of the order of 100, this term may contribute significantly.

To find $h_{re} = v_{be}/v_{ce}$ (at $i_b = 0$), we note that for $i_b = 0$:

$$i_e = i_c = v_{cb'}/r_c + \alpha i_e \quad \text{or} \quad i_e = v_{cb'}/[r_c(1 - \alpha)].$$

Further,

$$v_{be} = v_{b'e} = v_{ce} - v_{cb'} = -\mu_{ce}v_{cb'} + i_e r_e.$$

Eliminating i_e and v_{cb} from these expressions, we obtain, after some manipulating,

$$h_{re} = \frac{v_{be}}{v_{ce}} = \frac{-\mu_{ce}r_c(1 - \alpha) + r_e}{(1 - \mu_{ce})r_c(1 - \alpha) + r_e}. \tag{3.17}$$

Since $\mu_{ce} \ll 1$ and $r_c(1 - \alpha)$ is still much larger than r_e, we may write

$$h_{re} \approx -\mu_{ce} + r_e/[r_c(1 - \alpha)], \quad \text{for} \quad i_b = 0. \tag{3.18}$$

Clearly there are two opposing influences on the reverse voltage transfer ratio: the term $-\mu_{ce}$ takes into account the penetration of the collector field into the base; it indicates that for increasing V_{ce}, V_{be} must be reduced to keep I_b constant. The second positive term represents the voltage drop in r_e caused by the emitter current for $I_b = 0$. This current is $1/(1 - \alpha)$ times the reverse current through the collector-base junction, which acts in the same way as a real base current.

The forward current transfer ratio h_{fe} is related to α by

$$h_{fe} = \frac{i_c}{i_b} \approx \frac{\alpha}{1 - \alpha}, \qquad \text{for } v_{ce} = 0. \qquad (3.19)$$

This expression is found at once from (3.15) and $i_e = i_b + i_c$. (The parameter h_{fe} is sometimes denoted by β or α'.)

Finally, the output admittance $h_{oe} = i_c/v_{ce}$, for $i_b = 0$, can be related to the quantities of Fig. 3.19 as follows: as with the derivation of h_{re}, we have $i_c = v_{cb'}/[r_c(1 - \alpha)]$ if $i_b = 0$. Further,

$$v_{ce} = v_{cb'} + v_{b'e} = (1 - \mu_{ce})v_{cb'} + i_e r_e \approx v_{cb'} + i_c r_e;$$

therefore, after eliminating $v_{cb'}$, we find that

$$h_{oe} = \frac{i_c}{v_{ce}} = \frac{1}{r_e + r_c(1 - \alpha)} \approx \frac{1}{r_c(1 - \alpha)}, \qquad \text{for } i_b = 0. \qquad (3.20)$$

The output impedance is reduced by a factor of $(1 - \alpha)$, compared with the actual internal resistance of the base-collector junction. This effect is caused by reverse collector current flowing into the base and acting exactly like a real base current. It gives rise to an emitter current that is larger by a factor of $1/(1 - \alpha)$, reducing the output impedance by a factor of $(1 - \alpha)$.

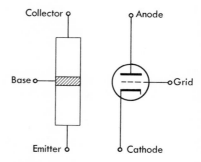

FIG. 3.20. Approximate equivalence between a transistor and a vacuum tube.

3.5.3   Basic transistor amplifier circuit

From the characteristic curves of Fig. 3.18 it is apparent that the operation of a transistor is roughly equivalent to that of a vacuum tube (actually a pentode), with the emitter playing the role of the cathode, the base that of the control grid, and the collector that of the anode, as indicated in Fig. 3.20. However, the input "signal" to the transistor is a change in *base current* rather than in *grid voltage*. The output signal in either case is a change in current—in collector current for a transistor and in anode current for a vacuum tube, which, for small changes, varies roughly linearly with the input signal. The fact that a current *must flow* into the base of a transistor amplifier to produce a change in output current, while no current need flow in the grid circuit of a vacuum tube, imposes a fundamental distinction between the two amplifier circuits: a transistor amplifier, unlike a vacuum-tube amplifier, must draw *power* from the source; the transistor amplifier therefore has a much smaller *input impedance*. These considerations, and others involved with stabilizing the operation of transistors, are of great importance in the selection of proper values of circuit components to achieve a reliable and useful transistor amplifier. We shall defer a detailed discussion of such matters until Chapter 4. For the present, we shall consider only a somewhat idealized amplifier circuit, that shown in Fig. 3.21, which will serve to illustrate how the h-parameters previously defined enter as equivalent physical variables.

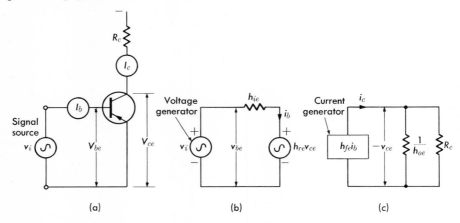

(a)   (b)   (c)

FIG. 3.21. Idealized transistor amplifier. (a) Basic circuit arrangement, (b) equivalent input circuit, (c) equivalent output circuit.

The basic circuit shown in Fig. 3.21(a) is the common-emitter amplifier arrangement. Through means which are at present unspecified, the circuit is initially biased to some equilibrium state, with base current $I_b^{(0)}$ and collector current $I_c^{(0)}$; the collector-to-emitter voltage $V_{ce}^{(0)}$ is then fixed in accordance with the characteristics of Fig. 3.18. The input-signal voltage source is connected between the base and emitter. When turned on, it produces a small-signal voltage v_i across its output terminals.

The voltage v_i will produce a base-signal current i_b, which can be calculated from the equivalent input circuit of Fig. 3.21(b). Here the input resistance h_{ie} appears simply as a resistor, and the feedback term h_{re} is merely a generator of emf $h_{re}v_{ce}$, in series with the circuit. The base signal current is then clearly

$$i_b = (v_i - h_{re}v_{ce})/h_{ie}. \tag{3.21}$$

In the output circuit shown in Fig. 3.21(c), the base current i_b produces a collector current

$$i_c = h_{fe}i_b, \tag{3.22}$$

which is represented by a current source. The output admittance h_{oe} appears as a resistance $1/h_{oe}$ in parallel with the load resistor R_c, which is in series with the collector. The current i_c, in turn, causes the collector signal

$$v_{ce} = \frac{-i_c(R_c/h_{oe})}{R_c + 1/h_{oe}}, \tag{3.23}$$

as we can see from the figure. In (3.23) the minus sign takes account of the 180-degree phase difference between the collector current and voltage; as the collector current rises, the voltage V_{ce} must decrease, as in a vacuum tube amplifier. We can now solve for the voltage gain of the circuit, $A_V = v_{ce}/v_i$, from Eqs. (3.21) through (3.23). Since v_{ce} appears in two equations, the exact solution would require a bit of algebraic manipulation. But this is something of an idealized circuit anyway, so we shall defer the exact solution in favor of an approximate solution, which fortunately corresponds to the most important practical cases. For the moment, we shall assume that h_{re} is very small, so that we may ignore the term $-h_{re}v_{ce}$ in (3.21) in comparison with v_i. Then the voltage gain would be given approximately by

$$A_V = \frac{v_{ce}}{v_i} \approx -\frac{i_c R_c}{i_b(1 + h_{oe}R_c)h_{ie}} = -\frac{h_{fe}}{h_{ie}}\frac{R_c}{(1 + h_{oe}R_c)}. \tag{3.24}$$

From this expression we can easily derive the current gain A_I by using $i_{R_c} = -v_{ce}/R_c$ and $i_i = v_i/h_{ie}$. We obtain

$$A_I = \frac{i_{R_c}}{i_i} = \frac{-v_{ce}}{R_c}\frac{h_{ie}}{v_i} = -\frac{h_{ie}}{R_c}A_V = h_{fe}\frac{1}{(1 + h_{oe}R_c)}. \tag{3.25}$$

For $R_c \ll 1/h_{oe}$, Eq. (3.25) reduces to $A_I \approx h_{fe}$, the forward-current transfer ratio. From (3.19), $h_{fe} \approx \alpha/(1 - \alpha)$. Since for a good transistor α can be about 0.99, $h_{fe} \approx 100$.

If two identical transistors in the common-emitter arrangement are cascaded, the second transistor offers a resistance h_{ie} in parallel with the collector resistance of the first. Usually $R_c \gg h_{ie}$; hence, we may replace R_c in Eq. (3.25) by h_{ie} and find that $A_I \approx -A_V$ for the current gain of the first transistor. Thus, the voltage gain of a cascaded stage can be of the order of -100. Note that the voltage and current gains are of opposite sign since the output voltage becomes more negative when the output current goes more positive.

The values of all the pertinent h-parameters can be obtained from the slopes of the characteristic curves evaluated at the points specified by the initial bias conditions: $I_b^{(0)}$, $I_c^{(0)}$, $V_{ce}^{(0)}$, and $V_{be}^{(0)}$. However, as is evident from Fig. 3.18, if we restrict ourselves to small signals and use a large enough collector supply voltage, so that V_{ce} does not become too small, the most important parameter, h_{fe}, will not change very much, and the gain will not depend strongly on the bias conditions.

Biasing circuits for transistor amplifiers, which we ignored in our simple example, are necessarily more complex than those in vacuum-tube amplifiers, and the actual circuit gain is also dependent on the details of the biasing circuit. Omission of these terms, together with the other approximations employed in deriving Eq. (3.24) and (3.25), makes the present result appear tentative. However, for most practical circuits, the voltage gain given by (3.24) is within 20% of the actual value, and since tabulated values of h_{fe} are seldom more precise than this, use of Eq. (3.24) is an adequate starting place for practical circuit design, as we shall see in Section 4.3.4.

3.6 PRACTICAL LIMITATIONS OF TRANSISTORS

Transistors, like semiconductor diodes, are made with pn-junctions and are therefore susceptible to all the woes that may befall diodes under improper operating conditions, and for essentially the same reasons. Since we considered these matters in some detail for diodes in Section 3.3, a brief treatment, stressing the peculiarities particular to transistors, should suffice to delineate the inherent limitations of these devices.

3.6.1. Current, voltage, and power limits

In normal operation, the emitter-base junction of a transistor is forward-biased, and the collector-base junction is reverse-biased. In some switching circuits, the transistor may be turned off by application of a reverse bias to the emitter-base junction. Care must be taken in the design of any transistor circuit, as with diodes, that neither of these junctions ever be allowed to become excessively hot to the point where interdiffusion can occur. Excessive heating can occur either from especially large currents being drawn in normal operation (exceeding rated temperature and power limits) or by voltage breakdown under reverse bias. The manufacturers usually specify a number of absolute maximum ratings, which must not be exceeded if reliable operation is to be maintained. These include the following critical parameters.

Symbol	Definition
$T_{\max}$	maximum junction operating temperature
$P_{c\,\max}$	maximum average collector dissipation
$I_{c\,\max}$	maximum collector current
BV_{cb}	collector-base breakdown voltage
BV_{ce}	collector-emitter breakdown voltage
BV_{eb}	emitter-base breakdown voltage

Direct collector-to-emitter breakdown occurs, particularly in transistors with very narrow base regions, by penetration of the electric field at the collector-base junction into the barrier at the emitter-base junction. Such failure is usually called *reach-through* or *punch-through* failure. Absolute maximum ratings, together with typical operating parameters, are listed in Table 3.4, for a variety of transistors.

3.6.2 High-frequency limits

Semiconductor diodes, as we have seen, are limited in the rate at which they can be turned off by the storage of excess minority carriers near the junction. This problem is, of course, also present at the emitter-base junction of a transistor. However, transistors have another important high-frequency limitation, which is analogous to the transit-time limit in a vacuum tube. Because of the finite time required for the injected minority carriers to cross the base and enter the collector, there is a delay in turning the transistor on. Since the injected carriers merely drift across the base by diffusion (they are not accelerated by an electric field to any appreciable extent during the trip across the base), the time involved will depend critically on the drift mobility and width of the base. The transit time may be relatively long, typically several microseconds, unless the base is very narrow and very pure. Even more important, the transit times of individual carriers may differ by amounts of the same order of magnitude, so that if an ac-current with a period of the order of the transit time is injected at the emitter-base junction, carriers which leave the emitter at a particular phase of the current will reach the collector junction at widely divergent phases. This dephasing will cause the collector current to be much smaller than it is at low frequencies, so that in addition to being delayed by the transit time, the output signal will also be reduced in amplitude. This behavior can be represented to a good approximation by the introduction of the complex current amplification factor

$$\alpha_f = \frac{\alpha}{1 + jf/f_{\alpha b}}, \tag{3.26}$$

where α is the dc-current amplification factor defined in Eq. (3.6); at $f_{\alpha b}$, called the α *cutoff frequency*, the absolute value of α_f is reduced to $1/\sqrt{2}$ of its low-frequency value, and the collector current lags 45° behind the emitter current. This would correspond to the frequency at which the gain of the *common-base* amplifier would drop to 0.707 of its maximum value. However, for the usual common-emitter circuit, the gain will fall off much more rapidly when h_{fe} falls to 0.707 of its low-frequency value. From Eqs. (3.19) and (3.26), it is apparent that the frequency $f_{\alpha e}$, at which the gain of the common-emitter amplifier falls by $1/\sqrt{2}$, is related to $f_{\alpha b}$ by

$$f_{\alpha e} = f_{\alpha b}/(1 + h_{fe}). \tag{3.27}$$

Since h_{fe} is usually about 50–100, $f_{\alpha e}$ is much smaller than $f_{\alpha b}$. Typical values of $f_{\alpha b}$ are given in Table 3.4.

Another serious limitation in the capabilities of transistors at high frequencies is caused by the capacity of the pn-junctions. The collector-to-base capacity, which can be of the order of 50 pF for low-frequency transistors, is particularly troublesome since it can give rise to undesirable feedback in addition to high-frequency attenuation. Special methods which have been developed to optimize high-frequency operation are discussed in the next section.

3.7 TRANSISTOR-FABRICATION METHODS

The desirable characteristics of transistors, as we have seen, depend to a great extent on the purity of the material used, the width of the base region, and the thermal contact to the collector, among other things, not the least of which are structural rigidity and cost. A wide variety of techniques has been developed to achieve maximum performance at minimum cost, but, as usual, these two desirable ends necessitate a considerable compromise. As a result, a large number of methods are currently used in manufacturing transistors; better performance is obtained at higher cost by use of more expensive materials and more elaborate processing techniques. A very cursory description of some of the current methods follows, together with some assessment of their limitations and benefits. The chief difference in the various methods arises from the manner in which the required pnp- or npn-junctions are formed.

3.7.1 Alloy transistors

Alloy transistors are usually the least expensive to fabricate, but, because the base region is frequently wide, conventional alloy transistors have a limited frequency response. The basic construction technique is illustrated in Fig. 3.22 for a pnp-transistor. Small pellets of an acceptor impurity metal, such as indium, are placed on opposite sides of a thin slab of n-material. When the wafer

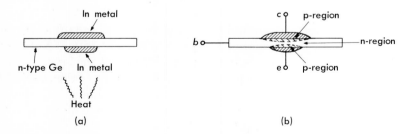

FIG. 3.22. Basic construction of a pnp alloy junction transistor. (a) Initial configuration with acceptor metal impurity deposited on opposite sides of the n-type wafer. (b) After heat treatment, emitter and collector p-type regions are formed by diffusion of impurities into the wafer.

is then heated to a high temperature, some of the acceptor atoms diffuse into the n-material, alloying with the semiconductor and creating p-regions on either side of the n-region. The remaining metal on the surface can be used for ohmic emitter and collector contacts, and an ohmic base contact can be added to complete the unit. To achieve uniformity in electrical characteristics, the wafer and pellet thicknesses, the contact area, and the alloying temperature must all be very carefully controlled. With this technique, it is difficult to attain uniformly thin base regions, and since f_{ab} varies inversely as the square of the base width, conventional alloy transistors are usually limited to values of f_{ab} of a few megacycles per second or less. However, since both the emitter and collector regions are thin and have a low resistance, little power is wasted in the body of the alloy transistor, and they can be made to operate at high power levels.

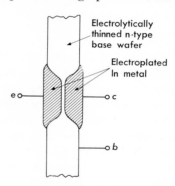

FIG. 3.23. Construction of micro-alloy transistor. The n-type base wafer is first thinned electrolytically, then the acceptor metal is electrodeposited by reversal of current in the bath. The assembly can then be heated to form emitter and collector junctions inside the thinned section of the wafer.

An important variant of the conventional alloy transistor is the *microalloy-* or *surface-barrier* transistor shown in Fig. 3.23. Here the base wafer is first thinned by electrolytic etching to provide a very thin base region; then, without the fragile wafer being moved, metal is electrolytically deposited on either side of the thinned region to equal or exceed the original wafer thickness, so that the piece is again mechanically strong. With slight heating, small alloy emitter and collector regions are formed in the thin base. This transistor has all the good features of a conventional alloy transistor, and besides, because of the very thin base, it can have a much higher value of f_{ab}, up to 100 Mcps or more. The cutoff frequency can be raised even further by starting with a wafer in which the emitter junction is already formed by diffusion and then using the microalloy technique to thin the material and form a low-resistance collector. In such a *microalloy diffused* transistor, values of f_{ab} of several hundred megacycles can be attained.

3.7.2   Grown-junction transistors

Pn-junctions can be formed in the body of a semiconductor during the crystal growth process, as the solid crystal is formed by pulling it slowly upward out of a hot liquid semiconductor "melt" which contains donor and acceptor atoms.

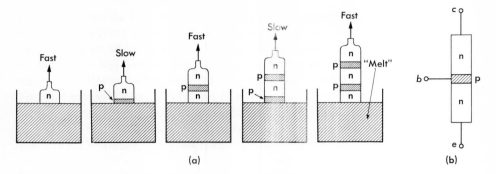

FIG. 3.24.   Rate growing. (a) Formation of alternate n- and p-type regions within a large crystal by varying the rate at which it is pulled from the liquid "melt," (b) leads attached to a tiny section of the crystal to form an npn-transistor.

Varying the rate at which the crystal is grown produces regions with an excess of either donors or acceptors. Slow growth favors formation of p-regions, while rapid growth produces n-regions. This method, called *rate growing*, can produce crystals with very steep gradients between p- and n-regions, and precisely controllable compositions. The transistors are made by slicing the large crystal into a large number of tiny npn-pellets, as shown in Fig. 3.24, to which leads can be attached. A major difficulty is encountered in making a reliable electrical connection to the thin base. Because of this problem, the base cannot be too narrow; therefore, typically, values of $f_{\alpha b}$ for rate-grown transistors are limited to about 10 Mcps. The power-handling capability is also limited, for the emitter and collector regions must in general be fairly thick. However, since compositions can be closely controlled, these transistors can be made with closely reproducible electrical characteristics.

3.7.3 Diffused transistors

The closest control of transistor characteristics can be achieved, at some increase in production cost, by the diffusion of donor or acceptor impurities into a semiconductor wafer from thin electrolytic or vapor-deposited layers. Frequently these techniques are combined with alloy-junction methods. Diffusion from the surface inevitably results in nonuniform composition, since the concentration of impurities tends to decrease exponentially with distance from the surface. This fact can be used to advantage in transistor design by deliberate use of a base in which the impurity concentration decreases from emitter to collector. This concentration gradient creates an intrinsic electric field across the base, which accelerates the injected minority charge carriers toward the collector, decreasing the transit time and increasing $f_{\alpha b}$. Devices of this type are usually called *drift* transistors. Emitter and collector junctions can be formed by alloy or microalloy techniques, which produce low-resistance emitter and collector regions.

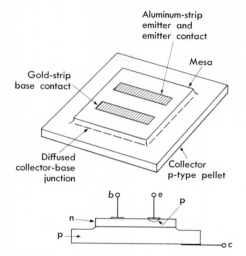

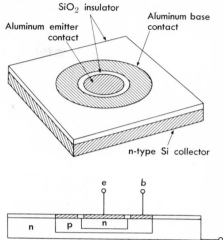

FIG. 3.25. Basic construction of a germanium mesa transistor. The collector-base junction is formed by diffusion before the mesa region is electrolytically etched out.

FIG. 3.26. Basic construction of a silicon planar transistor. The SiO_2 layer serves as a protective insulator.

Diffusion techniques can also be used with grown-junction transistors to enhance the impurity concentration in the base; such devices are usually called *grown diffused* transistors.

These techniques permit use of special wafer and electrode geometries which assist in attaining very high cutoff frequencies. Two important arrangements are the *mesa* and *planar* transistors, shown in Figs. 3.25 and 3.26. In both these transistors, the large wafer forms the *collector* instead of the base, so that mechanical rigidity is not affected by the base thickness. The base and emitter are on the same side of the wafer and are formed by diffusion of appropriate donors and acceptors. In the mesa transistor, the collector wafer is p-type, and the collector-base junction is formed by diffusion of donor arsenic atoms into a very thin layer at the top of the collector. A thin strip of acceptor aluminum is then vacuum-deposited over part of the base and diffused to form the emitter. A strip of gold alloy is vapor-deposited a few microns away from the emitter strip to form the base contact. Finally, a large part of the base-collector junction around the emitter and base contacts is etched away to form a mesa, thus reducing the collector-to-base capacity by a large amount. The silicon planar transistor is also formed by diffusion of base and emitter regions, but without a mesa-forming etch. In this transistor, the whole surface is subsequently oxidized to form a thin layer of protective SiO_2. Very-high-resistance films can be formed by a particular technique called *epitaxial* deposition. Such transistors, frequently called *planar epitaxial*, can have excellent high-frequency response and very stable electrical characteristics, with high values of breakdown voltage and low leakage currents.

3.8   OTHER SEMICONDUCTOR DEVICES

Since the discovery of transistors, a large number of other useful and frequently ingenious semiconductor devices has been developed, usually for special applications. In this section we shall briefly consider several of such devices. Because the variety of semiconductor applications appears boundless, and new devices with contrived, esoteric names appear almost daily, this list will be, at best, incomplete but, hopefully, will include those which may prove most durable.

FIG. 3.27. Schematic representation of pnip-transistor, with a thin layer of intrinsic semiconductor between the collector and base, to reduce the collector-base capacity.

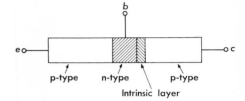

3.8.1   The pnip (or npin) transistor

The high-frequency operation of a transistor is determined by the base width as well as the magnitude of the collector-base capacitance. This capacitance must be small for maximum $f_{\alpha b}$. For a small capacitance in the mesa and planar transistors, the junction area must be kept small. The capacitance can be reduced also by the interposition of a layer of intrinsic, undoped, semiconductor between the base and collector, as in Fig. 3.27, forming a pnip- (or npin-) structure. The intrinsic layer serves as a dielectric, increasing the effective thickness of the base-collector junction and reducing the output capacitance.

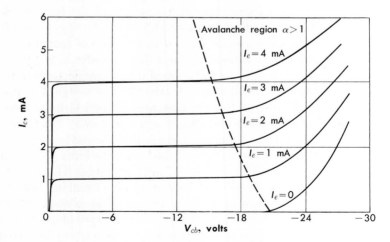

FIG. 3.28.   Common-base characteristics of an avalanche transistor. The current gain becomes greater than unity in the avalanche region.

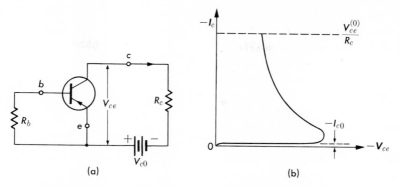

FIG. 3.29.   Avalanche transistor circuit. (a) Typical circuit arrangement, (b) current-voltage characteristics.

3.8.2   The avalanche transistor

When the reverse-bias voltage across the base-collector junction of a transistor is made too large, the junction may break down due to avalanche multiplication, causing large reverse currents. Ordinarily, the bias is limited to small values to avoid such effects. However, in special *avalanche* transistors, the unit is designed to operate in precisely this range, slightly below the actual breakdown voltage but in the region where avalanche multiplication of the collector current occurs, Typical characteristics are shown in Fig. 3.28. In the high-bias avalanche region. the current gain α is greater than unity, and current multiplication occurs. The collector current then increases from I_{c0} to a value limited only by the external resistance in the circuit. If a resistance is inserted in the emitter-base circuit, as shown in Fig. 3.29(a), the current-voltage characteristic of the collector exhibits a negative resistance region (Fig. 3.29b).

3.8.3   The field-effect transistor

The field-effect transistor (FET) is not a true transistor, for there is actually no base region through which minority carriers must flow. Instead, the device is more analagous to a vacuum tube, as shown in Fig. 3.30. The current flow

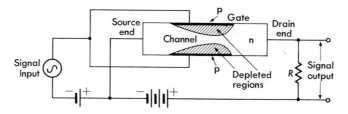

FIG. 3.30.   Schematic representation of a field-effect transistor.

between the *source* and *drain*, on opposite ends of the n-type bar, is
controlled by the magnitude of the opposing electric fields set up across the
channel defined by the diffused p-
region *gates.*   Since the gates are
reverse-biased, only a small reverse
saturation current flows, and the
device, like a vacuum triode, has a
very high input resistance. If the gate
bias is made sufficiently large, *pinchoff*
of the drain current occurs, as shown
in Fig. 3.31; not the striking similarity
between these characteristics and those
of the vacuum pentode.

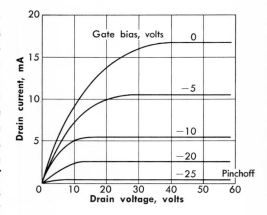

FIG. 3.31.   *I* vs. *V* characteristics of a
field-effect transistor.

3.8.4   The unijunction transistor

The unijunction transistor, shown schematically in Fig. 3.32, is actually a double-
base diode, not a transistor. It consists of a semiconductor bar with two ohmic
base contacts, B_1 and B_2, and a single rectifying emitter contact E. When no
emitter current flows, the device behaves like a voltage divider, so that a fraction
η of the base-to-base voltage V_{bb} would appear at the central emitter position.
If the emitter bias V_e is less than ηV_{bb}, the emitter diode will be cut off, and only
a small reverse current will flow in the emitter circuit. However, if V_e is made
larger than ηV_{bb}, a forward current will flow between the emitter and B_1. The
effective resistance between the emitter and B_1 will then decrease sharply, so
that the fraction of V_{bb} "biasing" the emitter junction in reverse also decreases.
As a result, the current in the emitter circuit will increase *even if V_e is decreased,*
giving a V vs. I characteristic with a very stable region of negative resistance,
as shown in Fig. 3.33.

3.8.5   The tetrode transistor

The tetrode transistor, shown in Fig. 3.34, is similar in construction to a normal
transistor except that two separate base connections are provided at opposite
ends of the actual base. A bias current is passed between the *normal* base and
the *extra* base, B_2. The transverse current sets up a potential drop which in-
hibits injection of carriers except in a small region near the normal base. This
squeezing of the base current reduces the effective area of the base beyond that
attainable mechanically, with a consequent decrease in base-collector capacitance
and an increase in $f_{\alpha b}$.

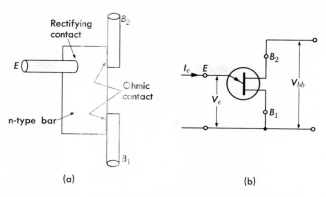

FIG. 3.32.   The unijunction transistor. (a) Construction, (b) symbolic representation.

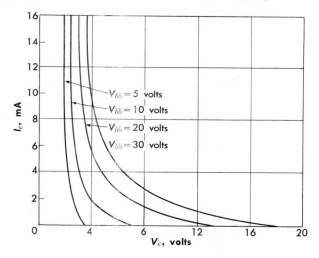

FIG. 3.33.   Typical emitter current-voltage characteristics of a unijunction transistor. The emitter current is essentially zero until V_e rises to a fraction of V_{bb}; then I_e rises rapidly even if V_e is decreased, giving a large region of negative resistance.

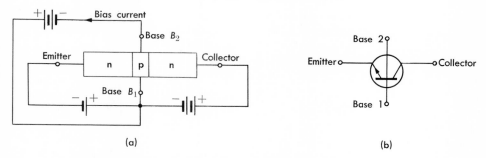

FIG. 3.34.   The tetrode transistor. (a) Construction, (b) symbol.

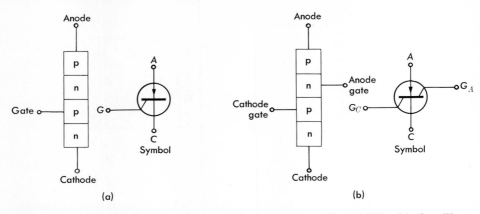

FIG. 3.35. npnp-devices. (a) The silicon-controlled rectifier (SCR), (b) the silicon-controlled switch (SCS).

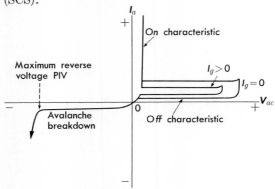

FIG. 3.36. *I* vs. *V* characteristics of a silicon-controlled rectifier.

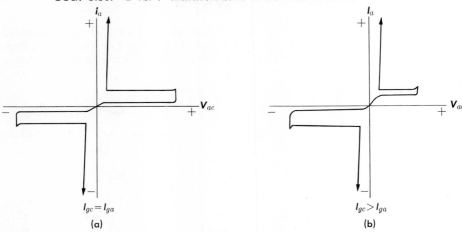

FIG. 3.37. *I* vs. *V* characteristics of a silicon-controlled switch (a) with equal gate currents, (b) with unequal gate currents.

3.8.6 pnpn-devices

Two extremely useful devices which employ three pn-junctions are the *silicon-controlled rectifier* (SCR) and *silicon-controlled switch* (SCS), shown schematically in Fig. 3.35. The structures are similar, except that only one *gate* connection is provided in the SCR, while two are provided in the SCS. The SCR operates very much like a thyratron, with a I vs. V characteristic such as is shown in Fig. 3.36. The anode-cathode current is maintained "off," even though the anode is positive with respect to the cathode, because of the reverse-biased gate region in between. When the gate is biased further forward or the anode voltage is increased, breakdown occurs and there is a large forward anode current. As in a thyratron, the gate regains control only when the anode current is turned off by reversal of the anode voltage. In a large number of current-control circuits SCR'S may be used in place of thyratrons, and are available to control currents as large as 500 A, with PIV ratings of over 1000 V. The SCS, because it has two gates, can be used in other ways: as a symmetrical pair of SCR'S operating on alternate half-cycles (Fig. 3.37a) or in various unsymmetrical switching arrangements where the two gates have different biases and signals.

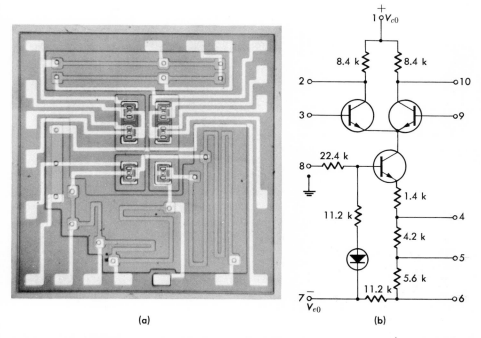

(a)   (b)

FIG. 3.38. An integrated circuit employing a silicon substrate (courtesy of Motorola, Inc.). The circuit is that of a difference amplifier (see Chapter 6), with a differential gain of about 140, a maximum peak-to-peak output voltage of 7 V, and a bandwidth of 1.4 Mcps. The actual circuit, shown in (a) is about 5 mm on a side. The equivalent electrical circuit is shown in (b).

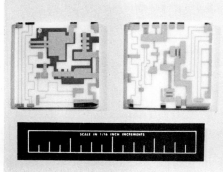

(a)

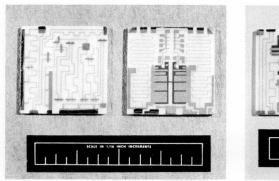

(b)

FIG. 3.39. An integrated circuit employing thin film deposition on an insulating substrate (courtesy of Motorola, Inc.). The circuit is that of a voltage-controlled oscillator (see Chapter 8), such as would be used in an FM telemetry system, and consists of the four substrates shown in (a). The equivalent electrical circuit is shown in (b).

3.8.7 "Integrated" semiconductor circuits

As we have seen, combinations of semiconductors and various metals can be used to form diodes, transistors, condensers, and resistors, depending on the relative composition, voltage, and proximity of the other connections. Recently it has become possible to "integrate" whole circuits which would normally employ all these elements as separate components, from two basic approaches. One technique involves the use of a tiny semiconductor wafer (a few millimeters on a side) as a substrate, in which the elements are formed by diffusion of appropriate impurities. An example of such a circuit is shown in Fig. 3.38. The second technique involves use of an insulating substrate where the elements are formed by deposition of thin films of metals and semiconductors; an example of a thin-film circuit is shown in Fig. 3.39. The semiconductor substrate technique suffers in the tolerance, reproducibility, and temperature effects in the passive element area and from parasitic interactions which can occur through the semiconductor substrate. Many of these difficulties are eliminated by use of insulating substrates, but the thin-film circuits suffer from poor reproducibility of the active element areas and from increased cost. Because of these limitations, semiconductor substrates are usually employed only for fairly simple circuits; attempts to integrate too many components onto a single wafer result in excessive rejection rates of completed units. Currently, both approaches are used and, with improved manufacturing techniques, it has become possible to provide a wide variety of integrated circuits with fairly reproducible characteristics at a cost not exceeding that of the individual components. It seems reasonable to expect that the manufacturing techniques will be advanced rapidly, and circuits as complex as a radio receiver and no larger than a postage stamp may be commonplace in another decade.

PROBLEMS

3.1   Find the forward current I_f as a function of the input voltage V_i for $R = 10\ \Omega$, 1 kΩ, and 10 kΩ, for

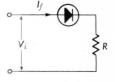

(a)   a germanium pn-junction diode with a reverse saturation current of 10 μA at 300°K.

(b)   a silicon pn-junction diode with a reverse saturation current of 0.01 μA at 300°K.

Neglect the internal ohmic resistance of the diodes and leads.

FIGURE 3.40

3.2   Find the effects of changing the temperature from 300°K to 400°K on the I vs. V characteristics of the two diodes in Problem 3.1, for $R = 1$ kΩ.

3.3   A germanium pn-junction diode has a reverse saturation current of 100 μA at 300°K. It is operated with a 2-V forward bias.

(a)   Compare the forward current and power dissipated in the diode if the ohmic resistance of the diode and leads is negligible to that for a similar diode with an ohmic resistance of 5 Ω.

(b)   Assuming that the diodes in (a) are not maintained at a constant temperature but rise in temperature by $\frac{1}{2}$°C/mW dissipated in the diodes, find the equilibrium temperature and current for the two cases.

3.4   For what value of the reverse voltage will the reverse current in a junction diode reach 95% of its saturation value at 300°K? For what forward bias will the forward current be 100 times the reverse saturation current? Repeat for temperatures of 200°K and 400°K.

3.5 Show that the effective capacity of a reverse-biased pn-junction (varactor) should vary approximately as $1/\sqrt{V}$, where V is the reverse-bias voltage. (Assume that the only effect of importance in determining the capacity is the effective width of the depletion layer.)

3.6 Show that the Zener breakdown voltage of a junction diode should vary approximately as the reciprocal of the acceptor concentration on the p-side when the donor concentration on the n-side is very large, as in an alloy junction. [*Hint:* Assume that the breakdown occurs at a fixed value of the *electric field* and is otherwise independent of the impurity concentration.]

3.7 The circuit diagram of Fig. 3.41 shows an arrangement of diodes to protect the meter M from serious overloads. The two diodes are silicon-junction rectifiers.

(a) Explain qualitatively the operation of the circuit.

(b) Suppose that the meter has a sensitivity of 50 μA full scale and that the series resistance R (which includes the internal resistance of the meter) is 2000 Ω. What should be the value of the reverse saturation current of each of the diodes in order for the meter to be protected against currents greater than twice full scale (100 μA) in the forward direction and full scale (50 μA) in the reverse direction for input voltages up to 50 times the nominal full-scale reading ($\pm$5 V between the terminals)?

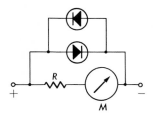

FIGURE 3.41

3.8 Show that the forward-current transfer ratio h_{fe} of a transistor should be an *increasing* function of temperature. Estimate the magnitude of the change to be expected for the temperature interval 200°K–400°K for typical germanium and silicon transistors when $h_{fe} = 50$ at 300°K. [*Hint:* Results obtained in Chapter 1 are required for solution of this problem.]

3.9 Show that the emitter-base voltage required just to produce cutoff ($I_e = 0$) in a transistor with a normally biased collector in the common-base configuration is

$$V_{ebc} = (kT/e) \ln (1 - \alpha).$$

3.10 Derive approximate relationships for the small-signal h parameters for a transistor in the common-base and common-collector configurations. Show that these are related to the common-emitter h parameters as follows.

	Common base	Common collector
Input resistance	$h_{ib} \approx \dfrac{h_{ie}}{1 + h_{fe}}$	$h_{ic} \approx h_{ie}$
Reverse-voltage ratio	$h_{rb} \approx \dfrac{h_{ie}h_{oe}}{1 + h_{fe}} - h_{re}$	$h_{rc} \approx 1 - h_{re}$
Forward-current transfer ratio	$h_{fb} \approx \dfrac{-h_{fe}}{1 + h_{fe}}$	$h_{fc} \approx -(1 + h_{fe})$
Output conductance	$h_{ob} \approx \dfrac{h_{oe}}{1 + h_{fe}}$	$h_{oc} \approx h_{oe}$

3.11   A transistor amplifier is connected in the common-emitter circuit shown in Fig. 3.21.   The transistor has the following values for the h-parameters: $h_{ie} = 2$ kΩ, $h_{re} = 0$, $h_{fe} = 50$, $1/h_{oe} = 50$ kΩ.

(a)   Find the value for the collector resistance R_c and the current gain A_I when the voltage gain of the amplifier, A_V, is 60.

(b)   What would be the voltage and current gain of the amplifier if the load were a second transistor with $h_{ie} = 2$ kΩ?

(c)   Given that the transistor has an α cutoff frequency f_{ab} of 2 Mcps, at what frequency will the gain of the common-emitter amplifier decrease by $1/\sqrt{2}$?

REFERENCES

Bridgers, H. E., J. H. Scaff, J. N. Shive, and F. J. Biondi (Editors), *Transistor Technology* (3 parts), van Nostrand, 1958–1959.

Hunter, L. P. (Editor), *Handbook of Semi-conductor Electronics*, McGraw-Hill, 1962.

Keonjian, E., *Microelectronics*, McGraw-Hill, 1963.

Levine, S. N., *Principles of Solid State Micro-electronics*, Holt, Reinhart and Winston, 1963.

Phillips, A. B., *Transistor Engineering*, McGraw-Hill, 1962.

Chapter 4

BASIC AMPLIFIER CIRCUITS

4.1 GENERAL CONSIDERATIONS

Certainly the most important application of vacuum tubes and semiconductor devices is in electronic amplifiers. By a suitable combination of these "active" devices with "passive" elements like resistors, condensers, and batteries, it is a straightforward matter to develop amplifier circuits in which the output signal is larger than the input signal. By a suitable interconnection of different amplifier circuits (often interspersed with other circuits), it is possible to construct an almost unlimited variety of fascinating and useful devices, from television sets to digital computers. In this chapter we shall be concerned only with the behavior of basic, simple amplifier circuits; a knowledge of their behavior and limitations is fundamental to any understanding of more complicated circuits.

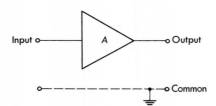

FIG. 4.1. Symbolic representation of amplifier with gain A.

Schematically, we can represent any amplifier by the simple block diagram of Fig. 4.1. The input signal is applied between the *input* and *common* (or *ground*) terminals, while the output signal appears between the output and common terminals. In complicated block diagrams the common terminal is usually omitted. The amplifier itself is shown here simply as a triangular box enclosing the letter A, which symbolizes the *gain* of the circuit:

$$A = \text{signal out/signal in.} \tag{4.1}$$

Customarily, the input and output signals are measured in the same units, and A is dimensionless. If the signals are voltages, A is the voltage gain of the amplifier; if they are currents, A is the current gain; and if they are powers, the

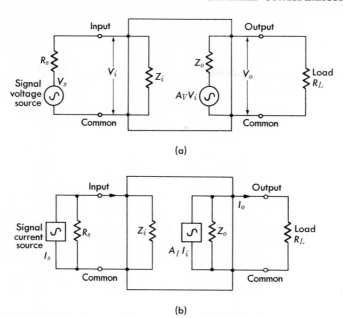

(a)

(b)

FIG. 4.2.   Four-terminal symbolic representation of (a) voltage amplifier and (b) current amplifier, showing input and output impedances and connections to signal source and load.

power gain. If we deal with voltage gain only, we shall denote the gain by A; where voltage and current gain are treated more or less simultaneously, as in transistor circuits, we shall use subscripts A_V and A_I, respectively.

The gain A defined by Eq. (4.1) is hopefully, but not necessarily, a real number. If the output signal is an exact scale replica of the input, then A is real, and the circuit is called a *linear* amplifier. If the output contains the same frequency components as the input, but not with exactly the same relative amplitudes and phases (as is generally the case), A is a complex number. If the output contains frequency components not originally present in the input, A is not only complex, it is quite complicated, and we usually employ a relationship somewhat different from (4.1) for such a nonlinear amplifier (see Section 5.1).

Thus, specification of the gain A of an amplifier tells us most of what we want to know about any circuit. However, two important additional characteristics must also be known if we are to consider interconnections of amplifiers between actual signal sources and actual loads, namely the input and output impedances of the amplifier. For example, for the voltage amplifier shown in Fig. 4.2(a), the actual signal voltage, V_i, appearing across the input terminals is not the electromotive force, V_s, of the signal generator but is $V_s Z_i/(Z_i + R_s)$. Similarly, the output voltage, V_o, appearing across the load resistance R_L is not AV_i but $AV_i R_L/(Z_o + R_L)$. Thus the true effective voltage gain of the circuit

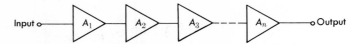

Input o———▷ A_1 ▷———▷ A_2 ▷———▷ A_3 ▷—————▷ A_n ▷———o Output

FIG. 4.3. Symbolic representation of series cascade amplifier, with output of one stage serving as input of following stage.

is not A but, rather,

$$A_{\text{eff}} = \frac{V_o}{V_s} = \frac{AZ_iR_L}{(Z_i + R_s)(Z_o + R_L)}. \tag{4.2}$$

Clearly $A_{\text{eff}} \approx A$ only if $Z_i \gg R_s$ and $Z_o \ll R_L$; otherwise, the effective gain is less than A. If amplifiers are connected in series, as in Fig. 4.3, the output of one stage serves as the input of the next. If the output impedances, Z_o, are all negligible compared with the input impedances Z_i, the effective gain of the combination is simply the product of the gains of the separate stages:

$$A(n) \approx A_1 \times A_2 \times \cdots \times A_n = (A_1)^n \qquad (Z_i \gg Z_o), \tag{4.3}$$

for n identical stages. If the ratio of output to input impedances is not negligible, then

$$A(n)_{\text{eff}} \approx A(n)[Z_i/(Z_i + Z_o)]^n. \tag{4.4}$$

For maximum voltage amplification, therefore, it is desirable to construct circuits with high input impedance and low output impedance.

For current and power amplifiers, on the other hand, circuit performance is optimized by quite different choices of Z_i and Z_o. For a current amplifier, we may use the equivalent circuit shown in Fig. 4.2(b). The current input to the amplifier is $I_sR_s/(R_s + Z_i)$, which will approach the source current if $Z_i \ll R_s$; similarly, the current delivered to the load will be a maximum if $Z_o \gg R_L$. Thus, for optimal *current* amplifiers, we require that $Z_i \ll Z_o$, which is exactly opposite the criterion for an optimal voltage amplifier. For a power amplifier, we would select Z_i and Z_o to maximize power transfer between stages. Since the power transferred from one amplifier stage to the next (identical) stage is, according to Fig. 4.2(a)

$$P = (AV_i)^2 Z_i/(Z_i + Z_o)^2, \tag{4.5}$$

we can find the maximum value of P by setting

$$\frac{dP}{dZ_i} = \frac{(AV_i)^2}{(Z_i + Z_o)^2}\left[1 - \frac{2Z_i}{Z_i + Z_o}\right] = 0;$$

the only solution is

$$Z_i = Z_o. \tag{4.6}$$

Thus, for optimum *power* amplification, we want the input and output impedances to be identical, a procedure frequently called *impedance matching*. Thus, in effect, the question of whether a given circuit is best suited for use as a voltage, current, or power amplifier really depends on the relative values of the input and output impedances rather than on the gain A. In the next section, we shall see how different circuit configurations naturally give different ratios of these impedances.

4.2   CLASSIFICATION OF AMPLIFIERS

To the uninitiated, there seem to be as many classes of amplifier circuits as of elementary particles in physics. Amplifier classifications have arisen for not necessarily cogent reasons now lost in history. We shall be mainly concerned in this chapter with a single class of amplifier circuits called Class A, *RC*-coupled common cathode or common emitter. For completeness, it is advisable to review first the general classification schemes currently in use.

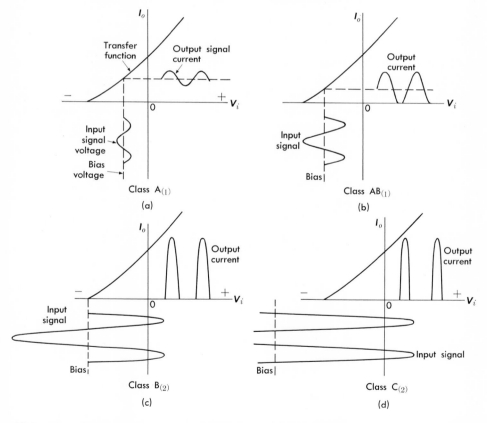

FIG. 4.4.   Classification of amplifiers by duty cycle. (a) Class A_1: 100% duty cycle, no grid current; (b) Class AB_1: duty cycle between 50% and 100%, no grid current; (c) Class B_2: 50% duty cycle, grid current; and (d) Class C_2: duty cycle less than 50%, grid current.

A. Classification by duty cycle. This classification, as shown in Fig. 4.4, charac-
terizes the fraction of the period of the input signal during which current actually
flows in the output circuit of the amplifier. If current always flows, as in Fig.
4.4(a), the operation is called Class A; this is the only case of importance for all
ordinary untuned voltage and current amplifiers, where a reasonably linear
response characteristic is desirable. When the current flows for more than half
the cycle but less than the full cycle, the operation is designated Class AB.
When current flows for about half the cycle, it is called Class B, while if current
flows for appreciably less than half the cycle, it is Class C. Classes other than A
are of importance only for power amplifiers (see Section 6.7); the efficiency of
an amplifier in delivering power to a load increases as the duty cycle is decreased
from Class A to AB to B to C, but the distortion of the amplifier also increases.
For vacuum-tube amplifiers, a subscript 1 or 2 is sometimes used in addition to
the class designation, to indicate whether or not any control-grid current flows
during the cycle; thus, in Class AB_1 no grid current flows, while in Class AB_2
there would be some grid current during a fraction of the signal period. The class
of operation is determined by the value of the preset dc bias voltage at the
amplifier input and the magnitude of the input signal, as shown in Fig. 4.4.

B. Classification by interstage coupling. It is almost always necessary to introduce
a coupling network between the output of one amplifier stage and the input to
the next stage, since the dc bias levels are generally quite different. For example,
the anode of a vacuum tube must be operated at a positive dc-voltage with
respect to the cathode for the tube to conduct, while the grid is generally biased

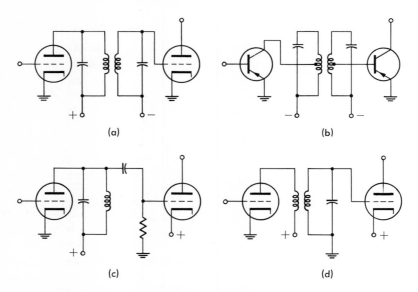

FIG. 4.5.   Methods of interstage coupling of tuned amplifiers: (a) and (b) double-
tuned; (c) and (d) single-tuned.

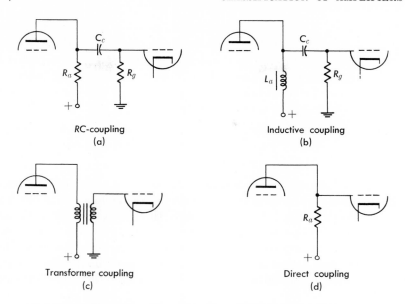

FIG. 4.6.   Methods of interstage coupling of untuned amplifiers.

negative. Therefore, we cannot simply connect the anode of one tube to the grid of the next. Various methods of interstage coupling are shown in Figs. 4.5 and 4.6. Those in Fig. 4.5 are for *tuned* amplifiers, which are designed to amplify in a narrow band of frequencies centered about the resonant frequency of the coupling network. The coupling networks in Fig. 4.6 are for untuned amplifiers. These are much more common and have the following general characteristics.

1. *RC-coupling.* This coupling, shown in Fig. 4.6(a), is the least expensive and by far the most frequently used interstage coupling network. The *blocking* or *coupling* condenser, C_c, serves to isolate the dc-level at the ouput of the first stage from that at the input of the next. In the circuit shown, the ac output voltage of the first stage is developed across the resistor R_a, whereas the input-signal voltage to the next is developed across R_g. Because of the presence of C_c, this circuit obviously cannot pass signals of very low frequency. The frequency limitations of the *RC*-coupled amplifier will be discussed in Section 4.3.

2. *Inductive coupling.* Use of an inductance in place of the resistance R_a in the output of the first stage, as shown in Fig. 4.6(b), permits coupling a larger signal since there is no dc-drop across the inductor. However, the low-frequency response of this circuit is much worse than that of the *RC*-circuit, and there is always appreciable distortion, so that inductive coupling is used only where fidelity of signal reproduction is not important and the possibility of providing a large signal justifies use of an inductor instead of a less expensive resistor.

3. *Transformer coupling.* Use of an interstage transformer, as shown in Fig. 4.6(c), provides the possibility of achieving increased over-all circuit gain or

impedance matching, depending on the ratio of primary and secondary turns. Moreover, since there is no dc-drop in the primary, the circuit can handle large signals. However, good linear transformers of broad frequency response are very expensive, generally much more than another amplifier stage; therefore, such circuits are usually used only when impedance matching is a critical requirement, as in the output of a power amplifier.

4. *Direct coupling.* In some circuits, it is essential to amplify very slowly varying signals. Then direct coupling may be used, with some other provision to readjust dc-levels to proper values. (See Section 6.6.)

C. Classification by common circuit element. As shown in Fig. 4.7, amplifiers are further classified according to which circuit element is common to the input and output ac-circuits. This choice determines the relative values of the gain and input and output impedances for the circuit to a large extent. As already noted, the functions of cathode, grid, and anode for tubes are similar to those of emitter, base, and collector, respectively, for transistors. Basic circuit arrangements with corresponding common elements therefore have analogous characteristics.

The following are the usual arrangements and their most salient characteristics.

1. *Common cathode (tube) or common emitter (transistor).* The input signal is applied between grid and cathode in the tube circuit and between base and emitter in the transistor, as shown in Fig. 4.7(a). The output signal is derived between anode and cathode or collector and emitter. This is by far the most commonly used circuit for either tube or transistor voltage amplifiers, and it provides fairly high gain. For tubes the input impedance is very high; for transistors, moderate. The output impedance is of the order of a few thousand ohms for triodes but usually higher for pentodes and transistors.

2. *Common grid (tube) or common base (transistor).* The input signal is applied between grid and cathode or between base and emitter, as in 1 above, but the output signal is now derived between anode and grid in the tube or between collector and base in the transistor, as shown in Fig. 4.7(b). The grid or base is usually connected to ground, and this circuit is sometimes called a *grounded-grid* or *grounded-base* amplifier. The circuit has a high voltage gain but a very low imput impedance; the output impedance is high for both tubes and transistors. The circuit provides good isolation between input and output. The tube circuit is used mainly for amplification at very high frequencies. (See Section 6.3.4.)

3. *Common anode (tube) or common collector (transistor).* In Fig. 4.7(c) the input signal is connected between grid and anode or between base and collector, since the anode or collector is maintained at ground for signal voltages; the output is taken between cathode and anode or between emitter and collector. Since the cathode or emitter voltages tend to follow the grid or base voltages, this configuration is usually called a *cathode follower* or *emitter follower*. This

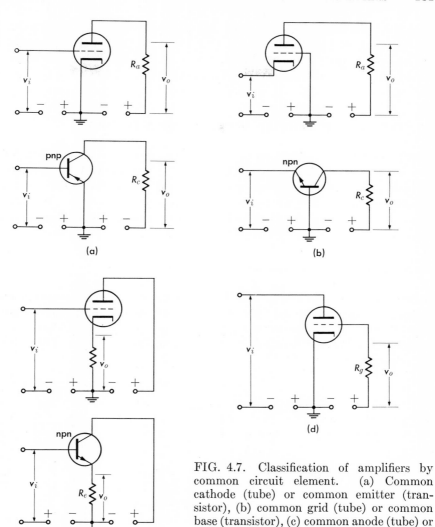

FIG. 4.7. Classification of amplifiers by common circuit element. (a) Common cathode (tube) or common emitter (transistor), (b) common grid (tube) or common base (transistor), (c) common anode (tube) or common collector (transistor), (d) inverted common cathode (tube).

circuit provides high input impedance and the lowest output impedance of the arrangements discussed here; the voltage gain, however, is always slightly less than unity. The circuit is widely used as a broad-band *transformer* to match a high-impedance amplifier to a low-impedance load, as with a coaxial cable (see Section 5.6).

4. *Inverted common cathode (tube).* In the special-purpose circuit shown in Fig. 4.7(d), in which the roles of the electrodes are just reversed from their ordinary use, the highest possible input impedance is provided. The output impedance is moderate, but the voltage gain is always much less than one. This

circuit is used only when the signal source is at a very high negative dc-level and when a very high input impedance is required, for example in connecting a gas nuclear counter tube to an amplifier. Note that the circuit is normally biased with the anode negative and the grid positive. There is no output unless grid current flows. There is no useful transistor analog for this circuit.

4.3 THE BASIC *RC*-COUPLED VOLTAGE-AMPLIFIER STAGE

Nearly all simple voltage amplifiers are based on the common-cathode or common-emitter circuits shown in Fig. 4.7(a). Previously, in Section 2.8.1 and Section 3.5.3, we discussed some general features of these amplifiers, such as the dependence of the gain on the tube or transistor parameters. We shall now examine the circuits in detail, to find practical criteria for proper design of voltage amplifiers.

4.3.1 Basic circuit requirements

In order for a vacuum tube or transistor to operate properly as an amplifier, the circuit must provide proper biasing voltages, as well as input and output networks through which signals can flow. As a minimum, the circuit must therefore include the following elements, which are illustrated in Figs. 4.8(a) through (c), respectively.

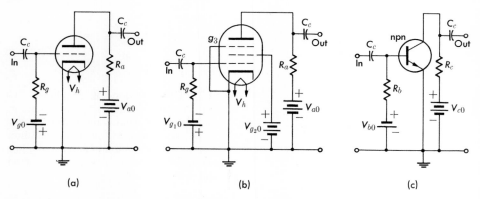

(a)   (b)   (c)

FIG. 4.8. Basic circuit requirements for *RC*-coupled amplifiers. (a) Triode, (b) pentode, (c) transistor.

A. Triode

1. A negative grid-bias voltage V_{g0} to set the control grid so negative with respect to the cathode that with the largest input signals used, the tube will neither draw grid current nor be cut off.

2. A positive anode supply voltage V_{a0}, chosen in combination with V_{g0} and R_a so as to locate the grid cutoff voltage V_{gc} sufficiently far below V_{g0}, say at

2 or 3 times V_{g0}. (The anode voltage is related to the grid cutoff voltage by $V_a \approx -\mu V_{gc}$, where μ is the amplification factor, because for this value of V_a the effective control voltage $V_{ec} = V_g + V_a/\mu = 0$.)

3. A grid resistor R_g in the grid circuit, which fixes the control-grid voltage at V_{g0} with respect to the cathode when there is no input signal and also provides an element across which the input signal can be impressed. If R_g were not included, the grid would be "floating" and could assume an arbitrary voltage. Ordinarily R_g is chosen large, of the order of a megohm, to keep the input impedance high.

4. A resistor R_a in series with the anode, across which the output voltage is developed.

5. Blocking or coupling condensers C_c to isolate the input and output from the dc-bias voltages.

6. Connections from the cathode heater to a source of rated voltage for the tube.

Usually the heater is connected to an ac-voltage through a step-down transformer operating from the line; one side of the heater voltage line, or the center tap of the transformer, is often connected to the common ground to minimize ac-pickup.

B. Pentode

1 through 6. These elements are the same as for a triode, but we require in addition:

7. A connection between the suppressor g_3 and the cathode; this is usually simply a wire across the tube socket or an internal connection in the tube; no additional bias voltage is ordinarily required.

8. A positive supply voltage V_{g20} to set the screen sufficiently positive with respect to the cathode that the cutoff voltage of g_1 does not become too small ($V_{g_1c} \approx -V_{g20}/\mu_{g_2g_1}$).

C. Transistor

This figure shows the arrangement for an npn-transistor; use reverse voltages for pnp.

1. A positive base-bias voltage, V_{b0}, to set the zero-signal base current at a level such that the transistor never reaches cutoff or saturation with the maximum expected input signal.

2. A positive collector-supply voltage, V_{c0}, completely analogous to the anode supply required for a vacuum tube.

3. An input resistor R_b in the base circuit that, together with V_{b0}, determines the zero signal base current and is further analogous to R_g in the tube circuit. The actual base-to-emitter voltage, $V_{b0} - I_bR_b$, is small, usually less than one volt, so that often $I_{b0} \approx V_{b0}/R_b$.

4. A resistor R_c in the collector circuit, analogous to R_a in the tube circuit.

5. Coupling condensers, C_c.

Fixing the values of the bias voltages and resistors completely determines the *operating* or *quiescent point* of the amplifier, i.e., the values of voltages and currents at which the circuit operates with no input signal.

4.3.2 Self-biasing circuits

All of the circuits shown in Fig. 4.8 are uneconomical since two or three separate power supplies are indicated. In practice we can seldom afford this luxury and, where possible, we try to operate the amplifier from a single power supply. We can then set the various elements to their required operating voltages by taking advantage of the fact that so long as the amplifier behaves in a reasonably linear manner, the *average* current flowing in any part of the circuit will be *independent of the signal voltage* (Class A operation). We utilize this fact to eliminate all but the anode or collector voltage supplies, setting the other elements at their proper voltage levels by adding more resistors, through which all or part of the current average flows. This technique, which is known as *self-biasing*, is not only economical, but it also results in more stable operation of the amplifier. Various self-biasing circuits are shown in Figs. 4.9 and 4.10. The biasing resistors are bypassed by large condensers (usually electrolytic) to keep the biases constant and independent of signal frequencies.

For the triode circuit, a resistor R_k is placed in series with the cathode, so that the cathode is now at a positive voltage $I_a R_k$ with respect to the control grid or, equivalently, the grid is at a voltage $-I_a R_k$ with respect to the cathode. The anode-to-cathode voltage is $V_{a0} - I_a(R_a + R_k)$. The self-biasing arrangement also tends to make the circuit somewhat self-regulating; for example, if the anode current should drop because of tube aging or lowered heater current, the bias voltage $I_a R_k$ would also decrease, tending to keep I_a constant.

For the pentode circuit, resistors R_k in the cathode circuit and R_{g_2} in the screen circuit have been added, shunted by the condensers C_k and C_{g_2}. The control

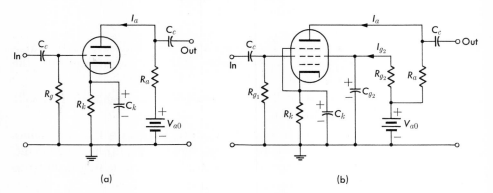

(a)   (b)

FIG. 4.9. Self-biasing circuits for tube amplifiers. (a) Triode, (b) pentode.

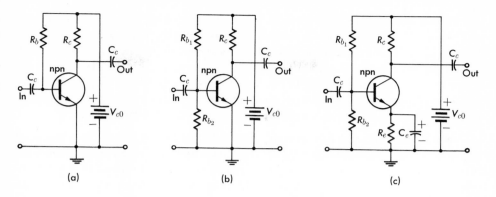

FIG. 4.10. Self-biasing circuits for transistor amplifiers. (a) Series resistor, (b) voltage divider, (c) stabilized bias circuit.

grid will now be at a voltage $-(I_a + I_{g_2})R_k$ with respect to the cathode, the screen at a voltage $V_{a0} - I_{g_2}R_{g_2} - (I_a + I_{g_2})R_k$, and the anode at a voltage $V_{a0} - I_a R_a - (I_a + I_{g_2})R_k$. The condenser C_{g_2}, like C_k, ensures that the screen voltage will depend only on the average screen current.

For the npn-transistor, we can in principle use the simple self-biasing circuits shown in Fig. 4.10(a) or 4.10(b), deriving the base bias voltage from a series resistor or a voltage divider.

Due to the strong temperature dependence of the reverse conduction of the base-collector diode, however, the operating point of these circuits is very unstable. Far more stable operation can be achieved with the circuit of Fig. 4.10(c), in which the emitter resistor R_e stabilizes the transistor current. The stabilizing effect is quite analogous to that of the cathode resistor in a tube circuit. It will be discussed in detail in the next section.

4.3.3 Selection of the operating point

We have seen how, with various resistors, condensers, and voltage supplies, we can bias the amplifier circuit to its operating point. Once selected, the operating point determines all the characteristics of the amplifier since the small signal parameters, μ, g_m, and r_p for tubes, and the h-parameters for transistors are then fixed. One extremely important question remains: With all these variables at our disposal, how do we go about choosing the best operating point for a particular amplifier? There are two general ways in which to proceed.

1. *Plagiarize.* Take a circuit designed by some professional of demonstrated competence or recommended by the tube or transistor manufacturer, and copy it, making small modifications to adapt it to your own requirements, if necessary. With all due deference to generations of textbook writers, this is honestly the best way to achieve a good amplifier in a minimum of time. There are a large

number of conflicting requirements to be reconciled in designing an optimal amplifier. If someone more expert has already done the hard work necessary to determine a reasonable compromise to achieve optimum results, it is no crime to adapt his circuit to your own requirements, at least as a starting point. (However, it is still frequently no trivial matter to decide which of many engineered circuits is best suited for your purposes and whether the particular circuit values found in the literature give truly optimal performance.)

2. *"Do it yourself."* (Recommended, naturally, for all students!) Starting with the measured (or copied) current-voltage characteristics of a tube or transistor and some educated guesses about a reasonable first choice for some of the parameters, determine the other parameters by graphical construction, and estimate the response of the circuit. Then try varying the initial assumptions, and recalculate the circuit response. (This second step is frequently simpler if you make a "breadboard" circuit in the laboratory and actually vary the parameters and measure the response.) By this iterative procedure, a reliable operating point, optimal for the particular application, can be found.

In this section, we shall be concerned only with the first part of the second procedure, assuming that some of the parameters are specified, for example, the tube or transistor, the anode or collector supply voltage, and the anode or collector resistor, R_a or R_c. It is then a simple matter to determine the values of the other parameters graphically, by what is sometimes called a *load-line* analysis. It is easiest to illustrate this procedure with some specific examples; the extension to other cases is straightforward.

Triode amplifier. This circuit arrangement is shown in Fig. 4.11; R_a has been selected as 50 kΩ, and the anode supply voltage is 250 V. We want to determine a value for R_k that will set the operating point; the values of R_g, C_c, and C_k affect the frequency response (see Sections 4.3.5 and 4.3.6) but not the operating point. The plate characteristics of the 12AU7 triode are shown in Fig. 4.12. Because the anode current flows through the resistors R_a and R_k, the tube cannot operate over an arbitrary range of these characteristics; the anode voltage is constrained to the range

$$V_a = V_{a0} - I_a(R_a + R_k), \qquad (4.7)$$

$$V_a \approx (250 - 50 I_a)\text{V} \qquad (I_a \text{ in mA}), \qquad (4.7a)$$

since R_k is expected to be much less than 50 kΩ. We can represent the constraint (4.7a) by the diagonal *load line* drawn over the plate characteristics in Fig. 4.12; allowed values of V_a and I_a *must lie along this line.* Note that the line has a slope $-1/R_a$; it is easily drawn by connecting

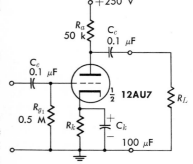

FIG. 4.11. Circuit of simple triode amplifier.

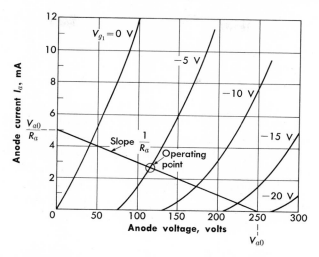

FIG. 4.12.   Plate characteristic curves of 12AU7 with load line for circuit of Fig. 4.11.

the point V_{a0}/R_a on the current axis with the point V_{a0} on the voltage axis. Allowable values of I_a and V_{g_1} are given by the intersection of the load line and the plate characteristics. These points can be replotted explicitly as in Fig. 4.13, with I_a shown as a function of V_{g_1}. From this curve, or simply by inspection of the intersection of the load line with the plate characteristic, we can now select an operating point to achieve the desired amplifier characteristic, for the output signal will be simply $R_a \, \Delta I_a$. Suppose, as a typical example, that we want the output to be as faithful a reproduction of the input as possible; we would then select the most linear portion of the I_a vs. V_{g_1} curve as our bias point. A reasonable choice would be $I_a \approx 2.7$ mA, $V_{g_1} \approx -5$ V. Since $V_{g_1} = -I_a R_k$ at zero input, we have thus determined the proper choice for R_k:

$$R_k = -V_{g_1}^{(0)}/I_a^{(0)}. \qquad (4.8)$$

For our circuit, $R_k \approx 1.8$ kΩ.

Normally both R_k and R_a would be only 10% precise resistors, so that our ignoring the value of R_k relative to R_a in Eq. (4.7a) is within the limits of our precision. If we must specify values of the components to greater precision, or if R_a has been chosen much smaller, it is a simple matter to work with Eq. (4.7) rather than (4.7a) in constructing the load line, first estimating a value for R_k and then solving by an iterative process to find a self-consistent value.

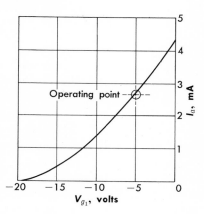

FIG. 4.13.   Transfer characteristics of 12AU7 for load line of Fig. 4.12.

The average power dissipated in R_a will be $I_a^2 R_a$ or about 0.3 W, hence, we would choose a half-watt or one-watt resistor for R_a. Since the power dissipated in R_k is only $I_a^2 R_k \approx 0.01$ W, a very-low-power resistor will suffice for R_k. Finally, the anode supply must furnish at least $I_a \approx 2.5$ mA to the circuit, at a cost of $V_{a0} I_a \approx 0.6$ W. We now know enough about the circuit to build it.

Pentode amplifier. We follow the same procedure as for a triode, starting from the pentode plate characteristics and constructing the load line of slope $-1/R_a$. However, we must now also select an operating screen voltage V_{g_2} to provide optimum I_a vs. V_{g_1} characteristics, using either the manufacturer's suggested values of screen voltage or working from different sets of I_a vs. V_a characteristics with V_{g_2} as a parameter. Our choice of $I_a^{(0)}$ then also specifies the screen current I_{g_2}. The screen-bias resistor R_{g_2} can then be determined from the condition

$$V_{g_2} = V_{a0} - I_{g_2} R_{g_2} \quad \text{or} \quad R_{g_2} = \frac{V_{a0} - V_{g_2}}{I_{g_2}}. \tag{4.9}$$

The cathode-bias resistor R_k is now determined by

$$R_k = \frac{-V_{g_1}^{(0)}}{I_a^{(0)} + I_{g_2}}. \tag{4.10}$$

Transistor amplifier. In transistor amplifiers the operating point may shift considerably with changes of the ambient temperature. The common-emitter circuit is particularly unstable in this respect; as already noted in Section 4.3.2, the stability can be improved by the use of a biasing arrangement with a by-passed resistor in the emitter lead. The relative effectiveness of the different biasing arrangements in achieving stable operation with varying temperature can be understood in terms of the dependence of the actual collector current I_c on the reverse saturation current I_{c0}. We define a *stability factor*

$$M = \Delta I_c / \Delta I_{c0}, \tag{4.11}$$

which is a convenient measure of the stability of a circuit; when M is small, the circuit is relatively insensitive to temperature changes. The value of M depends not only on the transistor but also on the circuit configuration. For typical germanium transistors, I_{c0} is of the order of a few microamperes at room temperature, increasing by 5–10% per centigrade-degree rise in temperature. For silicon transistors, base-bias stabilization is far less important because I_{c0} is usually much smaller.

In the common-base circuit (Fig. 4.7b), where the collector and emitter circuits are completely separate, I_{c0} has little influence on the emitter current I_e. Since $I_c = \alpha I_e + I_{c0}$, and only I_{c0} depends on temperature, it follows that $\Delta I_c \approx \Delta I_{c0}$ and $M \approx 1$. In the common-collector circuit of Fig. 4.7(c), but even more in the common-emitter circuit, M may become much larger than

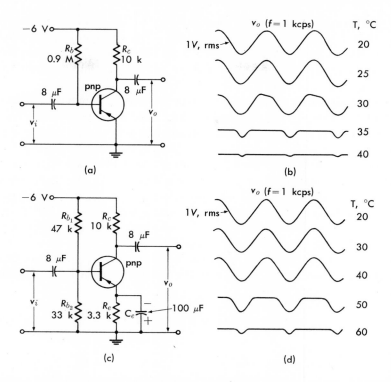

FIG. 4.14.   Relative effectiveness of different biasing circuits on actual operation of transistor amplifier. (a) Circuit of unstabilized amplifier, (b) output signal at different temperatures with constant sinusoidal input signal for circuit of (a), (c) circuit of stabilized amplifier, (d) output signal at different temperatures with constant sinusoidal input signal for circuit of (c).

unity.   In these circuits I_{c0} contributes to the conductivity of the base-emitter junction in exactly the same way as the base current (provided the external base resistance R_b is high), so that a change in I_{c0} has the same effect on I_c as a change in I_b.

For the simple uncompensated circuit of Fig. 4.10(a), the collector current is

$$I_c = A_I(I_b + I_{c0}) + I_{c0}, \qquad (4.12)$$

where A_I is the current gain of the circuit, which can be quite large, limited only by the value of h_{fe}. Thus, for this case, $M \approx A_I + 1$. A practical example of this circuit is given in Fig. 4.14(a). The transistor is a normal low-power low-frequency pnp alloy junction unit with $h_{fe} = 50$ and $I_{c0} \approx 2\ \mu A$ at $T = 20°C$.   For the circuit values chosen, we find that $A_I \approx 34$, so that $M \approx 35$.   Because R_b has been chosen so that $I_c \approx 300\ \mu A$, half the -6 V supply voltage appears across the 10-k resistor R_c and half between the collector and emitter.   This condition should provide the maximum undistorted output signal. However, when the temperature is raised to 36°C, I_{c0} increases by about 7 μA, so that I_c increases by $7M \approx 250$ μA. The voltage drop across R_c increases to $(300 + 250) \times 10^{-2}$ V $= 5.5$ V, so that only 0.5 V remains between collector and emitter. The collector-to-base voltage is reduced to almost zero, and the transistor is no longer an effective amplifier.

The output signal of this amplifier stage for various temperatures is shown in Fig. 4.14(b). The curves are actual tracings of oscilloscope photos. The input signal is a constant sinusoidal voltage adjusted to give a 1-V rms signal output at 20°C.

In the practical stabilized base-bias circuit of Fig. 4.14(c), stability is achieved by addition of the resistor R_e (bypassed by a large condenser C_e) in series with the emitter; the forward bias is now provided by the divider R_{b_1}, R_{b_2}. The resistor R_e tends to provide stabilization in the same manner as the cathode resistor R_k in the vacuum-tube circuit. If I_c starts to increase slowly, the voltage drop across R_e will increase proportionately, resulting in a *decrease* of both V_{be} and V_{ce}. The change in V_{be} causes a decrease in I_b, which in turn produces an *amplified* decrease in I_c; in this way the circuit is markedly self-stabilizing. Quantitatively, we can write

$$\Delta I_c = \alpha' \, \Delta I_e + \Delta I_{c0} = M \, \Delta I_{c0}, \qquad (4.13)$$

where $\alpha' = A_I/(1 + A_I)$.

When the emitter voltage changes by an amount $\Delta I_e R_e$, the base voltage will change by about the same amount, causing a decrease in base current by an amount

$$\Delta I_b \approx -\Delta I_e R_e / R_b, \qquad (4.14)$$

where $R_b = R_{b_1} R_{b_2}/(R_{b_1} + R_{b_2})$ is the effective series resistance in the base circuit, equal to the parallel combination of R_{b_1} and R_{b_2}. The decrease in base current, of course, tends to counteract the increase in collector current. Collecting terms, we obtain

$$\begin{aligned} \Delta I_c &= A_I \, \Delta I_b + (1 + A_I) \, \Delta I_{co} \\ &= -(1 + A_I)(\Delta I_c - \Delta I_{co}) R_e/R_b + (1 + A_I) \, \Delta I_{co}. \end{aligned} \qquad (4.15)$$

Solving for M, we have

$$M = \frac{\Delta I_c}{\Delta I_{c0}} = \frac{R_b + R_e}{R_b + (1 + A_I)R_e} \, (1 + A_I). \qquad (4.16)$$

The value of M thus depends on the ratio R_b/R_e, decreasing as this ratio is made smaller. For the resistance values used in the circuit of Fig. 4.14(c), $M \approx 6$, almost six times smaller than in the circuit of Fig. 4.14(a), and the useful temperature range is accordingly extended as is shown by the oscilloscope tracings of Fig. 4.14(d). The actual value chosen for M must always be some sort of compromise, for if we make R_b too small, the input impedance is reduced to the point where the amplifier gain decreases. On the other hand, if we make R_e too large, we need a larger collector supply voltage to keep V_{ce} sufficiently large to avoid saturation.

We now turn to the task of finding the proper operating point for the base-bias stabilized circuit, given in Fig. 4.15, together with its equivalent dc-bias circuit. Since the current gain A_I of this circuit will depend on both the operating point and the equivalent resistance in the base circuit [$R_b = R_{b_1} R_{b_2}/(R_{b_1} + R_{b_2})$], and the stability factor M depends on both R_b and A_I, a complete solution can become rather complicated. In effect, we have the following set of simultaneous equations to satisfy:

$$\text{for the collector circuit,} \quad V_{c0} = I_c R_c + V_{ce} + I_e R_e; \quad (4.17a)$$

$$\text{for the base circuit;} \quad V_{b0} = I_b R_b + V_{be} + I_e R_e; \quad (4.17b)$$

$$\text{for the stability factor,} \quad M \approx \frac{(R_b + R_e)(1 + A_I)}{R_b + (1 + A_I)R_e}; \quad (4.17c)$$

$$\text{by definition,} \quad R_b = \frac{R_{b_1} R_{b_2}}{R_{b_1} + R_{b_2}}, \quad (4.17d)$$

$$V_{b0} = \frac{V_{c0} R_{b_2}}{R_{b_1} + R_{b_2}}; \quad (4.17e)$$

$$\text{for current conservation,} \quad I_e = I_c + I_b. \quad (4.17f)$$

These six equations contain the fourteen parameters V_{c0}, I_c, R_c, V_{ce}, I_e, R_e, V_{b0}, I_b, R_b, V_{be}, M, A_I, R_{b_1}, and R_{b_2}. The known characteristics of the transistor provide information about the values of I_c as a function of V_{ce} and I_b, of I_b as a function of V_{be} and V_{ce}, and of A_I. Thus, from Eqs. (4.17) and the characteristics, we have a total of nine simultaneous equations relating fourteen unknowns. For a complete solution, we obviously must define values for any five of the parameters and then solve for the remaining nine.

Rather than attempt a complete solution, we usually proceed by specifying some of the parameters, making reasonable guesses about some of the others, and solving for the rest to any desired order of accuracy. For example, since I_c is usually much larger than I_b, we could assume that $I_e R_e \approx I_c R_e$ in (4.17a) and (4.17b); since V_{be} is usually very small, about -0.3 V, we could take $V_{be} \approx 0$ in (4.17b); since the current gain A_I is usually of the order of h_{fe}, we could assume that $1 + A_I \approx h_{fe}$ in (4.17c). Then (4.17a, b, c) reduce to

$$V_{c0} \approx I_c(R_c + R_e) + V_{ce}, \quad (4.18a)$$

$$V_{b0} \approx I_b R_b + I_c R_e, \quad (4.18b)$$

$$M \approx \frac{(R_b + R_e)h_{fe}}{R_b + h_{fe} R_e}. \quad (4.18c)$$

These approximate relations, plus the two definitions (4.17d, e), permit us to

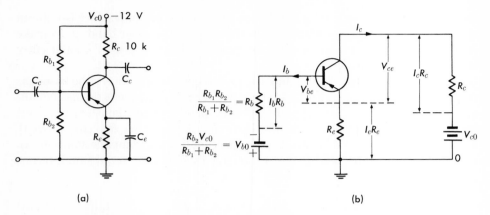

FIG. 4.15.   Transistor amplifier. (a) Actual circuit, (b) equivalent dc-circuit.

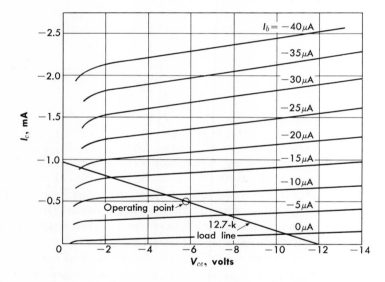

FIG. 4.16. I_c vs. V_{ce} characteristics of 2N384 pnp-transistor in circuit of Fig. 4.15.

find a first-order solution from the characteristic curves and determine a resonable operating point.

As an illustration we can solve the circuit of Fig. 4.15(a). As a starting point, we select values for the collector resistor $R_c = 10$ kΩ and the supply voltage $V_{c0} = -12$ V. The characteristics of the pnp-transistor used (type 2N384) are shown in Fig. 4.16. Equation (4.18a) specifies the load line for the circuit, with a slope $-1/(R_c + R_e)$. However, contrary to the situation in the tube circuit where $R_k \ll R_a$, we cannot assume that $R_e \ll R_c$, for R_e must be reasonably large to provide adequate stabilization. We shall select $M \approx 5$ in (4.18c) and, by making a sensible choice for $R_b \gg h_{ie}$ so that the circuit gain will be reasonably high, we can solve for R_e by using the value of $h_{fe} \approx 50$ from the characteristics. For this transistor, we expect that $h_{ie} \approx 1.5$ k; therefore, we choose $R_b = 12$ k. From (4.18c) we know that $R_e \approx 2.7$ k. We can then construct the load line of slope $-1/12.7$ k on the characteristics as shown in Fig. 4.16 and, from inspection of this curve or from the equivalent I_c vs. I_b characteristic of Fig. 4.17, we choose a suitable operating point: $I_c^{(0)} = 0.5$ mA, $I_b^{(0)} = 9\,\mu$A. Finally, solving for R_{b_1} and R_{b_2}, we find that $R_{b_1} \approx 100$ k, $R_{b_2} \approx 14$ k.

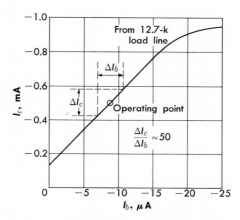

FIG. 4.17. I_c vs. I_b characteristics of 2N384 for load line of Fig. 4.16.

This solution is generally sufficient to permit us to construct and test the circuit. Of course, a more exact analytical solution can be obtained by use of the I_b, V_{be}, and V_{ce} characteristics of the transistor, Eqs. (4.17), and a little more algebra. However, unless we are working from the actual *measured* characteristics of the transistor, a more detailed analysis is hardly justified since the published characteristics are seldom identical with the actual characteristics within better than 20% uncertainty. For critical circuit requirements, it is far better to take the first-order solution, build a breadboard of the circuit, and make final adjustments in the laboratory if necessary.

4.3.4   Midfrequency gain characteristics

Once the operating point of the amplifier has been established, it is a fairly simple matter to determine the characteristics of the circuit as an ac-voltage amplifier. This can be done in one of two ways, either by a graphical load-line construction from the measured tube or transistor characteristics or by algebraic analysis. The first procedure is more exact than the second, particularly where the actual shape of the output signal (including possible distortion) is required for fairly large input signals, but is considerably more time-consuming. We shall consider both techniques here, but stress the simpler algebraic method.

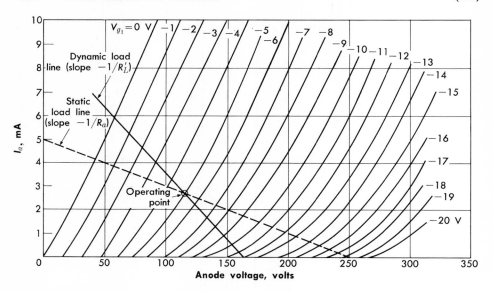

FIG. 4.18.   Plate characteristics of 12AU7, with static and dynamic load lines.

Tube circuit. The graphical technique is similar to that employed to determine the operating point, except that we use a *dynamic* load line instead of the *static* load line used before. This construction is shown in Fig. 4.18 for the common-cathode triode circuit shown in Fig. 4.11. The static load line passing through the operating point ○ has a slope $-1/R_a$ or, more precisely, $-1/(R_a + R_k)$ since the actual dc anode current passes through R_a and R_k in series. However, the alternating signal current, which we shall again denote by the lower-case symbol i_a, passes through the parallel combination of R_a and R_L if the frequency is sufficiently high that C_k and C_c offer zero impedance. (This condition defines the *midfrequency* characteristics.) Accordingly, we draw a dynamic load line through ○ with a slope $-1/R'_L$, where R'_L is the parallel combination $R_a R_L/(R_a + R_L)$. The intersections of the dynamic load line with the plate characteristics define the *dynamic transfer characteristic* shown in Fig. 4.19, and give i_a as a function of the alternating signal input voltage at the grid v_g. Since the alternating signal output voltage v_o is simply $-i_a R'_L$, we can graphically find the precise shape of the output for any input voltage, even for large signals, as shown in Fig. 4.20. This procedure is useful not only for triode amplifiers but also for other tube or transistor circuits.

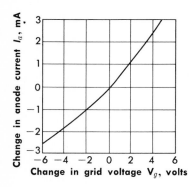

FIG. 4.19.   Dynamic transfer characteristics of 12AU7 for dynamic load line of Fig. 4.18.

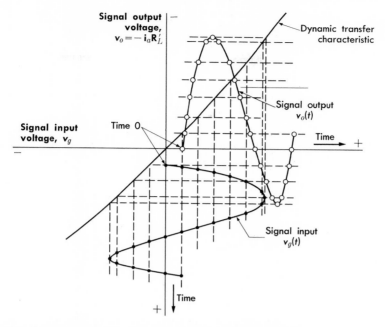

FIG. 4.20.   Graphical construction of amplifier output signal from dynamic transfer characteristic. For each point of the input signal (closed circle) the value of the output signal (open circle) is determined by "reflection" from the transfer characteristic. Case shown is for Class-A operation.

The algebraic analysis is valid only for small input and output signals, when the circuit behaves linearly and when it may be assumed that the tube parameters are dependent only on the operating point, not on the magnitude of the signals.

Such an analysis has already been presented in Chapter 2 for the simplified triode amplifier circuit shown in Fig. 2.18, to clarify the meaning of the characteristic tube parameters. For small ac-signals, the only difference in the circuit shown in Fig. 4.21 is the presence of a load resistor R_L, which effectively is in parallel with R_a. Denoting the parallel combination of R_L and R_a by

$$R'_L = R_L R_a/(R_a + R_L),$$

we may rewrite Eqs. (2.25) and (2.26) derived in Chapter 2 for the anode signal as

$$v_o = v_a = -g_m v_g (1/r_p + 1/R'_L)^{-1}, \quad (4.19)$$

$$v_o = v_a = -\mu v_g R'_L/(r_p + R'_L), \quad (4.20)$$

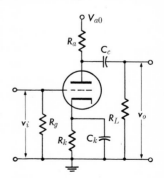

FIG. 4.21.   *RC*-coupled vacuum-tube amplifier.

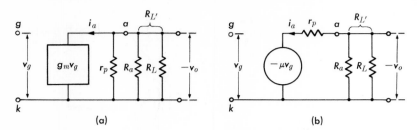

FIG. 4.22.   Midfrequency equivalent circuits for vacuum-tube amplifier of Fig. 4.21. (a) Current generator, (b) voltage generator.

or Eqs. (2.27) and (2.28) for the voltage gain as

$$A = -g_m(1/r_p + 1/R'_L)^{-1}, \tag{4.21}$$

$$A = -\mu R'_L/(r_p + R'_L). \tag{4.22}$$

Since $\mu = g_m r_p$, (4.19) and (4.20) as well as (4.21) and (4.22) are identical, of course.

The relations of Eqs. (4.19) and (4.20) are expressed by *equivalent circuits* as given in Fig. 4.22. These circuits are simply convenient symbolic representations of the actual linear equations governing the action of small signals on the tube. In the circuit of Fig. 4.22(a), we represent the action of the tube as an equivalent current generator, $g_m v_g$, of infinite internal impedance with a resistance r_p in parallel. The resistance R'_L is also in parallel with this system. Since the anode current flows counterclockwise through this circuit, a minus sign must be given to the voltage v_o developed by the current generator across r_p and R'_L in parallel. This circuit is the most convenient for pentodes, where usually $r_p \gg R'_L$. In this case r_p can be omitted, and we simply have $v_o = -g_m R'_L v_g$.

The circuit of Fig. 4.22(b) is more convenient for triodes. Here the tube is represented by a voltage source $-\mu v_g$ with the internal impedance r_p in series, connected to the effective load resistance R'_L.

From this diagram we also find the output impedance of the circuit, defined as the ratio of the *open-circuit* signal voltage (load R_L disconnected) to the *short-circuit* signal current (current with $R_L = 0$ across terminals):

$$Z_o = r_p R_a/(r_p + R_a). \tag{4.23}$$

Since normally the tube will draw no grid current, the input impedance is simply

$$Z_i = R_g. \tag{4.24}$$

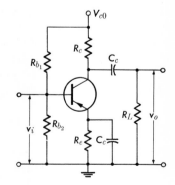

FIG. 4.23. *RC*-coupled transistor amplifier.

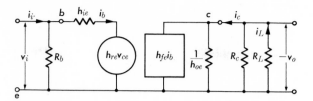

FIG. 4.24. Equivalent circuit of transistor amplifier of Fig. 4.23, showing bias and load resistors.

Transistor circuit. We shall discuss the small-signal behavior of the common emitter circuit shown in Fig. 4.23. Proceeding from the treatment already given in Chapter 3 for the basic circuit of a common-emitter amplifier, we can draw the complete equivalent-circuit diagram of Fig. 4.23 at once if we assume that all condensers offer essentially zero impedance. Thus we obtain Fig. 4.24, which is entirely analogous to Fig. 3.21(b) and (c). By replacing R_c with $R'_L = R_c R_L/(R_c + R_L)$ to take into account the presence of a load resistance in parallel with R_c in Eq. (3.24), we find [under the same condition as imposed on (3.24), namely, $h_{re}v_{ce} \ll v_i$] for the voltage gain:

$$A_V = -\frac{h_{fe}}{h_{ie}}\left(\frac{R'_L}{1 + h_{oe}R'_L}\right) = -\frac{h_{fe}}{h_{ie}}\left(h_{oe} + \frac{1}{R_c} + \frac{1}{R_L}\right)^{-1}. \qquad (4.25)$$

The current gain is affected by the presence of the resistance $R_b = R_{b_1}R_{b_2}/(R_{b_1} + R_{b_2})$ at the input, through which a part of the input current flows. To make allowance for this, we must modify Eq. (3.25) of Chapter 3 by the factor $R_b/(R_b + h_{ie})$.

Further, if we define the current gain as the ratio of the *load* current to the input signal current, we must multiply Eq. (3.18) by another factor, $R_c/(R_c + R_L)$, to take into account the fraction of the collector current flowing through R_c. Thus we obtain

$$A_I = \frac{i_L}{i_i} = \left(\frac{R_c}{R_c + R_L}\right)\left(\frac{R_b}{R_b + h_{ie}}\right)h_{fe}\left(\frac{1}{1 + h_{oe}R'_L}\right)$$

$$= \left(\frac{R_b}{R_b + h_{ie}}\right)\frac{h_{fe}}{R_L}\left(h_{oe} + \frac{1}{R_c} + \frac{1}{R_L}\right)^{-1}. \qquad (4.26)$$

In many circuits, we choose R_L much smaller than R_c or $1/h_{oe}$; then

$$A_V \approx -h_{fe}R_L/h_{ie} \qquad (4.27)$$

and

$$A_I \approx h_{fe}R_b/(R_b + h_{ie}). \qquad (4.28)$$

If the load is another similar transistor, $R_L \approx h_{ie}R_b/(R_b + h_{ie})$, then $A_V \approx -A_I$, as already observed in Chapter 3.

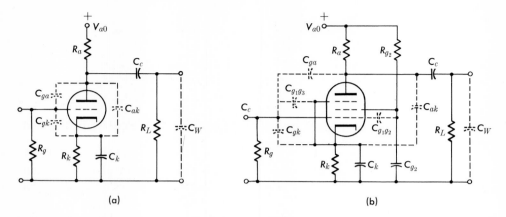

FIG. 4.25.   Distributed capacities in vacuum-tube amplifiers. (a) Triode, (b) pentode.

Finally, for the input and output impedances of the circuit, we readily obtain

$$Z_i = h_{ie}R_b/(R_b + h_{ie}),\tag{4.29}$$

$$Z_o = (h_{oe} + 1/R_c)^{-1}.\tag{4.30}$$

4.3.5   Characteristics at low and high frequencies

In the midfrequency range of operation of the RC-coupled amplifier, by definition none of the condensers we put into the circuit—the coupling condensers
C_c or the bypass condensers C_k, C_{g2}, or C_e—offered any impedance to the flow
of the alternating signal current.   However, it is clear that at low frequencies
the effects of these condensers must become noticeable because their reactance
$1/\omega C$ is inversely proportional to frequency.   It would appear, offhand, that
there is no natural high-frequency limit to the operation of the amplifier, since
certainly all the condensers which are effectively short circuits at mid-frequencies
will still have zero impedance at higher frequencies.   This is true if we are concerned only with the condensers we placed in the circuit.   However, there are
other inherent capacities, placed in the circuit by nature, which we have thus
far ignored.   These are the interelectrode and wiring capacities, shown in
Fig. 4.25 for the triode and pentode circuits; since they are in parallel with the
input and output resistances, they cause the gain to fall off at high frequencies.
We have so far ignored these parallel distributed capacities in the midfrequency
range, assuming that they have infinite impedance.   We shall now consider the
response of the tube and transistor circuits for sinusoidal signals of low and high
frequencies.

A. Low frequencies.   The low-frequency equivalent circuit of the amplifier is
shown in Fig. 4.26, where the effect of the limited frequency response of the
coupling condensers appears explicitly.   For the moment, we shall assume that

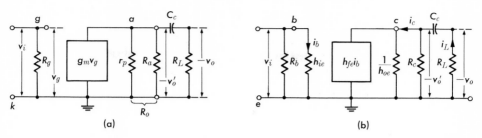

FIG. 4.26. Low-frequency equivalent current circuits for *RC*-coupled amplifiers. (a) Tube, (b) transistor.

the bypass condensers C_k, C_{g2}, and C_e are very large, so that we can still assume that they have effectively zero impedance even at the frequencies where the impedance of the coupling condenser C_c is large. The effects of the finite size of the bypass condensers on the transient response will be discussed in Section 4.3.6. Since we could ignore the effects of the parallel capacities at midfrequencies, they can obviously be ignored at lower frequencies.

In the low-frequency circuit, only a fraction of the signal voltage present between the left side of the coupling condenser and ground (across R_a or R_c) will appear across the load R_L. For a sinusoidal signal of frequency $\omega = 2\pi f$, the ratio of the output signal v_o across the load R_L to the signal v'_o will be

$$\gamma = R_L/(R_L - j/\omega C_c), \qquad (4.31)$$

where $j = \sqrt{-1}$. The signal v'_o appearing between anode and ground or between collector and ground must also change from its value at midfrequencies, since the anode or collector current now flows through an impedance consisting of the parallel combination of r_p, R_a, and $R_L - j/\omega C_c$, for the tube, which is larger than the midfrequency impedance of just r_p, R_a, and R_L in parallel. The same argument holds, of course, for the transistor if we simply substitute $1/h_{oe}$ for r_p, and R_c for R_a. To avoid unnecessary algebra, let us define the parallel combination of the resistances to the left of C_c (r_p and R_a for the tube, $1/h_{oe}$ and R_c for the transistor) as the *output resistance* R_o, consistent with (4.23) and (4.30). Then the ratio of v'_o to the midfrequency output signal will be

$$\beta = \frac{R_o(R_L - j/\omega C_c)(R_o + R_L)}{R_o R_L(R_o + R_L - j/\omega C_c)}. \qquad (4.32)$$

The actual output voltage across R_L at low frequencies will then be simply the product $\gamma\beta$ times its value of midfrequencies; thus $\gamma\beta$ is also the ratio of the amplifier gain at low frequencies to its midfrequency value. Substituting from (4.31) and (4.32) and simplifying, we obtain

$$\frac{A_l(\omega)}{A} = \gamma\beta = \frac{1}{1 - j/\omega C_c(R_o + R_L)}. \qquad (4.33)$$

Usually we define the *lower cutoff frequency* (or "lower 3-db cutoff") as

$$f_l = \frac{1}{2\pi C_c(R_o + R_L)}.$$
(4.34)

Then (4.33) can be rewritten as

$$\frac{A_l(f)}{A} = \frac{1}{1 - j(f_l/f)}.$$
(4.35)

Equation (4.35) is in complex notation. (See Appendix A.) The absolute value of this quantity tells us how the magnitude of the output signal falls off as a function of f at low frequencies,

$$\frac{|A_l(f)|}{|A|} = \frac{1}{\sqrt{1 + (f_l/f)^2}}.$$
(4.36)

At a frequency $f = f_l$, the amplitude has fallen to $1/\sqrt{2}$ of its midfrequency value. The imaginary part of (4.35) gives the *phase shift* of the signal at low frequencies relative to that at midfrequencies. The phase angle will be positive (the output leads the input), and is

$$\phi = \tan^{-1}(f_l/f).$$
(4.37)

Note that the phase shift is 45° at $f = f_l$.

In most vacuum-tube circuits, the load resistance R_L is simply the grid resistor of the next stage, R_g, and usually $R_g \gg R_o$. On the other hand, in transistor circuits the load is often the base input resistance of the next stage, which is frequently much less than R_o. Therefore, (4.34) may usually be approximated as follows:

for the tube, $f_l \approx 1/2\pi C_c R_g,$ (4.38)

for the transistor, $f_l \approx 1/2\pi C_c R_o \approx 1/2\pi C_c R_c,$ (4.39)

since in general $R_c \ll 1/h_{oe}$.

B. High frequencies. The high-frequency equivalent circuit of the vacuum-tube amplifier is shown in Fig. 4.27. Here we can ignore the coupling and bypass condensers; the reponse now depends on the effect of the distributed capacities. The output voltage will fall off at high frequencies since the impedance through which the anode current flows now consists of a parallel condenser, C_p, across the effective parallel resistance R_p (parallel combination of r_p, R_a, and R_L). The ratio of the gain at high frequencies to the midfrequency gain will then be

$$\frac{A_h(\omega)}{A} = \frac{1}{1 + j\omega C_p R_p}.$$
(4.40)

As before, we define an *upper cutoff frequency* (or "upper 3-db cutoff"):

$$f_h = \frac{1}{2\pi C_p R_p}.$$ (4.41)

Then

$$\frac{A_h(f)}{A} = \frac{1}{1 + j(f/f_h)},$$ (4.42)

and the magnitude of the gain falls off as

$$\frac{|A_h(f)|}{|A|} = \frac{1}{\sqrt{1 + f^2/f_h}},$$ (4.43)

while the phase angle by which the output lags the input is

$$\phi = -\tan^{-1}(f/f_h).$$ (4.44)

The gain falls by a factor of $1/\sqrt{2}$ and the phase shift is $-45°$ at $f = f_h$.

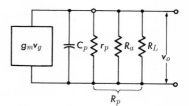

FIG. 4.27. High-frequency equivalent current circuit for tube amplifier.

Equations (4.43) and (4.44) are also appropriate for a transistor amplifier, but often the upper cutoff frequency f_h is closely related to that of the transistor, $f_{\alpha e}$, given in Eq. (3.27), rather than the value defined by (4.41).

There are a number of terms contributing to C_p. First, there are the geometrical capacities of the tube, between the anode and the grounded suppressor, screen grid, and cathode, which we may simply lump together as the output capacity C_o. Next, there are the capacities of all wiring between the anode pin and the load R_L. These are caused partly by the proximity to other wires or to the chassis and partly by *self-capacitance* due to the finite size of the components, especially the coupling condenser (a sphere of radius = 1 cm has a self-capacitance of about 1 pF remote from all other conductors). These capacities will be lumped together as the wiring capacity C_w. If the load R_L is actually the input to another amplifier stage, there are additional capacities to be considered: more wiring capacity (which we shall simply lump together with C_w) and the input capacity of the next tube, C_i. This capacity consists of the capacity between the grid and the cathode and all other grounded electrodes, denoted here by C_{gk}. It will also depend on the capacity between grid and anode, C_{ga}, although the latter cannot simply be added to the other terms. The special effect of the grid-anode capacity is shown in Fig. 4.28. It makes a connection between the grid and a

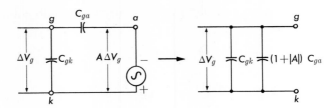

FIG. 4.28.   Miller effect in triode amplifier, showing special significance of grid-anode capacity.

point where the signal at the grid has been amplified by a factor of the *gain A* of the stage; since A is large and *negative*, the signal fed back through C_{ga} tends to cancel the input signal. A rise of grid voltage ΔV_g is accompanied by a drop $A \, \Delta V_g$ at the anode, causing the voltage across C_{ga} to change by $(1 + |A|) \, \Delta V_g$. Therefore a charge $\Delta Q_g = C_{ga}(1 + |A|) \, \Delta V_g$ must be supplied to the grid, which means that the effective grid-to-anode capacitance has increased to

$$C_{ga}^{\text{eff}} = \frac{\Delta Q_g}{\Delta V_g} = (1 + |A|)C_{ga}.$$

This phenomenon is known as the *Miller effect*. Thus, the total input capacitance can be written as

$$C_i = C_{gk} + (1 + |A|)C_{ga}. \tag{4.45}$$

Combining all the parallel capacities, we obtain for the total distributed capacity between two cascaded stages

$$C_p = C_w + C_o + C_{gk} + (1 + |A|)C_{ga}. \tag{4.46}$$

The Miller effect seriously limits the performance of triodes at high frequencies. One of the chief virtues of pentodes is that the insertion of the screen grid between the control grid and anode reduces C_{ga} to a negligible value; hence, pentodes provide far better high-frequency response than triodes (but they also are noisier; see Section 10.3).

FIG. 4.29. Amplitude and phase characteristics of *RC*-coupled amplifier. The gain is given in decibels (db) relative to that at midfrequency. The decibel value of the voltage gain $A(f)$ relative to the midfrequency voltage gain A is given by $\text{db} = 20 \log_{10} [A(f)/A]$.

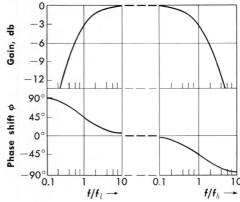

The frequency characteristics of an *RC*-coupled amplifier, in accordance with the relationships just derived, are shown in Fig. 4.29.

The input and output impedances of the amplifier at low and high frequencies are also changed from their values at midfrequency, as can readily be seen from the equivalent circuits. If we include C_c as part of the output circuit (an arbitrary choice), then for the vacuum tube, we have

$$Z_{il} = R_g, \tag{4.47}$$

$$Z_{ih} = \left[\frac{1}{R_g} + j\omega\left(C_{gk} + (1 + |A|)C_{ga} \right) \right]^{-1}, \tag{4.48}$$

$$Z_{ol} = \left[\frac{r_p R_a}{r_p + R_a} - \frac{j}{\omega C_c} \right], \tag{4.49}$$

$$Z_{oh} = \left[\frac{1}{r_p} + \frac{1}{R_a} + j\omega(C_o + C_w) \right]^{-1}. \tag{4.50}$$

The analysis of the high-frequency behavior of the basic common-emitter transistor amplifier stage is much more complicated than that of the vacuum-tube stage because of the following two physical differences:

1. *Charge carrier transit-time effects*, while negligible for the tube circuit, play a predominant role in the transistor circuit. Up to about the common-emitter cutoff frequency $f_{\alpha e}$, these effects may be represented to a good approximation by Eq. (3.27), but for higher frequencies the phase shift increases more rapidly than suggested by this equation; at a frequency of $10f_{\alpha e}$, the phase shift will generally exceed 180°.

2. *The internal capacities*, which for a tube are present directly between the pins at the tube base, in a transistor are separated from the external emitter, base, and collector connections by internal resistances, particularly the base resistance. Furthermore, only a fraction of the internal capacities in a transistor is of an electrostatic nature; the greater part arises from space-charge effects and therefore depends on the applied voltage across the junction regions, as discussed at the end of Section 3.2.1 for the *varactor*.

An approximate analysis, valid up to frequencies of the order of $f_{\alpha e}$, is often based on equivalent circuits in which the two effects just mentioned are represented by appropriate *RC*-combinations ("hybrid-pi," and "modified-T" circuits). One important difference with the tube circuit evident from such an analysis is the marked increase in voltage feedback across the collector-base capacity at high frequencies, which may become important at frequencies even below $f_{\alpha e}$.

For a more complete treatment of the behavior of transistor amplifiers at high frequencies, the reader should consult the references at the end of this chapter, in particular the books by Cattermole and by Joyce and Clarke.

4.3.6 Transient response

The signals which we must amplify are rarely simple sine waves. They frequently resemble rectangular pulses, particularly in radar, nuclear, and computer circuits. An ideal rectangular pulse of width T can be decomposed into two sudden voltage jumps. A positive pulse, for example, consists of a positive jump, followed after a time T by a negative jump of equal magnitude. One such jump is called a transient; we will consider the response of the RC-coupled tube-amplifier stage to a single transient. We can decompose such a transient or, in general, any signal into sinusoidal components by means of Fourier analysis. If the response of the amplifier to sinusoidal signals is known, we can synthesize these components again after they have passed through the amplifier, with their proper relative amplitudes and phases. On the other hand, if the transient response of the amplifier is known, we can determine its frequency response. The mathematical device used in both cases is the Fourier transform. This procedure is sound but tedious. It is far simpler to consider the effect of a transient on the coupling and distributed-capacity RC-sections directly.

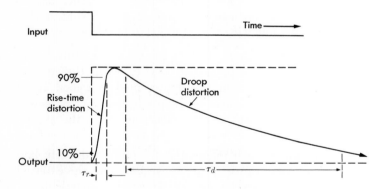

FIG. 4.30. Response of amplifier to a rectangular step voltage, showing rise time and droop distortion.

As shown in Fig. 4.30, an ideal transient will suffer two types of distortion. Because of the distributed capacity parallel to the anode resistor, the amplified pulse will have a finite rise time τ_r, in general defined as the time for the signal to rise from 10% to 90% of its final value.

Because of the RC-coupling network, the original flat top of the transient will exhibit a droop, characterized by a droop time τ_d, the time in which the signal falls from 90% to 10% of its maximum value. In practice, we usually have $\tau_d \gg \tau_r$, and therefore the rising and decaying part of the pulse can be considered separately.

For the rising part of the pulse we can again consider the equivalent circuit diagram of Fig. 4.27. In this circuit the tube acts as a current generator $g_m v_g$, supplying current to the parallel combination of C_p and R_p. A sudden decrease of V_g by an amount $-\Delta V_g$ at a time $t = 0$ produces a sudden decrease $-\Delta I_a$ of the anode current. The anode voltage now starts rising as C_p charges across R_p to a new equilibrium value. When this value is reached, no more current flows into C_p, and the change of current $-\Delta I_a$ has produced a rise of anode voltage $\Delta V_o = \Delta I_a R_p = g_m R_p \Delta V_g$.

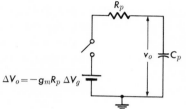

FIG. 4.31. Equivalent circuit of amplifier for calculation of rise-time distortion; the switch is closed at $t = 0$.

$$\Delta V_o = -g_m R_p \Delta V_g$$

The effect of the amplifier therefore is equivalent to the charging of C_p, connected, at a time $t = 0$, through R_p to a voltage source ΔV_o. This is illustrated by the simple equivalent circuit of Fig. 4.31. The well-known charging law of a condenser for this case can be written as

$$v_o = \Delta V_o (1 - \epsilon^{-t/R_p C_p}). \tag{4.51}$$

Thus, in a time $t = R_p C_p$, the voltage will have risen to a value $(1 - 1/\epsilon) \approx 63\%$ of its final value and the rise time will be

$$\tau_r = 2.2 R_p C_p = 2.2/(2\pi f_h) \approx 0.35/f_h, \tag{4.52}$$

with f_h as defined in Eq. (4.41).

Since $\tau_d \gg \tau_r$, the change of voltage across the coupling condenser during the rising part of the pulse is negligible, and we may take "time zero" for the flat-topped part of the transient as the moment at which the output signal has reached the value $\Delta V_o = -g_m R_p \Delta V_g$. As the coupling condenser charges, v_o decreases exponentially to zero. From the equivalent circuit diagram of Fig. 4.26(a), we see that the effect is now that of C_c charging through $R_o + R_L$ in series, so that the output voltage follows the law

$$v_o = \Delta V_o \epsilon^{-t/(R_o + R_L) C_c}. \tag{4.53}$$

In analogy with τ_r, we find for the droop time,

$$\tau_d = 2.2(R_o + R_L) C_c \approx 0.35/f_l, \tag{4.54}$$

with f_l taken from Eq. (4.34).

Because of the simple dependence of the rise time on f_h and the droop time on f_l, measuring the distortion of a transient (or a rectangular voltage pulse of sufficient duration) is a simple way to determine f_h and f_l with an oscilloscope and a square-wave generator.

Influence of the bypass condensers on the transient response. The actual droop response may be much worse than is indicated by Eq. (4.54), because of the charging of the cathode and screen bypass condensers, C_k and C_{g_2}, or the emitter bypass condenser C_e during the flat portion of the pulse, a fact which we have ignored thus far. When the cathode or emitter condensers start charging after a sudden jump at the input, this increases the effective tube grid or transistor base bias, and the output voltage will change until the condenser is charged. These changes will influence the shape of the tail of the transient. To simplify matters we will consider the influence of cathode and screen-grid voltage separately; further, the decay of the output voltage caused by the charging of the coupling capacitor C_c will be disregarded for the moment.

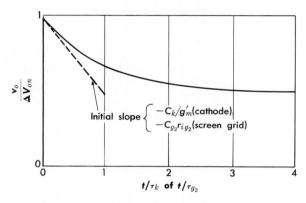

FIG. 4.32. Drooping of transient due to incomplete bypassing of cathode ($\tau_k = C_k R_k/(1 + R_k g_m')$) or screen grid ($\tau_{g_2} = C_{g_2} R_{g_2} r_{i g_2}/(R_{g_2} + r_{i g_2})$).

1. *Influence of C_k (V_{g_2} fixed).* A sudden change ΔV_i at the input is accompanied by a jump of the anode current $\Delta I_{an} = g_m \Delta V_i$. The cathode will now start to follow the grid voltage as the charge on C_k changes. This will continue until the cathode voltage has changed by an amount $\Delta V_k \approx \Delta V_i R_k g_m'/(1 + R_k g_m')$ (see cathode follower, Section 5.6); g_m' is the mutual conductance at the cathode (for pentodes this is 10 to 50% larger than the usual mutual conductance g_m at the anode because the screen-grid current contributes to the cathode current).

Finally, only a fraction, $\Delta I_a \approx g_m \Delta V_k \approx g_m \Delta V_i(1 + R_k g_m')$, of the original current change ΔI_{an} remains. Thus the output voltage changes exponentially (Fig. 4.32) from an initial value $\Delta V_{on} = -R_a \Delta I_{an} = -R_a g_m \Delta V_i$ to a final value $\Delta V_{o1} \approx \Delta V_{on}/(1 + R_k g_m')$ as

$$v_o \approx \frac{1 + R_k g_m' \epsilon^{-t/\tau_k} \Delta V_{on}}{1 + R_k g_m'}. \tag{4.55}$$

The time constant of the cathode circuit, τ_k, is equal to the product of C_k and the effective resistance between cathode and ground. This resistance is approximately equal to R_k in parallel with the internal cathode resistance $1/g_m'$ of the tube; so

$$\tau_k \approx \frac{C_k R_k}{1 + R_k g_m'}. \tag{4.56}$$

The output voltage v_o, in accordance with Eq. (4.55), is shown in Fig. 4.32. From (4.55) and (4.56), the initial slope of the transient characteristic is found to be $(dv_o/dt)_{t=0} = (-g_m'/C_k)\Delta V_{on}$. We see that the output voltage changes by 10% in a time $t_k \approx 0.1 C_k/g_m'$. For example, for a tube with $g_m' = 5$ ma/V and a cathode bypass capacitor $C_k = 500\ \mu\text{F}$, $t_k \approx 0.01$ sec.

Since it is not practical to make C_k very much larger, we see that it is difficult to reproduce voltage jumps with a flat top lasting for more than a few milliseconds without excessive distortion in a stage like the one discussed here. If it is required to amplify such signals without distortion, it is better not to bypass R_k at all. The gain is then reduced to $A/(1 + R_k g_m')$ but, at the same time, some degree of signal feedback is obtained, which results in improved linearity of the amplifier (see Section 5.1). Another method of preventing distortion of long pulses is connecting the cathode directly to ground. In this case an independent negative grid-bias supply is needed. We can now obtain full gain, but the stabilizing influence of R_k on the dc tube current and therefore on the gain is lost.

2. *Influence of C_{g_2} (V_k fixed).* As with C_k, we find that

$$v_o = \frac{r_{ig_2} + R_{g_2}\epsilon^{-t/\tau_{g_2}}}{r_{ig_2} + R_{g_2}}\Delta V_{on},$$

$$\tau_{g_2} = C_{g_2}\frac{R_{g_2}r_{ig_2}}{r_{ig_2} + R_{g_2}}, \tag{4.57}$$

where r_{ig_2} is the *differential screen resistance*. In this case the slope directly after a jump is $(dv_o/dt)_{t=0} = -\Delta V_{on}/C_{g_2}r_{ig_2}$, which leads to a change of the output voltage by 10% in a time $t_{g_2} \approx 0.1 C_{g_2}r_{ig_2}$. If we consider, for example, a tube with $\mu_{g_2g_1} = 50$, $g_m = 5$ mA/V, and $I_{g_2}/I_a = \mathcal{E} = 0.2$, we have $r_{ig_2} = \mu_{g_2g_1}/\mathcal{E}g_m = 50$ k. Choosing for the screen bypass capacitor a practical value, $C_{g_2} = 25\ \mu\text{F}$, we find that $t_{g_2} = 0.25$ sec. We see that for many applications, C_{g_2} need not be taken inconveniently large.

3. *Influence of C_e.* The influence of the emitter bypass condenser in the stabilized base-bias transistor circuit (see Fig. 4.15) is qualitatively analogous to that of C_k in the tube circuit. The exponential transition of the output voltage from an initial value ΔV_{on} to a final value V_{on}/p is again represented by an expression of the form

$$v_o = \Delta V_{on}\frac{1 + (p - 1)\epsilon^{-t/\tau_e}}{p}, \tag{4.58}$$

which is analogous to Eq. 4.55.

However, since a change of emitter voltage by the charging of C_e has an effect on the base current, the base resistance R_b, as well as the internal impedance of the signal source, is involved in this case. Because of this, the expressions for p and τ_e are more complicated here than for a tube circuit. We will give only approximate results for a couple of special cases, without derivation.

(a) Infinite signal-source impedance and $h_{ie} \ll R_b \ll R_e h_{fe}$:

$$p \approx h_{fe} R_e / R_b, \qquad \tau_e \approx R_b C_e / h_{fe}. \tag{4.59}$$

(b) Zero signal-source impedance and $R_e \gg h_{ie}/h_{fe}$:

$$p \approx h_{fe} R_e / h_{ie}, \qquad \tau_e \approx h_{ie} C_e / h_{fe}. \tag{4.60}$$

As an example, we take a transistor with $h_{fe} = 50$, so adjusted that $h_{ie} = 1$ k. Values $R_b = 10$ k and $R_e = 2$ k are chosen, and $C_e = 500\ \mu\text{F}$. Under these conditions we find that the output voltage droops by 10% in a time $t_e \approx 10^{-2}$ sec for case (a) and in a time $t_e \approx 10^{-3}$ sec for case (b). This demonstrates that for a transistor circuit the droop may depend strongly on the internal impedance of the signal source.

4.4 MULTISTAGE AMPLIFIERS

When a higher gain is required than can be obtained in a single RC-coupled amplifier stage of the type discussed in Section 4.3, several such stages can be connected in cascade. After n identical stages, the gain is the nth power of the gain of one stage, loaded by the input resistance of the next stage.

The frequency and transient response of a cascade amplifier is always worse than that of a single stage. The lower cutoff frequency rises and the upper cutoff frequency falls. For example, if in one stage the gain at a low frequency f is reduced from its midfrequency value by a factor of $\alpha = 1/\sqrt{1 + (f_l/f)^2}$, where f_l is the lower cutoff frequency, then clearly, after n stages, it will be reduced from its nth-power midfrequency value by a factor of α^n.

To obtain the new lower cutoff frequency f_{ln} of the n-stage amplifier, we set $\alpha^n = 1/\sqrt{2}$, from which we obtain

$$f_{ln} = \frac{1}{\sqrt{2^{1/n} - 1}} f_l. \tag{4.61}$$

In exactly the same way, the frequency f_h decreases and we find for the new upper cutoff frequency:

$$f_{hn} = \sqrt{2^{1/n} - 1}\, f_h. \tag{4.62}$$

The coefficient of f_h is reduced from 1 to 0.643 for $n = 2$ and for $n = 4$ to 0.435. Thus, after four stages the upper cutoff frequency is reduced to less than half its value for one stage and the lower cutoff frequency is raised by a factor of more than two.

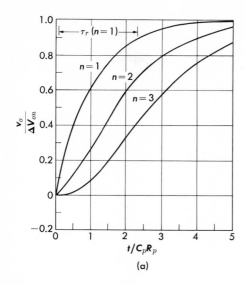 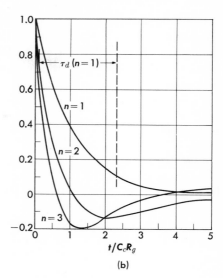

(a) (b)

FIG. 4.33.   Transient response of one-, two-, and three-stage RC-coupled amplifiers (number of stages $= n$). (a) Rising part, (b) decaying part. It is assumed that $C_p R_p$ is very much smaller than $C_c R_g$.

The effect of cascading identical stages on the *transient response* is illustrated in Fig. 4.33.

In Fig. 4.33(a) the rising part of the pulse is shown for 1, 2, and 3 stages, and in Fig. 4.33(b) the drooping part. It is clearly seen that the rise time increases while the droop time decreases as stages are added. In general, the total rise time of an n-stage amplifier with rise times of the individual stages $\tau_{1r}, \tau_{2r}, \ldots, \tau_{nr}$, is given to a good approximation by

$$\tau_r \approx \sqrt{\tau_{1r}^2 + \tau_{2r}^2 + \cdots + \tau_{nr}^2}, \tag{4.63}$$

which, for the special case of n identical stages $(\tau_{1r} = \cdots = \tau_{nr})$ reduces to

$$\tau_r \approx \tau_{1r}\sqrt{n}. \tag{4.64}$$

If we combine this result with Eqs. (4.62) and Eq. (4.52), we obtain

$$\tau_r \approx 0.35\sqrt{n(2^{1/n} - 1)}/f_{hn}. \tag{4.65}$$

For any value of n, the coefficient of $1/f_{hn}$ lies between 0.29 and 0.35. Equation (4.65) is useful for estimating the upper cutoff frequency of a multistage amplifier if the rise time is known, or vice versa.

There is no simple general relation between the lower cutoff frequency and the droop time of an n-stage amplifier. As is seen from Fig. 4.33(b), the droop time decreases very rapidly when stages are added, and also the decaying part crosses the zero line. For an n-stage RC-coupled amplifier, the zero line is crossed $n - 1$ times, which gives the transient the appearance of a damped oscillation. This effect must be carefully considered in pulse amplifiers. Positive parts of the signal following the first peak may be incorrectly interpreted as new pulses.

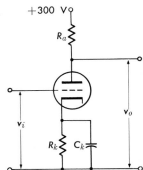

PROBLEMS

4.1 Using the manufacturer's published character-istics for a 12AX7 tube, find the small-signal mid-frequency voltage gain for the self-biased amplifier circuit shown in Fig. 4.34:

   (a) for a fixed value R_a = 50 kΩ, as R_k is varied from 100 Ω to 10 kΩ,

   (b) for a fixed value R_k = 1 kΩ, as R_a is varied from 5 kΩ to 500 kΩ.

   (c) Repeat (a) and (b) for a 6AU6 pentode with a fixed screen voltage of 200 V.

FIGURE 4.34

4.2 A pentode has a plate resistance r_p = 1 MΩ and a transconductance g_m = 3 mA/V. What must be the value of g_m for a triode with r_p = 50 kΩ if the triode and pentode amplifiers have identical anode resistors R_a = 50 kΩ, and, with the same input voltage, produce the same output voltage

   (a) across an infinite load resistance,

   (b) across a load resistance of 100 kΩ?

4.3 (a) For each circuit shown in Fig. 4.35, find the value for C_c so that the gain of each stage at a frequency of 50 cps is half that at 1000 cps.

   (b) Repeat for an amplifier with four identical RC-coupled stages.

(C_k and C_e are assumed to be very large, so that they do not affect the frequency response.)

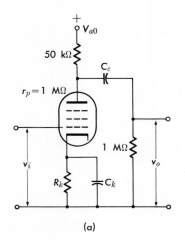

(a)

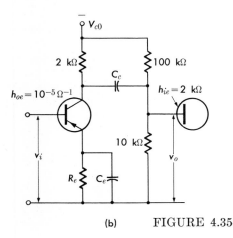

(b)   FIGURE 4.35

4.4 For the triode shown in Fig. 4.36, $C_{ga} = C_{gk} = 3 \text{ pF}; \mu = 60; r_p = 15 \text{ k}\Omega$.

(a) Find the midfrequency gain of the amplifier.

(b) Find approximate values for the input impedance of the amplifier at frequencies of 2 kcps, 20 kcps, 200 kcps, and 2 Mcps.

4.5 (a) Given that the input signal for the amplifier circuit of Problem 4.4 is derived from a signal generator which is equivalent to an emf of 0.1 V rms in series with an output resistor of 10 kΩ, what is the rms output voltage at each of the frequencies in Problem 4.4(b)?

(b) How does the amplifier output voltage vary at a frequency of 200 kcps, as the output impedance of the signal generator varies from 100 Ω to 100 kΩ?

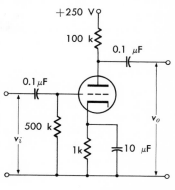

FIGURE 4.36

4.6 A cascade amplifier is made of four identical RC-coupled pentode amplifier stages, as shown schematically (bias connections omitted) in Fig. 4.37. The circuit parameters, identical for each stage, are $g_m = 3 \text{ mA/V}$, $r_p = 1 \text{ M}$, $C_c = 0.1 \text{ μF}$, $R_g = 1\text{M}$, $R_a = 50 \text{ k}$, $C_{ga} = 0$, $C_{gk} = 12 \text{ pF}$, $C_{ak} = 8 \text{ pF}$. Find the midfrequency gain and the upper and lower "3-db" frequencies (at which the gain drops to $1/\sqrt{2}$ of its midfrequency value) for the whole amplifier.

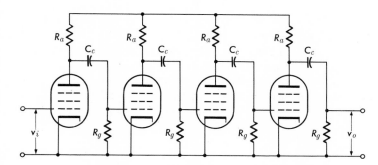

FIGURE 4.37

4.7 Suppose that a cascade amplifier consists of a large number n of identical RC-coupled stages, each with the same g_m, R_a, and R_g, and the same effective input and output capacities, C_i and C_o. Show that the limiting value of the product of the over-all gain A_n and the over-all upper cutoff frequency f_{hn} is simply $g_m/(2\pi(C_i + C_o))$, independent of the other circuit parameters. From this result, discuss the relative merits of triodes and pentodes for use in broadband (high f_h) cascade amplifiers.

4.8 An RC-coupled amplifier provides an output voltage of 20 V for an input voltage of 0.1 V at a midfrequency of 2000 cps. The lower 3-db frequency of the amplifier is 100 cps and the upper 3-db frequency 20 kcps.

(a) What is the midfrequency voltage gain in decibels?

(b) What is the db voltage gain at 50 cps and 40 kcps?

(c) Plot the variation in voltage gain on a db scale from 10 cps to 100 kcps.

4.9 For the transistor shown in Fig. 4.38, $h_{re} = 0, h_{fe} = 50, h_{oe} = 2 \times 10^{-5} \, \Omega^{-1}, I_{co} = -10 \, \mu A$.

(a) Find approximate quiescent values of I_b, I_c, and V_{ce}. (Assume $V_{be} \approx 0$.)

(b) For the values found in (a), the input impedance $h_{ie} \approx 1.3 \, k\Omega$. Find the current and voltage gain of the amplifier at mid-frequencies.

(c) Find the lower 3-db frequency of the amplifier for infinite load impedance, ignoring possible effects due to imperfect bypassing by the 50-μF emitter condenser.

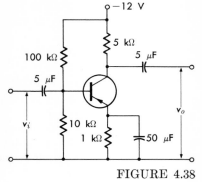

FIGURE 4.38

4.10   Draw the small-signal equivalent voltage-source circuits for each of the circuits in Fig. 4.39, omitting the dc bias voltages, and derive expressions for the voltage gain of each circuit.

4.11   The diagram in Fig. 4.40 shows a simple "tone control" circuit for an audio-frequency amplifier. Determine approximate minimum and maximum values for the relative gain of the amplifier at a frequency of 100 cps as a function of the setting of R_3 (with R_5 adjusted to its midpoint), and at a frequency of 10 kcps as a function of

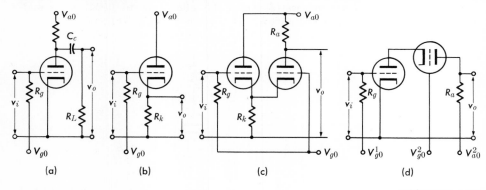

FIGURE 4.39

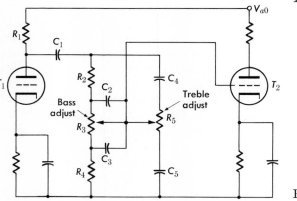

FIGURE 4.40

the setting of R_5 (with R_3 adjusted to its midpoint) for the following values of the circuit parameters:

$$T_1 = T_2 = \tfrac{1}{2} \, 12\text{AU}7$$

$$R_1 = 100 \text{ k}\Omega, \qquad C_1 = 0.1 \, \mu\text{F}$$
$$R_2 = 220 \text{ k}\Omega, \qquad C_2 = 0.001 \, \mu\text{F}$$
$$R_3 = 500 \text{ k}\Omega, \qquad C_3 = 0.01 \, \mu\text{F}$$
$$R_4 = 22 \text{ k}\Omega, \qquad C_4 = 0.0005 \, \mu\text{F}$$
$$R_5 = 500 \text{ k}\Omega, \qquad C_5 = 0.005 \, \mu\text{F}$$

(Assume that low-frequency and high-frequency controls do not interact.)

REFERENCES

Alley, C. L., and K. W. Atwood, *Electronic Engineering*, Wiley, 1962.

Cattermole, K. W., *Transistor Circuits*, Heywood, 1959.

Cooke-Yarborough, E. H., *An Introduction to Transistor Circuits*, Oliver and Boyd, 1957.

Joyce, M. V., and K. K. Clarke, *Transistor Circuit Analysis*, Addison-Wesley, 1962.

Landee, R. W., D. C. Davis, and A. P. Albrecht, *Electronic Designers Handbook*, McGraw-Hill, 1957, Chapter 3.

Ryder, J. D., *Engineering Electronics*, McGraw-Hill, 1957, Chapters 4–8.

Terman, F. E., *Radio Engineers Handbook*, McGraw-Hill, 1943, Section 5.

Valley, G. E., and H. Wallman, *Vacuum Tube Amplifiers*, McGraw-Hill, 1948.

Chapter 5

FEEDBACK AMPLIFIERS

5.1 GENERAL FEATURES

The performance of an amplifier can be radically modified if part of the output signal is connected back to the input—a process known as *feedback*. In general, feedback systems may have many outputs and many inputs, the signals may be of a mechanical rather than an electrical nature, and the feedback may occur by mechanical rather than electrical means. Indeed, the subject of feedback encompasses, in principle, the whole field of control devices, including servo systems and even biological systems. The latter can frequently be well simulated by simple electronic circuits with feedback. In this chapter we shall restrict our attention to feedback in electronic amplifiers, where the quantities of interest at the input and output are voltages or currents. A block diagram of a feedback amplifier is shown in Fig. 5.1. A signal βs_o is derived from the output signal s_o by means of the feedback network. In general, the term β represents some operation on s_o; in the simplest case (and the most common), β is merely a real number by which s_o is multiplied. The signal βs_o from the feedback network is added to the original input signal s_i in a summing network, so that the sum $s_i + \beta s_o$ appears at the output of this network as the input to the amplifier. If the amplifier is linear and has a gain A_0, the output is

$$s_o = A_0(s_i + \beta s_o). \tag{5.1}$$

Relative to the original input signal s_i, the gain of the amplifier with feedback, A_f, is evidently

$$A_f = \frac{s_o}{s_i} = \frac{A_0}{1 - \beta A_0}. \tag{5.2}$$

If the quantity βA_0, which is called the feedback factor, is positive, then A_f is greater than A_0, and the gain of the amplifier is increased because of the feedback; this case is called *positive* feedback. So long as $0 < \beta A_0 < 1$, the amplifier is stable. However, as βA_0 approaches $+1$, the gain becomes increasingly sensitive to small changes in A_0. From (5.2), we see that if $\beta A_0 = +1$, the gain with feedback becomes infinitely large. In this case, the amplifier is said to be regenerative; it produces an output with no input signal. This is just the condition for self-excited oscillation, and will be discussed separately in Chapter 8. Parenthetically, we may note at this time that while it is possible to make $\beta A_0 = +1$ to achieve "infinite gain," the amplifier becomes nonlinear as the signal grows and A_0 (and hence βA_0) decreases. It takes some finesse to keep βA_0 exactly $+1$ to make a good linear oscillator.

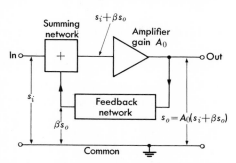

FIG. 5.1.   General form of feedback amplifier.

For most of the circuits in this chapter, we shall be concerned with *negative* feedback, where $\beta A_0 < 0$. For this case, we see from (5.2) that $A_f < A_0$; the amplifier gain has been decreased. However, as we shall see, this loss is offset by a number of salutary benefits, in particular the following.

1. *Constancy of gain.* The gain A_0 of an amplifier without feedback is, as we have seen, subject to changes due to variation in g_m of tubes with age, changes of supply voltage and, particularly for transistors, changes in temperature. Suppose that due to any variation, the gain A_0 should change by an amount δA_0, so that $A_0 \rightarrow A_0 + \delta A_0$. From (5.2), we know that the gain of the feedback amplifier changes by a fractional amount:

$$\frac{\delta A_f}{A_f} = \frac{\delta A_0}{A_0}\left(\frac{1}{1 - \beta A_0}\right). \tag{5.3}$$

The relative variation in gain is reduced by a factor of $1 - \beta A_0$, which can be a large positive quantity for negative feedback amplifiers, 100 or more, for example. In fact, if βA_0 is negative and large, (5.2) reduces to

$$A_f \approx 1/\beta. \tag{5.4}$$

The gain of the feedback amplifier is then almost completely independent of the gain of the amplifier, depending only on the values of the elements in the feedback network. Since these can be purely passive elements like resistors and condensers, we can achieve circuits of exceedingly constant gain by use of negative feedback.

2. *Reduction of distortion.* We have thus far treated our amplifiers as though they were truly linear, that is, as though the output were purely a multiple of

the input. This, of course, is a considerable idealization, as is evident from the shape of the transfer characteristics. All real amplifiers are nonlinear to some extent. In this case the gain function $A_0(s_i)$, rather than being simply a constant, can be expressed as a power series:

$$A_0(s_i) = A_{1_0} + A_{2_0}s_i + A_{3_0}s_i^2 + A_{4_0}s_i^3 + \cdots \qquad (5.5)$$

The output signal in the absence of feedback is then

$$s_o = A_0(s_i)s_i = A_{1_0}s_i + A_{2_0}s_i^2 + A_{3_0}s_i^3 + A_{4_0}s_i^4 + \cdots \qquad (5.6)$$

The first term, $A_{1_0}s_i$, gives the linear part of the output; the second quadratic term includes second harmonics of each of the input frequencies; the third term, third harmonics, etc.; these effects are called *harmonic distortion*. In addition, if the input signal contains two or more frequencies, $f_1, f_2, \ldots$, the second and higher terms generate beat frequencies, $f_1 + f_2$, $f_1 - f_2$, $2f_1 - f_2$, etc., an effect known as *intermodulation distortion*. If, as is usually the case, we want a linear amplifier, all terms in s_o except $A_{1_0}s_i$ represent unwanted signals. The use of negative feedback in the amplifier provides a great reduction in distortion, for the feedback signal βs_o contains the same fraction of the desired linear signal $A_{1_0}s_i$ and each of the distortion terms, $A_{2_0}s_i^2$, $A_{3_0}s_i^3$, etc. However, since only s_i was present in the original input, the feedback signal, which reduces the linear gain by a factor of $(1 - \beta A_0)$, tends to reduce the distortion terms by a factor of $(1 - \beta A_0)^2$. Thus, in the feedback amplifier, the distortion is reduced by a factor of $1 - \beta A_0$, relative to that in the amplifier without feedback.

Sometimes a combination of positive and negative feedback can be used to effect an even greater decrease in distortion. Such a circuit is shown in Fig. 5.2. Positive feedback is used around the first stages of the amplifier, where the signal level and the distortion will be small (since the distortion terms depend

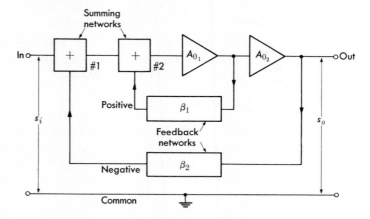

FIG. 5.2. Feedback amplifier with both positive and negative feedback.

on second and higher powers of the signal amplitude), while negative feedback is applied from a later stage where the signal level is high. The over-all gain of the amplifier is increased by the positive feedback in the first section, so that the factor $1 - \beta A_0$ is larger because A_0 now includes the effects of the positive feedback.

The above beneficial effects occur when the signal fed back from the output to the input is a fraction of the output voltage or of the output current. For other effects, we must distinguish between these cases.

5.2 VOLTAGE FEEDBACK

Two cases of voltage feedback are shown in Fig. 5.3. In the circuit of Fig. 5.3(a) the feedback voltage is connected in *series* with the signal voltage at the amplifier input terminals, whereas in that of Fig. 5.3(b), the signal and feedback voltages are connected in *parallel*. The parallel arrangement is commonly called an *operational amplifier;* this circuit will be discussed separately in Section 5.9. In this section we shall concentrate on the series voltage-feedback circuit of Fig. 5.3(a). As we shall see, with this connection the output impedance of the amplifier decreases and the input impedance increases with increasing negative feedback. The amplifier thus becomes a more ideal voltage amplifier.

A fraction, $[R_2/(R_1 + R_2)]v_o$, of the output voltage is derived from a voltage divider, which should not load the amplifier appreciably. This fraction is applied to the input in series with the signal v_i so that the difference $v_i - [R_2/(R_1 + R_2)]v_o$ appears between the input terminals. If we define $\beta = R_2/(R_1 + R_2)$, the voltage gain is

$$A_f = \frac{v_o}{v_i} = \frac{A_0}{1 - \beta A_0} \approx \frac{R_1 + R_2}{R_2} \quad \text{if} \quad |\beta A_0| \gg 1. \tag{5.7}$$

We denote by Z_{oo} the output impedance of the amplifier without feedback, which was defined in Section 4.1 as the ratio of the open-circuit voltage to the short-circuit current. This is equivalent to the ratio of a small change in output voltage v_{oo}, applied externally, to the resulting change in current i_{oo}, with a

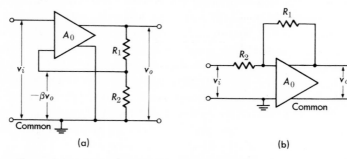

(a)   (b)

FIG. 5.3. General form of amplifier with voltage feedback. (a) Series feedback, (b) parallel feedback.

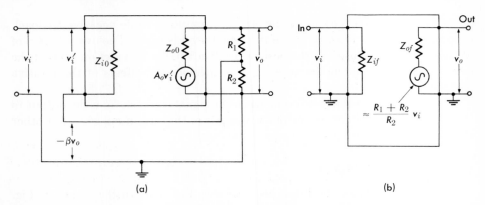

FIG. 5.4. (a) Four-terminal equivalent circuit of series-voltage-feedback amplifier, showing actual input and output impedances, (b) four-terminal equivalent circuit showing effective input and output impedances.

constant input signal voltage. Using this criterion, we can easily find the effect of negative feedback on the output impedance by considering the equivalent circuit diagram of Fig. 5.4(a). The voltage change v_{o0} gives rise to a signal, $v_i' = -\beta v_{o0}$, at the amplifier input, which after amplification by a factor of A_0 produces a change $A_0 v_i' = -\beta A_0 v_{o0}$ at the bottom of Z_{o0}. At the top of Z_{o0} a change v_{o0} is impressed, so that the actual total voltage change across Z_{o0} is $(1 - \beta A_0)v_{o0}$. To realize such a change of voltage across Z_{o0}, an extra current, $i_{o0} = [(1 - \beta A_0)v_{o0}]/Z_{o0}$ must pass through Z_{o0}; this current must be delivered from the external voltage source that causes the change v_{o0}. The effective output impedance of the feedback amplifier therefore is

$$Z_{of} = \frac{v_{o0}}{i_{o0}} = \frac{Z_{o0}}{1 - \beta A_0}. \tag{5.8}$$

It is apparent that the output impedance is reduced by the same factor as the gain for negative feedback. A voltage-feedback amplifier thus behaves like a voltage source with a low internal impedance. Such an amplifier can be connected to a low-impedance load with little loss in signal.

The input impedance of the amplifier will increase as a result of negative-voltage feedback if the feedback signal is actually connected in series at the input, as shown in Fig. 5.4(a). (As we shall see in Section 5.9, the input imped-ance of the amplifier is *decreased* for parallel negative-voltage feedback.) The actual current change in the input impedance Z_{i0}, caused by a change of input voltage v_{i0}, will be reduced by the feedback action. A change, v_{i0}, at the top of Z_{i0} is accompanied by a change, $\beta v_o = (\beta A_0/1 - \beta A_0)v_{i0}$, of the same sign at the bottom of Z_{i0}. The total voltage change across Z_{i0} is

$$v_{i0}[1 - \beta A_0/(1 - \beta A_0)] \approx v_{i0}/(1 - \beta A_0),$$

and the change of input current is

$$i_{i0} = v_{i0}/[(1 - \beta A_0)Z_{i0}].$$

Thus, the input impedance of the voltage-feedback amplifier is

$$Z_{if} = v_{i0}/i_{i0} = Z_{i0}(1 - \beta A_0). \tag{5.9}$$

Such an amplifier presents a high impedance to the input signal generator if βA_0 is large and negative. The use of series negative-voltage feedback to increase the effective input impedance is sometimes called *bootstrapping*, since the lower end of the actual input impedance is literally "lifted by its own boot-straps" above ground potential by the feedback action.

Equations (5.8) and (5.9) are also valid for $\beta A_0 > 0$; thus for positive series voltage feedback, $Z_{of} > Z_{o0}$ and $Z_{if} < Z_{i0}$.

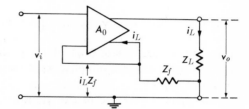

FIG. 5.5. General form of amplifier with current feedback.

5.3 CURRENT FEEDBACK

If the feedback signal is proportional to the actual current delivered to the load, the case is designated as current feedback. A typical example is shown in Fig. 5.5, where the feedback signal is derived across an impedance Z_f in series with the load impedance Z_L. Here Z_f is assumed negligible compared with the load Z_L or the amplifier output impedance Z_{o0}. The output current is $i_L = v'_o/(Z_{o0} + Z_L)$, where v'_o is the voltage across the series combination of Z_L and Z_{o0}. The actual output voltage across Z_L is $v_o = i_L Z_L$; the feedback voltage is $-i_L Z_f = -v'_o Z_f/(Z_{o0} + Z_L)$. Since $v'_o = A_0(v_i - i_L Z_f)$, we find immediately for the voltage gain

$$A_f = \frac{v_o}{v_i} = \frac{A_0}{1 + Z_{o0}/Z_L + A_0 Z_f/Z_L} \approx \frac{Z_L}{Z_f} \tag{5.10}$$

if $A_0 Z_f/Z_L \gg 1 + Z_{o0}/Z_L$.

To calculate the effective output and input impedances of the amplifier with feedback, Z_{of}, we consider Fig. 5.6(a). The output impedance Z_{of} is given as the ratio of the open-circuit voltage to the short-circuit current. If the output Z_{i0} is accompanied by a change $-\beta v_0 = -[\beta A_0/(1 - \beta A_0)]v_{i0}$, at the bottom of Z_{i0}. The total voltage change across Z_{i0} is the difference of these two changes

$$v_{i0}[1 + \beta A_0/(1 - \beta A_0)] = v_{i0}/(1 - \beta A_0),$$

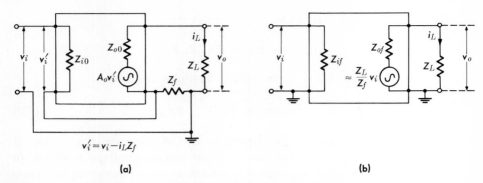

$$v_i' = v_i - i_L Z_f$$

(a)   (b)

FIG. 5.6. (a) Four-terminal equivalent circuit of current-feedback amplifier showing actual input and output impedances, (b) four-terminal equivalent circuit showing effective input and output impedances.

and the effective output impedance is

$$Z_{of} = v_o''/i_L' = Z_{oo}(1 + A_0 Z_f/Z_{oo}),$$ (5.11)

increased by a factor of $(1 + A_0 Z_f/Z_{oo})$ from its value without feedback. The high effective output impedance tends to keep the current through the load constant.

The input impedance of the amplifier with current feedback, like that with voltage feedback, is increased from its nominal value Z_{i0}, and for the same reason; if the feedback signal is actually connected in series with the input signal, then the current flowing in the input is proportional only to the voltage difference $v_i - i_L Z_f$, rather than to v_i, and the input impedance is

$$Z_{if} = \frac{v_i Z_{i0}}{v_i - i_L Z_f} = Z_{i0}\left[1 + \frac{A_0 Z_f}{Z_{oo} + Z_L}\right].$$ (5.12)

5.4 FREQUENCY CHARACTERISTICS AND STABILITY OF FEEDBACK AMPLIFIERS

Thus far we have ignored the effect of phase shifts on the response of the feedback amplifier, although we know from the previous chapter, in which the simple RC-coupled amplifier was studied, that phase shifts occur at the low- and high-frequency ends of the spectrum. These can have a serious effect on the performance of the feedback amplifier, especially if for any frequency the cumulative effect of the phase shifts exceeds 180°; then, if we provide negative feedback at midfrequencies, where the phase shift is zero, we will have *positive* feedback at frequencies where the phase shift is 180°. If the amplifier gain at one of these frequencies is sufficiently high that $\beta A_0 \geq 1$, the amplifier will be regenerative at that frequency, and all the beneficial effects of the negative feedback will be lost. The phase and amplitude characteristics of the amplifier

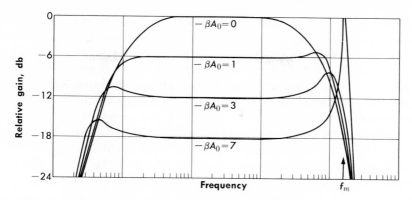

FIG. 5.7. Frequency characteristics of feedback amplifier of Fig. 5.9 for different values of the midfrequency feedback factor βA_0. For $|\beta A_0| \geq 8$, the amplifier is regenerative and will oscillate at a frequency f_m.

without feedback (and also those of the feedback network) thus determine whether the amplifier will be stable when feedback is applied. The "growth" of instability in an amplifier with increasing feedback is illustrated in Fig. 5.7.

The phase shifts in the amplifier and feedback network can be taken into account if we let β and A_0 be complex (this does not change the validity of any of the formulas). The feedback term βA_0 is frequently plotted as a function of frequency in the complex plane, as shown in Fig. 5.8 (called a Nyquist diagram).

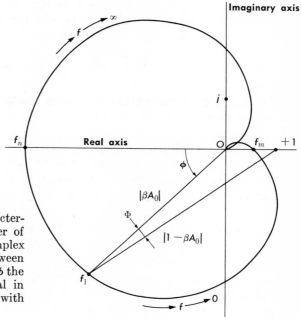

FIG. 5.8. Frequency characteristics of the feedback amplifier of Fig. 5.9, plotted in the complex plane. Φ is the phase angle between the input and output voltages, ϕ the total phase shift of the signal in amplifier and feedback network with open feedback loop.

Such a plot presents several characteristics of the feedback amplifier at a glance. The distance from the origin O to some point f_1 on the curve gives the absolute value $|\beta A_0|$ of the feedback factor at the frequency f_1; the angle ϕ between the line joining O and f_1 and the real axis represents the phase shift of the signal at the output of the feedback network with respect to the input signal. If the curve makes a closed loop about the point $+1$, the amplifier will be regenerative (Nyquist criterion). For a constant and real β, (e.g., when the feedback network consists of a frequency-independent voltage divider), the phase angle Φ between the input and output voltage of the feedback amplifier can also be read from the figure. This angle remains small so long as $|\beta A_0| \gg 1$. Thus, the phase shift of the amplifier is also reduced by negative feedback.

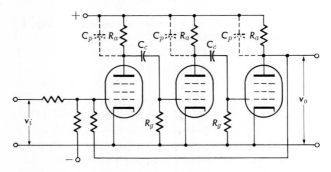

FIG. 5.9.   Three-stage feedback amplifier subject to oscillation at a high frequency.

In order for regeneration to occur, the total phase shift must add up to 180°. Such a condition can easily arise in a three-stage amplifier with identical stages, for 60° phase shift per stage. For example, in the circuit shown in Fig. 5.9, there are only two series-coupling networks $R_g C_c$, but three parallel networks $R_a C_p$. For three equal time constants $R_a C_p$, the feedback amplifier will become regenerative when there is a 60-degree phase shift at the output of each stage if, at that (high) frequency, f_H, the total gain $A_0(f_H)$ times the feedback fraction β is ≥ 1. From (4.43) and (4.44), we note that $\phi = 60°$ when $f_H/f_h = \sqrt{3}$. At this frequency, the gain per stage is reduced by a factor of $1/\sqrt{1 + \sqrt{3}^2} = 1/2$, and the total amplifier gain is reduced by $(1/2)^3 = 1/8$. Thus, this amplifier will oscillate if the magnitude of the feedback factor $|\beta A_0| \geq 8$ at mid-frequencies. With such a low feedback factor, we can hardly hope to attain all the benefits of negative feedback which seemed apparent. Fortunately, there is a straightforward solution to this problem: we simply make one of the time constants, $R_a C_p$, *much different from the other two*. In this way, when the phase shift accumulates to 180°, the gain has already decreased to such an extent that $|\beta A_0| < 1$. To ensure stable operation, it is recommended that the critical regenerative condition never be closely approached in circuit design. Good rules to follow are: $|\beta A_0| \leq 0.3$ for a phase shift of 180°, and for $|\beta A_0| > 1$, the phase of the feedback signal should never be between 140 and 220°.

In practical feedback amplifiers, additional phase shifts are introduced by imperfect bypassing of screen grids or cathodes or by frequency-sensitivity of the feedback network. Such effects may give rise to regeneration even in two-stage amplifiers. Care must also be taken to avoid feedback through inadvertent coupling of the output signal by proximity of wires or by currents flowing in "ground loops" in the chassis. These may provide undesired positive feedback in addition to the negative feedback and, unfortunately, when given the choice, the amplifier follows the path of positive feedback toward regenerative operation, for all the negative feedback which might be superposed.

5.5 DC VOLTAGE AND CURRENT FEEDBACK

Amplifier characteristics can be improved not only by feeding back part of the output signal but also by feedback stabilization of the dc-currents in the active circuit elements. Networks which provide voltage or current feedback only for very slow changes, and not at signal frequencies, can be obtained by bypassing the feedback resistors with large capacitors, for example. Effectively, this has already been shown in the $R_k C_k$-network used for self-bias of the vacuum tube and the $R_e C_e$-network used to stabilize the transistor. A higher degree of dc-stabilization can be obtained by feedback across more than one stage if direct coupling is used between stages; sometimes a combination of current and voltage feedback is used to obtain favorable properties.

5.6 THE CATHODE FOLLOWER AND THE EMITTER FOLLOWER

The simplest example of a vacuum-tube voltage-feedback amplifier is the common anode circuit of Fig. 4.7(c), usually designated a *cathode follower*. In this circuit (see Fig. 5.10) the entire output voltage is fed back to the input, so that the effective input signal is $v_i' = v_i - v_o$ and $\beta = -1$. The voltage

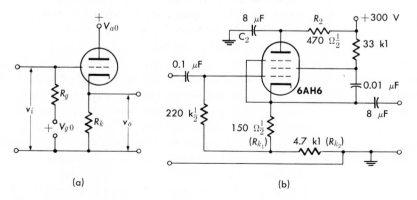

FIG. 5.10. (a) Basic circuit of a triode cathode follower, (b) detailed circuit of a cathode follower using a pentode. The network $R_2 C_2$ reduces the influence of rapid current fluctuations in the tube on the power supply voltage.

gain without feedback is that of a triode with a resistor R_k in the anode lead (but with inverted sign since v_k and v_i have the same sign, whereas v_a and v_i have opposite signs). From Eq. (2.28) we see that

$$A_0 = \mu R_k/(R_k + r_p) = g_m R_k/(1 + g_m R_k/\mu).$$

Therefore, from (5.2) the voltage gain with feedback is

$$A_f = \frac{g_m R_k}{1 + g_m R_k (1 + \mu)/\mu}. \qquad (5.13)$$

This value is always less than 1. For very large $g_m R_k$ the gain approaches a limiting value, $\mu/(\mu + 1)$, which is very close to 1. So long as $g_m R_k < \mu$, which is usually the case, we may write, to a good approximation,

$$A_f \approx \frac{g_m R_k}{1 + g_m R_k}. \qquad (5.14)$$

From Eq. (5.8) we obtain, for the output impedance,

$$Z_{of} \approx \frac{R_k}{1 + g_m R_k} \left(\approx \frac{1}{g_m} \text{ if } g_m R_k \gg 1 \right). \qquad (5.15)$$

Values of g_m typically range from 1 to 10 mA/V, corresponding to output impedances ranging from 100 to 1000 Ω.

For the circuit to work properly, sufficient current must flow through the tube. Because a rather large cathode resistor is usually chosen (1–10 kΩ), a positive grid bias is required. This can be obtained from a separate source, $+V_{g0}$ as is indicated in Fig. 5.10(a), or by return of the grid resistor to a tap on the cathode resistor, as shown in the detailed circuit of Fig. 5.10(b). Since in this circuit $R_{k_1} \ll R_{k_2}$, practically the whole cathode signal is present at the bottom of R_g, which increases the effective input resistance to

$$Z_{if} \approx R_g (1 + g_m R_k), \qquad (5.16)$$

in accordance with Eq. (5.9). This is a good approximation so long as $g_m R_k < \mu$. For very large values of $g_m R_k$, Z_{if} approaches a limiting value, $R_g(1 + \mu)$. The same mechanism which increases the input resistance reduces the effective grid-to-cathode capacitance C_{gk} by a factor of about $1 + g_m R_k$. In the circuit of Fig. 5.10(b) the screen grid is capacitively connected to the cathode, causing g_2 to follow the cathode and thereby reducing $C_{g_2 g_1}$ by a factor of $1 + g_m R_k$.

While the operation of the *emitter follower* closely resembles that of the cathode follower in many respects, there are also some typical differences. In the emitter follower, base current must always flow, whereas in a properly adjusted cathode follower no grid current is drawn. This necessitates some care in analyzing the operation of the emitter follower. In principle this can again be accomplished by use of the general feedback concepts laid down in Eqs. (5.2), (5.8), and (5.9), but we prefer to give a direct analysis, using the common-emitter small-signal h-parameters, with which we are already familiar. (We do not introduce the common-collector h-parameters which are closely related to the common-emitter parameters, because these are much less often given in transistor data sheets.)

In Fig. 5.11 the circuit of an emitter follower with an npn-transistor is given. From the circuit we see that

$$v_i = v_i' + v_o, \qquad (5.17)$$

$$v_o = i_e R_e = -v_{ce}. \qquad (5.18)$$

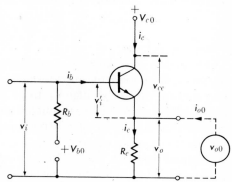

From the definitions of the h-parameters (Section 3.5.2), we know that

$$v_i' = i_b h_{ie} + v_{ce} h_{re}, \qquad (5.19)$$

$$i_c = i_b h_{fe} + v_{ce} h_{oe}. \qquad (5.20)$$

FIG. 5.11.   Basic circuit of npn-emitter follower.

Completing these equations with

$$i_e = i_b + i_c, \qquad (5.21)$$

we can eliminate all unwanted variables from (5.17) through (5.21) and obtain for the voltage gain

$$A_f = \frac{v_o}{v_i} = \frac{(1 + h_{fe}) R_e}{h_{ie} + R_e[(1 + h_{fe})(1 - h_{re}) + h_{oe} h_{ie}]}. \qquad (5.22)$$

Since normally $h_{fe} \gg 1$ and always $h_{re} \ll 1$, this expression can be reduced to

$$A_f \approx \frac{(h_{fe}/h_{ie}) R_e}{1 + (h_{fe}/h_{ie}) R_e (1 + h_{oe} h_{ie}/h_{fe})}. \qquad (5.23)$$

The ratio $h_{fe}/h_{ie} = g_m^{(t)}$ is defined as the transistor transconductance; the term $h_{fe}/(h_{oe} h_{ie}) = \mu^{(t)}$ can be called the transistor amplification factor, and we may write (5.23) as

$$A_f = \frac{g_m^{(t)} R_e}{1 + g_m^{(t)} R_e (1 + \mu^{(t)})/\mu^{(t)}}, \qquad (5.23')$$

which is identical to the expression (5.13) derived for the cathode follower. For transistors, μ-values are larger by an order of magnitude than for tubes. Therefore, (5.23') can be written as

$$A_f = \frac{g_m^{(t)} R_e}{1 + g_m^{(t)} R_e} \qquad (5.24)$$

for all practical cases.

In calculating the output impedance of the emitter-follower circuit, the internal impedance of the source that delivers the signal must be taken into account since an externally impressed change of output voltage causes a change in the base current. Let us assume that the internal signal-source resistance is incorporated in the external base resistance R_b. Then, a variation, i_b, of the base current at constant source voltage will cause a variation

$$v_i = -i_b R_b \tag{5.25}$$

of the base voltage.

The output impedance Z_{of} can again be defined as the ratio of a voltage change v_{o0} impressed by an external source (see Fig. 5.11) on the emitter and the resulting current change i_{o0} to be delivered by this source. A part, $i'_{o0} = v_{o0}/R_e$, of this current flows through the emitter resistor; the rest, $i''_{o0} = i_{o0} - i'_{o0}$, compensates the change of emitter current: $i_e = -i''_{o0}$.

From the circuit we see again that $v_{o0} = -v_{ce}$ and $v_{o0} + v'_i = v_i$. Combining these equalities with Eq. (5.19) through (5.21) and (5.25), we derive for the output impedance, once more neglecting h_{re},

$$Z_{of} = \frac{v_{o0}}{i_{o0}} = \frac{1}{1/R_e + h_{oe} + (1 + h_{fe})/(R_b + h_{ie})}. \tag{5.26}$$

In practice, the emitter follower usually derives its input signal from a high impedance source, so that $R_b \gg h_{ie}$. On the other hand, R_b is generally small compared with the ratio h_{fe}/h_{oe}. Under these conditions (5.26) reduces to

$$Z_{of} \approx \frac{1}{1/R_e + (1 + h_{fe})/R_b}. \tag{5.27}$$

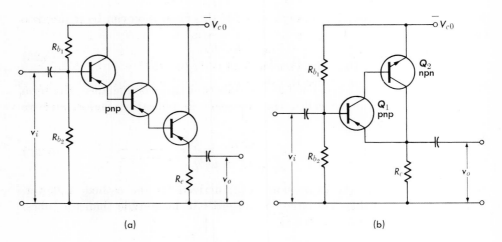

(a)   (b)

FIG. 5.12.   (a) Three-stage cascade emitter follower, (b) emitter follower with pnp/npn complementary pair.

Clearly, this is the parallel combination of the external emitter resistor and an impedance $R_b/(1 + h_{fe})$. Thus, the emitter follower serves as an impedance transformer that steps down the effective resistance at its input by a factor of $1 + h_{fe}$. This factor in practice ranges from 20–100.

When an emitter follower is connected to a low-impedance source so that $R_b \ll h_{ie}$, we may write

$$Z_{of} \approx \frac{1}{1/R_e + (1 + h_{fe})/h_{ie}} \approx \frac{R_e}{1 + g_m^{(t)} R_e} \approx \frac{1}{g_m^{(t)}} \qquad \text{if} \quad R_e g_m^{(t)} \gg 1. \quad (5.28)$$

This expression is identical with (5.15). Values of $g_m^{(t)}$ range from 10–100 mA/V, corresponding to $Z_{of} \approx 10$–$100\ \Omega$.

A similar analysis yields for the input impedance of the emitter follower,

$$Z_{if} \approx \frac{1}{1/R_b + 1/(h_{ie} + (1 + h_{fe}) R_e)}. \quad (5.29)$$

In this result, we neglected h_{re} and assumed that $R_e \ll 1/h_{oe}$. Often we will choose R_e such that $h_{fe} R_e \gg h_{ie}$. Under this condition we find that the input impedance consists of the parallel combination of the base resistor R_b and an impedance $(1 + h_{fe}) R_e$. Thus, at the emitter-follower input the resistance loading its output appears stepped up by a factor of $1 + h_{fe}$, and high values of the input impedance can be obtained (typically varying from 100 kΩ to a few MΩ). Only when R_e is very small will the input impedance approach the value of h_{ie} found for the grounded emitter circuit.

If the input-output impedance transformation ratio provided by one stage is insufficient, two or more stages may be cascaded, as shown in Fig. 5.12(a). Another method for increasing the transformation ratio is shown in Fig. 5.12(b), where a pnp/npn complementary transistor pair is used, resulting in a particularly simple circuit. This circuit can be regarded as a two-transistor feedback loop, in which the entire output signal of Q_2 is fed back to the emitter of Q_1. It has better linearity than the cascaded emitter follower but is more liable to regeneration. The impedance transformation ratio for the circuits of Fig. 5.12

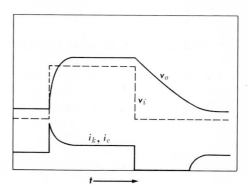

FIG. 5.13. Distortion of a rectangular voltage pulse in a capacitively loaded cathode or npn emitter follower.

is to a good approximation equal to the product of the current transfer ratios, h_{fe}, of the individual transistors.

The analysis just presented for the cathode follower and the single-stage emitter follower is no longer valid if the input signal is so large that g_m or h_{fe} changes appreciably. In particular, if the input signal is a very large positive pulse, and there is a capacitive load across the output, the output signal may be appreciably distorted on the trailing edge of the pulse, as shown in Fig. 5.13. This effect arises because the capacitive loading prevents the cathode or emitter voltage from following the fast negative-going input pulse, so that the tube or transistor are *cut off;* the output impedance then rises to the full value of R_k or R_e (since $A_0 = 0$ if the tube or transistor is cut off), and the discharge time of the capacitive load is much longer than the charging time on the rising portion of the pulse when the tube or transistor conducts a high current.

This difficulty can be overcome by certain circuits, which are discussed in the next section.

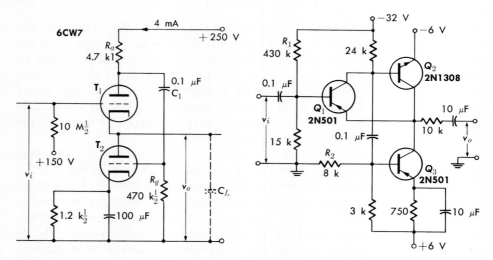

FIG. 5.14. Practical White cathode-follower circuit.   FIG. 5.15. Practical White emitter-follower circuit.

5.7   WHITE CATHODE AND EMITTER FOLLOWERS

The White circuits provide a symmetrical response to positive and negative signals. They can be considered as two-stage feedback amplifiers in which the total output signal is fed back to the input. They therefore provide a voltage gain slightly smaller than unity, combined with a very low output impedance and a very high input impedance. The tube circuit of Fig. 5.14 provides the output impedance

$$Z_{of} \approx 1/g_m^2 R_a'. \tag{5.30}$$

In the circuit shown, $g_m = 4\,\text{mA/V}$ and $R'_a = R_a r_p/(R_a + r_p) = 2.6\,\text{k}\Omega$, so that $Z_{of} \approx 25\,\Omega$. Since the circuit is ac-coupled through C_1, the anode signal of T_1 is incompletely transmitted to T_2 at very low frequencies. This causes the output impedance for very slow changes to rise to about $1/g_m \sim 250\,\Omega$ (T_2 then acts only as a large cathode resistance $R_k = r_p = 35\,\text{k}\Omega$). Signal feedback in this case is larger than dc-feedback by a factor of $g_m R'_a$. It is possible, however, to use dc-coupling from T_1 to T_2 if we must have a frequency-independent value of Z_{of}.

The response of the circuit to large positive and negative jumps of the input voltage under a capacitive load is shown in Fig. 5.16. For positive jumps the load capacity C_L is charged rapidly through T_1 since this tube is highly conducting while T_2 is cut off. For negative jumps the roles of T_1 and T_2 are reversed— T_2 conducts while T_1 is cut off.

A pleasant feature of this circuit is that the quiescent current can be small; large currents must be delivered only during fast changes. For a normal cathode follower a small quiescent current is possible only when fast positive jumps are required at the output.

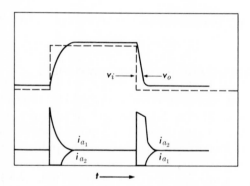

FIG. 5.16.   Distortion of a rectangular voltage pulse in a White cathode follower. Note the much faster decay of v_o compared with the normal cathode-follower output shown in Fig. 5.13.

A practical White emitter follower for fast pulses is shown in Fig. 5.15. The difference between input and output signals appears between base and emitter of Q_1, and the amplified difference signal at the collector of Q_1 is fed in parallel to the complementary pair Q_2(npn) and Q_3(pnp). In this manner the pnp-transistor is turned on for positive input pulses; the npn-transistor, for negative pulses. Resistor R_1 sets the quiescent current of Q_1; R_2 sets that of Q_3; and the difference between these currents flows in Q_2. Like the tube circuit, the transistor circuit is biased to a small quiescent current. Under capacitive load, large currents flow only during transients. The maximum output signal across a $100\text{-}\Omega$ load resistor is about ± 6 V, and the response of such a device is linear within 1%.

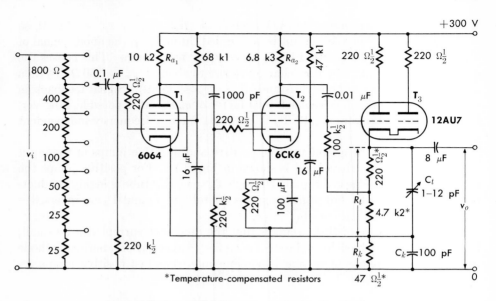

FIG. 5.17.   Circuit of a practical multistage wide-band vacuum tube amplifier with voltage feedback.

5.8   PRACTICAL MULTISTAGE FEEDBACK AMPLIFIERS

Examples of practical amplifier circuits employing negative feedback across several stages are shown in Figs. 5.17 and 5.18. Figure 5.17 shows a three-stage vacuum-tube amplifier frequently used for pulse amplification in nuclear circuits, providing good linearity for positive output pulses of up to 100 V. The signal from the input attenuator is amplified in pentodes T_1 and T_2 (gain $A_0 = g_{m_1} R_{a_1} g_{m_2} R_{a_2}$) and applied to the cathode follower T_3. A fraction of the output signal determined by the ratio of R_t and R_k is fed back to the cathode of T_1. The gain of the amplifier $A_f \approx R_t/R_k$. The bandwidth of the amplifier shown is about 5 Mcps, and the rise time $\approx 0.07\ \mu$sec. The two condensers C_t and C_k provide compensation for the feedback attenuator (see Section 9.2.2). The trimmer C_t should be so adjusted that a transient does not show any overshoot at the output, as can be checked with a fast pulse generator and an oscilloscope. For excessively small values of C_t the amplifier will become regenerative. The output impedance of the amplifier is about 10 Ω, but the actual maximum positive signal that can be delivered is limited by the maximum current that can be delivered by T_3 without grid current being drawn, while the maximum negative signal is limited by cutoff of T_3. For the circuit shown, with a load resistor of 1000 Ω, $v_{o\ \max} \approx +70$ V or -17 V. The width of pulses applied to the amplifier should be at least a few times the rise time, because for shorter pulses the benefits of negative feedback are lost. The amplifier then behaves more like an integrator (see Section 9.2.4).

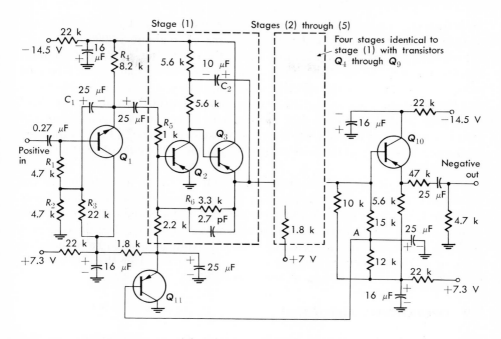

FIG. 5.18. Multistage transistor feedback amplifier with 5 cascaded feedback loops, each providing a gain of −3.3 [slightly simplified circuit diagram, taken from Philips service notes; Q_1 = OC141 (Philips) or equivalent npn medium-power fast-switching transistor, Q_2- through Q_{10}-AFZ12 (Philips) or equivalent vhf transistor, Q_{11}-OC47 (Philips) or equivalent pnp transistor]. Feedback loops are indicated by heavy lines.

The circuit of a practical multistage transistor feedback amplifier providing a gain of −330 and a rise time of about 0.1 μsec is shown in Fig. 5.18. Feedback loops with different purposes are used in this circuit. The input stage consists of an emitter follower Q_1. The input impedance of this stage is increased by the presence of condenser C_1, which feeds back the emitter signal to the bottom of R_1. This method of increasing the input impedance of a feedback amplifier has been discussed in Section 5.2 (see Eq. 5.9). At signal frequencies, the resistors R_2 through R_5 in parallel constitute the external emitter resistance $R_e \sim 700\ \Omega$, and the effective base resistance, $R_b' \approx R_1[1 + h_{fe}/h_{ie})R_e]$, is about 120 k$\Omega$ ($h_{fe} = 50$, $h_{ie} \approx 2$ k). Inserting this value of R_b' for R_b into Eq. (5.29), we find for the input impedance $Z_{if} \approx 30$ kΩ, in good agreement with the manufacturer's data.

The output signal from the emitter follower is applied through R_5 to the first of five identical transistor feedback loops in cascade, each providing a voltage gain $A = -R_6/R_5 = -3.3$. The first loop consists of the pair of transistors Q_2, Q_3, with Q_2 acting as a common-emitter amplifier directly coupled to the emitter follower Q_3. The effective collector resistance of Q_2 is increased exactly the same way as the base resistance of the input stage: the output signal is fed back from Q_3 to a tap on the collector resistor through C_2. By this method the open-loop voltage gain A_0 of the stage is increased to about -3000.

Feedback around the loop is provided by the connection of R_6 directly from the emitter of Q_3 to the base of Q_2. This method of feedback, called *parallel voltage feedback*, reduces the effective input impedance of Q_2 to a very low value ($\sim 1\ \Omega$) and, since $-A_0 \gg R_6/R_5$, sets the voltage gain of the feedback amplifier very close to $A \approx -R_6/R_5$ (see Section 5.9). The ouput impedance of the loop is also reduced to a low value by the voltage feedback ($\sim 1\ \Omega$), so that the 1-kΩ input resistance of the next stage does not lower the gain of the first stage appreciably.

In addition, dc-feedback is provided around all stages to stabilize the dc-transistor voltages. For this purpose, voltage variations slower than about 1 cps are taken from point A and returned to the first amplifier stage through transistor Q_{11}, which is connected as an emitter follower. The dc-loop gain is about -100, causing an open-loop change in voltage level to be reduced by a factor of 101. The gain stability of the amplifier is better than 0.5% in 24 hours for temperature changes of less than 10°C.

5.9 OPERATIONAL AMPLIFIERS

The parallel-voltage-feedback amplifier circuit shown schematically in Fig. 5.3(b) and again in Fig. 5.19(a) is frequently called an *operational amplifier*. The name is derived from the fact that by proper choice of the source and feedback impedances, Z_s and Z_f, the output voltage v_o can be made to represent the effect of a predetermined mathematical function operating on the input signal v_i—such as multiplication or division by a constant, integration, differentiation, or addition. Such circuits are frequently used in analog computers, as well as in a large number of other applications.

The performance of the circuit can be readily understood in terms of the parallel negative feedback between the input and output through the impedance

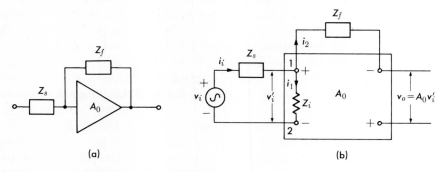

FIG. 5.19. Schematic representation of operational amplifier. (a) Two-terminal equivalent circuit, (b) four-terminal equivalent circuit showing input impedance and pertinent voltages and currents.

Z_f. The output voltage v_o will, of course, be simply $A_0 v_i'$, where v_i' is the actual voltage appearing between input terminals 1 and 2 in Fig. 5.19(b). If we denote by $Z_i' = v_i'/i_i$ the effective input impedance (including the effects of the feedback impedance Z_f) between terminals 1 and 2, we have

$$v_i' = i_1 Z_i = v_i Z_i'/(Z_s + Z_i'). \tag{5.31}$$

With reference to the output circuit, we note that

$$v_i' - v_o = v_i'(1 - A_0) = i_2 Z_f. \tag{5.32}$$

Solving for i_1 and i_2 and summing, we obtain

$$i_1 + i_2 = i_i = v_i'(1/Z_i + (1 - A_0)/Z_f) \approx v_i'(1 - A_0)/Z_f \tag{5.33}$$

if $|Z_i| \gg |Z_f/(1 - A_0)|$. The effective input impedance Z_i' is therefore

$$Z_i' = v_i'/i_i = Z_f/(1 - A_0). \tag{5.34}$$

Note that if A_0 is very large and negative, Z_i' is *very small;* there is a *virtual short circuit* across the input terminals, virtual because the actual current drawn, $i_1 = v_i'/Z_i$, is essentially zero if Z_i is large. Thus, to a good approximation, $i_2 \approx i_i$, and the total input current effectively passes through the feedback resistor Z_f to the output.

Combining (5.31) and (5.34), we may solve for the gain of the whole circuit:

$$A_f = \frac{v_o}{v_i} = \frac{A_0 v_i'}{v_i} = \frac{A_0 Z_f}{Z_s(1 - A_0)} \approx -\frac{Z_f}{Z_s} \tag{5.35}$$

if $(1 - A_0) \gg 1$. For proper operation of the circuit, A_0 must be very large and negative, so that all the approximations made are valid to high precision.

The functional relationship between v_o and v_i, then, depends only on the choice of the impedances Z_s and Z_f. Various possible combinations, shown in Fig. 5.20, are as follows.

(a) *Multiplication, division, or inversion.* If $Z_s = R_1$ and $Z_f = R_2$, then $v_o = -(R_2/R_1)v_i = -kv_i$, where k is a constant. If $R_1 = R_2$, then $v_o = -v_i$, corresponding to an inversion of v_i.

(b) *Integration.* If $Z_s = R$ and $Z_f = C$, because of the virtual short circuit across the input, $i_i \approx v_i/R \approx i_2$ and $v_o \approx -(1/C) \int i_2 \, dt \approx -(1/RC) \int v_i \, dt$.

(c) *Differentiation.* If $Z_s = C$ and $Z_f = R$, because of the virtual short circuit across the input, $i_i \approx C(dv_i/dt) \approx i_2$ and $v_o \approx -i_2 R \approx -RC(dv_i/dt)$.

(d) *Addition.* If $Z_{s_1} = Z_{s_2} = Z_{s_3} = \cdots = Z_{s_n} = R_1$, and $Z_f = R_2$, because of the virtual short circuit, $i_i \approx v_{i_1}/R_1 + \cdots + v_{i_n}/R_1 \approx i_2$ and $v_o \approx -i_2 R_2 \approx -R_2/R_1(v_{i_1} + v_{i_2} + \cdots + v_{i_n})$.

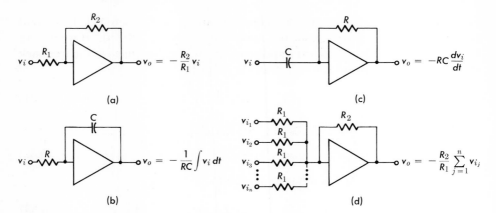

(a)   (c)

(b)   (d)

FIG. 5.20. Connections for operational amplifier. (a) Inverter-multiplier, (b) integrator, (c) differentiator, (d) adder.

The major limitation of the operational amplifier, as in any negative feedback circuit, arises from the deleterious effects of phase shifts, which can lead to unstable operation at high and low frequencies. The low-frequency instability can be avoided by use of a direct-coupled amplifier (see Section 6.6), and the high-frequency instability by unsymmetrical limiting of the high-frequency gain of one or more of the amplifier stages, as discussed in Section 5.4. This requirement limits the high-frequency capability of the whole circuit. The circuit thus usually acts less efficiently as a differentiator (where the derivative dv_i/dt contains mainly the highest-frequency components present in v_i) than as an integrator, where principally the lowest-frequency components of v_i are

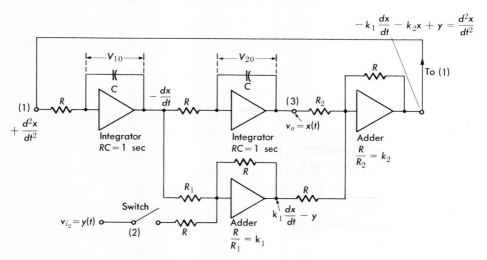

FIG. 5.21. Analog computer for solution of differential equation $(d^2x/dt^2) + k_1(dx/dt) + k_2x = y.$

important. In practical analog-computer circuits, therefore, the equations to be solved are best cast in integral form, if possible.

As an example, the differential equation

$$\frac{d^2x}{dt^2} + k_1 \frac{dx}{dt} + k_2 x - y(t) = 0$$

can be solved by the circuit arrangement shown in Fig. 5.21. An input signal $v_{i_1} = d^2x/dt^2$, derived from the circuit itself, is applied to the input terminal (1) and a signal $v_{i_2} = y(t)$ to input terminal (2). Initial conditions $(dx/dt)_0$ and x_0 can be fixed by presetting the initial voltages, V_{10} and V_{20}, across the integrator condensers before starting. When the switch is then closed, the solution $x(t)$ appears at the output terminal (3).

PROBLEMS

5.1 A feedback amplifier is to be constructed from a three-stage RC-coupled amplifier to provide a total gain of 1000. The gain should not vary by more than 1% while the g_m of the individual tubes may vary from 2.2 to 2.5 mA/V. What is the minimum value of the gain of the amplifier *without* feedback?

5.2 In the circuit in Fig. 5.22, R_k is selected so that the tubes operate with $\mu = 100$, $r_p = 75$ kΩ. The signal source has an internal resistance of 10 kΩ, as shown.

(a) What is the maximum value of R_f for which the circuit will operate stably? (Neglect phase shifts in the coupling and decoupling networks.)

(b) When R_f is half the value found in (a), what are the gain and the effective input and output impedances of the amplifier?

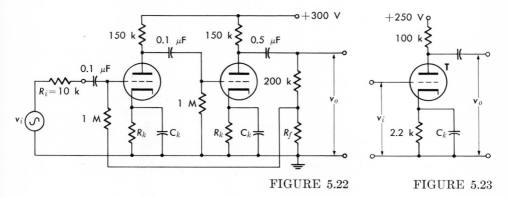

FIGURE 5.22   FIGURE 5.23

5.3 Find the midfrequency gain of the amplifier in Fig. 5.23 when the tube (T) is $\frac{1}{2}$12AU7, $\frac{1}{2}$12AT7, or $\frac{1}{2}$12AX7, and C_k is very large. Compare the relative gain of the three amplifiers under this condition with that when C_k is absent.

5.4 The three RC-coupled amplifier stages A_1, A_2, and A_3 in Fig. 5.24 each provide a midfrequency gain of 50; A_1 and A_3 have a lower 3-db cutoff frequency f_l of 10 cps

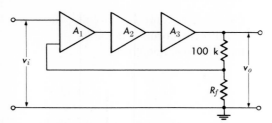

FIGURE 5.24

and an upper 3-db cutoff frequency f_h of 100 kcps. The voltage divider across the output provides negative series voltage feedback to the input.

(a) For what value of R_f will the over-all gain of the amplifier be 500?

(b) If the actual input impedance of A_1 is 0.5 MΩ, what will be the effective input impedance of the amplifier?

(c) When the actual output impedance of A_3 is 20 kΩ, what will be the effective output impedance of the amplifier?

(d) What is the minimum value of f_l and the maximum value of f_h for stage A_2 for which the amplifier will operate without regeneration?

(e) What is the over-all bandwidth $f_h - f_l$ for the entire amplifier with stage A_2 limited as determined in (d)?

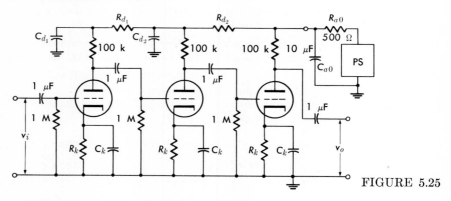

FIGURE 5.25

5.5   In a multistage amplifier, undesired positive feedback can occur through the common power supply (PS), particularly when it has a relatively high internal impedance. This feedback can cause the circuit to break into oscillation at a low frequency, a phenomenon sometimes called "motorboating." This effect can be eliminated by use of "decoupling" networks $R_{d_1}C_{d_1}$, $R_{d_2}C_{d_2}$, as shown in Fig. 5.25. Suppose that the power supply has an effective output resistance $R_{a0} = 500$ Ω shunted by a capacity $C_{a0} = 10$ μF. In the above circuit, the self-bias networks R_kC_k set the operating points of the 12AX7 tubes at $\mu = 100$, $r_p = 62$ kΩ.

(a) What is the midfrequency gain of the whole amplifier?

(b) What is the lower 3-db cutoff frequency of the whole amplifier?

(c) When the decoupling networks $R_{d_1}C_{d_1}$, $R_{d_2}C_{d_2}$ are omitted, at approximately what frequency would the circuit break into "motorboating" oscillation? (Assume that the C_k are infinite, and note that the time constant $R_{a0}C_{a0}$ is much smaller than the coupling constants between the amplifier stages.)

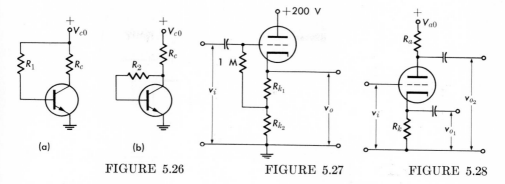

FIGURE 5.26   FIGURE 5.27   FIGURE 5.28

(d) What values of the components in the decoupling networks will ensure that "motorboating" cannot occur even if R_{a0} would rise to 2 kΩ and C_{a0} would fall to 2 μF?

5.6   (a) Compare the performance of the bias circuits in Fig. 5.26(a) and (b) on the stability of the amplifiers with changes in h_{fe} or I_{c0}. Show that for (a), the quiescent collector current

$$I_c \approx h_{fe}(V_{c0}/R_1 + I_{c0}), \qquad \text{while for (b),} \qquad I_c \approx h_{fe}(V_{c0} + I_{c0}R_2)/(R_2 + h_{fe}R_c).$$

(b) Find the current and voltage gain of the amplifier for each arrangement.

5.7   In the cathode-follower circuit shown in Fig. 5.27, $R_{k_1} + R_{k_2} = 10$ kΩ. Find values for R_{k_1} and R_{k_2} to provide maximum peak-to-peak output voltage for a sinusoidal input signal, when the tube is a 12AX7, 12AT7, or 12AU7. Find the output impedance and input impedance for each case. (Assume that the condition for maximum peak-to-peak output voltage is achieved when the tube neither draws grid current on positive excursions nor is cut off on negative excursions.)

5.8   Find the small-signal gain and the output impedance for each output terminal in Fig. 5.28. What is the special characteristic of the two output signals when $R_a = R_k$?

5.9   Compare the advantages and disadvantages of each of the four methods shown in Fig. 5.29 for biasing a cathode follower, relative to their effects on the maximum

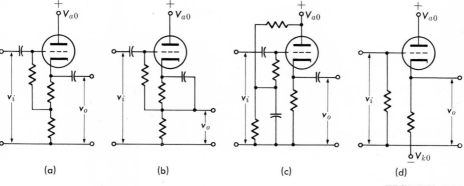

(a)   (b)   (c)   (d)

FIGURE 5.29

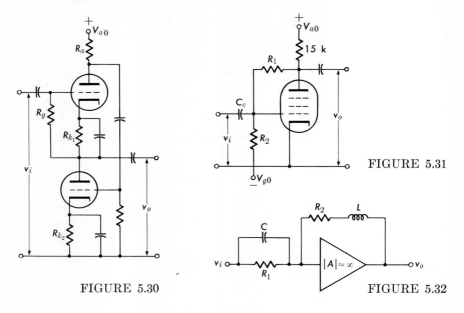

FIGURE 5.31

FIGURE 5.30

FIGURE 5.32

peak-to-peak output signal attainable, on input impedance, output impedance, and frequency response.

5.10   The circuit shown in Fig. 5.30 is sometimes called a "double cathode follower." Show that for identical triodes with high μ, with $R_a \gg r_p$ and $R_{k_1} \approx R_{k_2} \ll R_a$, the output impedance is approximately $1/\mu g_m$.

5.11   Derive an approximate expression for the voltage gain of the amplifier circuit shown in Fig. 5.31 as a function of frequency for various values of R_1 and R_2, assuming both much larger than 15 kΩ. Assume that for different values of R_1 and R_2, V_{g0} is adjusted to keep the g_m of the pentode constant at 5 mA/V. Consider in particular the limiting cases $R_1 \gg R_2$ and $R_1 \ll R_2$. Assume that the input signal is derived from a signal generator of internal impedance R_i.

5.12   Derive a general expression for v_o in terms of v_i and the parameters given in Fig. 5.32. Show that for $v_i = V_{i0} \sin \omega t$, the output voltage is exactly 90° out of phase with the input voltage when $\omega = \sqrt{R_2/LCR_1}$.

REFERENCES

Bode, H. W., *Network Analysis and Feedback Amplifier Design*, van Nostrand, 1959.

Korn, G. A. and T. M., *Electronic Analog Computers*, McGraw-Hill, 1956.

Landee, R. W., D. C. Davis, and A. P. Albrecht, *Electronics Designers Handbook*, McGraw-Hill, 1957, Chapters 18 and 19.

Smith, O. J. M., *Feedback Control Systems* (mathematical), McGraw-Hill, 1958.

Chapter 6

SPECIAL AMPLIFIER CIRCUITS

6.1 INADEQUACIES OF *RC*-COUPLED AMPLIFIERS

In the preceding chapters we concentrated almost exclusively on the behavior of the *RC*-coupled voltage amplifier since this is certainly the most important single amplifier configuration, and a detailed knowledge of its characteristics and limitations is essential for any understanding of complex circuits. However, simple *RC*-coupled circuits cannot fulfill all the functions required of electronic amplifiers. In particular, they are limited in the following respects.

1. *Bandwidth.* Reproduction of the fast signals encountered, for instance, in nuclear physics and radar requires amplifiers of extraordinarily broad bandwidths, larger than achievable with simple *RC*-coupling.

2. *High-frequency operation.* Communication of intelligence over large distances requires that the signals be radiated from one point to another. For efficiency, the antennas required must be of the order of the wavelength of the transmitted signal. Thus the intelligence must be translated to a high frequency, in the range of 0.5–500 Mcps, to keep the antennas at a reasonable size. Because of the effects of parallel capacities, *RC*-coupled amplifiers are useless over most of this range.

3. *Low-frequency operation.* It is frequently necessary to amplify signals of extremely low frequency, of 0.1 cps or even less. The requirement of a series blocking condenser in *RC*-coupled amplifiers makes them useless for frequencies of much less than 1 cps.

4. *Power amplification.* *RC*-coupled amplifiers are inefficient for applications where power must be delivered to a load since, unless the load can be connected directly in the anode or collector circuit, much power is wasted in the resistors which must be present in the output circuit. In addition, there is no provision for impedance matching to optimize power transfer to the load.

Special amplifier circuits have been developed for each of these applications, and we shall review some of them briefly in this chapter. A full treatment of each of these classes of amplifier circuits is beyond the scope of the present book; we shall therefore restrict our attention to a discussion of the general circuit requirements and a few typical examples of each type.

189

6.2 WIDE-BAND (VIDEO) AMPLIFIERS

The transition between "normal" and "wide-band" amplifiers is somewhat arbitrary, but the special designation is usually given to amplifiers with band-widths of at least a few hundred kilocycles per second, corresponding to rise times of a few microseconds or less. From Eqs. (4.21), (4.41), and (4.52), we see that the ratio of the gain to the rise time of a single-stage RC-coupled tube amplifier is

$$\eta = \frac{|A|}{\tau_r} \approx 0.45 \frac{g_m}{C_p}. \tag{6.1}$$

This expression shows that tubes for wide-band amplifiers should have high mutual conductance combined with low interelectrode capacities. In a wide-band amplifier with two or more identical stages in cascade, C_p is the sum of the output capacity C_o and the input capacity C_i of a tube augmented by the capacitance of the tube sockets and the wiring, C_w. For low-power stages C_w will usually lie between 5 and 15 pF; $C_o + C_i$ between 5 and 30 pF. The quality of a wide-band-amplifier tube is often expressed by a figure of merit, $g_m/(C_o+C_i)$. A high value of this quantity is obtained for tubes with small spacing, d_{gk}, between control grid and cathode. Although the grid-to-cathode capacitance C_{gk} increases in inverse proportion to d_{gk}, g_m increases more rapidly, so that g_m/C_{gk} becomes larger as the grid-to-cathode distance is decreased. In Table 6.1 some representative values of the figures of merit of special wide-band tubes are

TABLE 6.1

Figure of Merit of Tubes for Broad-Band Amplifiers

Type	C_i',* pF	C_o, pF	g_m, mA/V	I_a, mA	$g_m/(C_i'+C_o)$,* $(\mu\mathrm{sec})^{-1}$
6AU6	5.5	5.0	5.2	10	420
6AC7	11.0	5.8	9.0	10	430
6AG5	6.5	1.8	5.0	7	490
6CB6	6.5	3.0	6.2	13	510
6AK5	4.0	2.8	5.0	8	570
6EW6	9.9	2.5	14.5	10	850
6688	7.5	3.0	16.6	13	1100
7788	16	3.8	50	35	1700
EFP60†					
(anode)	9	6	25	20	1400
(dynode)	9	11	−20	−16	880

* C_i is usually tabulated for a cold tube (heater off). When the cathode is heated and the tube is drawing its rated current as listed in column 5, there is an additional input capacity $\Delta C_i \approx$ 0.3 to 1 + (0.2 to 0.35)g_m pF which must be added. This term is included in $C_i' = C_i + \Delta C_i$ in column 6.
† Secondary-emission tube; the negative current tabulated under I_a in the last row is the dynode current.

given. High values of the figure of merit can be obtained with secondary-emission tubes: secondary emission provides a considerable gain in mutual conductance without much increase of the parasitic capacitances. The EFP 60 (see Table 6.1) is an example of this. Since mutual conductance increases with anode current, the highest value of the figure of merit is obtained by operation of the tube close to its maximum allowable anode current.

In this section we shall concentrate on techniques for maximizing the bandwidth of vacuum-tube amplifiers. Many of these are also suitable with transistors, but in the latter case it is usually more convenient simply to employ transistors with a high cutoff frequency. Transistors with maximum usable frequencies greater than 10^9 cps are currently available, and the upper limits are steadily increasing as manufacturing techniques improve.

6.2.1   High-frequency compensation

There are several methods for increasing the bandwidth of an RC-coupled amplifier at constant gain. One or more compensation coils with suitable inductances are often incorporated into the coupling network for this purpose. Two possible methods are shown in Figs. 6.1 and 6.2. Figure 6.1 indicates the simple method of *shunt compensation;* a small coil is connected in series with the anode resistor.

The influence of this inductance can be qualitatively understood if we consider its effect on the anode current. After a jump i_a of the anode current, the parasitic capacity C_p initially absorbs the whole amount i_a; as the output signal v_o

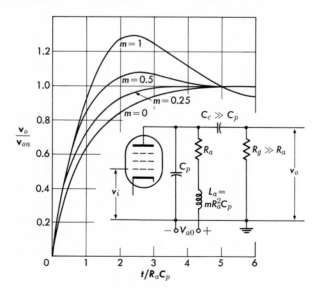

FIG. 6.1.   Transient characteristic of a shunt-compensated amplifier stage.

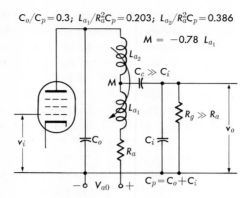

FIG. 6.2.   Coupling network with good transient response.

develops across C_p, an increasing fraction of i_a will flow through R_a so that C_p is charged more slowly. Without the inductance L_a, the fraction of the current through R_a is equal to v_o/R_a; therefore, the current charging C_p will decrease proportionally to $v_{on} - v_o$. Hence, v_o will approach its final value, v_{on}, exponentially. The inductance L_a in a series with R_a initially blocks the current through R_a, so that the whole amount i_a remains available for a longer time for charging C_p. In this way C_p is charged more rapidly. If the inductance L_a is chosen larger than $0.25R_a^2C_p$, at which value the circuit $L_aC_pR_a$ is critically damped, a damped oscillation will be excited in this circuit for each sudden change of anode current. As shown in Fig. 6.1, the output voltage in this case overshoots its final value v_{on}. Sometimes a certain amount of overshoot can be tolerated in order that a shorter rise time be obtained. For shunt compensation the following ratios of gain-to-rise time are found:

$$\text{for } \frac{L_a}{R_a^2C_p} = m = 0.25, \qquad \eta = 0.65\,\frac{g_m}{C_p} \qquad \text{(no overshoot)};$$

$$\text{for } \frac{L_a}{R_a^2C_p} = m = 0.5, \qquad \eta = 0.89\,\frac{g_m}{C_p} \qquad \text{(6.5\% overshoot).}$$

(6.2)

Comparison of these values of η with those obtained without compensation (see Eq. 6.1) shows that they are higher by a factor of 1.4 and 2, respectively.

A further improvement may be obtained by use of coupling networks in which the contributions of C_o and C_i to the parasitic capacitance are separated by another coil. An example of such a coupling network is shown in Fig. 6.2, where a practical value of the ratio $C_o/(C_o + C_i) = 0.3$ has been assumed. For the inductance and resistance values given in the circuit, the figure of merit becomes

$$\eta = 1.4(g_m/C_p), \qquad (6.3)$$

at an overshoot of only 1%.

In order to adjust these networks properly, the values of C_o, C_i, L_{a_1}, and L_{a_2} must be measured accurately; also the ratio of C_o and C_i just quoted must be maintained. Without accurate adjustment and checking with a good wide-band oscilloscope, the advantages of the more complicated coupling networks are often illusory.

Cathode and screen-grid compensation. In Section 4.3.6, we considered the influence of the finite value of cathode or screen bypass condensers on the shape of the output signal after a sudden change of input voltage. As shown in Fig. 4.32, the anode current exhibits a peak, the duration of which is determined by the magnitude of the cathode or screen grid bypass condenser, or both. By choosing a small value for this condenser, the duration of the peak can be adjusted so that it is just sufficient to charge the parasitic capacity more rapidly, reducing the rise time. The highest reduction of the rise time without overshoot is obtained by choosing

$$C_k R_k = C_p R_p. \tag{6.4}$$

An explicit calculation shows that the rise time is then reduced from $\tau_r = 2.2 C_p R_p$ (for $C_k = 0$) to $\tau_r' = 2.2 C_p R_p / (1 + R_k g_m')$.

Cathode or screen-grid compensation does *not* improve the gain/rise-time ratio because negative feedback in the cathode circuit reduces the gain by the same factor as the rise time. Cathode compensation is most useful in obtaining a large output signal from a tube with a small maximum anode dissipation: A certain desired rise time can be obtained at a larger value of the anode resistor, and therefore a larger signal can be obtained at a given maximum anode dissipation.

Cathode compensation works properly only if the input signal does not drive the tube to cutoff or into the positive grid region. When, for instance, the tube is nearly cut off by the input signal, the mutual conductance becomes very small and the expected reduction of rise time is not achieved.

Screen-grid compensation (choose $C_{g_2} R_{g_2} = C_p R_p$) in principle has the same result as cathode compensation; when there is an unbypassed screen grid, a reduction of the rise time by a factor of about $1 + R_{g_2}/r_{i g_2}$ is obtained. In practice this factor usually cannot be made as large as that obtained with cathode compensation.

6.2.2 Low-frequency compensation

In capacitively coupled amplifiers, a sufficiently long decay or droop time τ_d following a sudden voltage change at the input often can be obtained only if we choose very large coupling condensers. If we wish to avoid this, low-frequency compensation can be used. A suitable method is shown in Fig. 6.3. If we choose R_1 large compared with the anode resistor R_a and take

$$R_a C_a = R_g C_c, \tag{6.5}$$

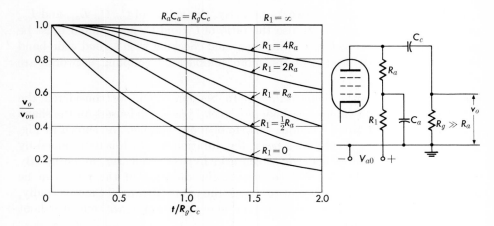

FIG. 6.3. Improvement in the droop response of the transient characteristic by a network R_1C_a in the anode supply lead.

the coupling capacitor C_c and the bypass capacitor C_a are charged equally rapidly after a current jump i_a, because i_a is distributed between R_a and R_g in a constant ratio. It follows that the output voltage across R_g remains constant so long as i_a remains constant.

In practice, R_1 cannot be chosen larger than a few times R_a, for otherwise the dc anode voltage would be too low or an abnormally high supply voltage V_{a0} would be needed. Figure 6.3 indicates the behavior of v_o for several values of R_1. It is apparent that considerable improvement is obtained for reasonable values of R_1. In particular, the initial slope of the characteristic is always zero, a consequence of condition (6.5). Without compensation, the initial slope is always negative: $(dv_o/dt)_{t=0} = -v_{on}/R_gC_g$.

Besides providing an improved transient response, R_1C_a at the same time furnishes an extra filter for the supply voltage.

6.2.3 Distributed amplifiers

As shown in Section 6.2.1, the gain/rise-time ratio, $\eta = A/\tau_r$, of a stage of a wide-band amplifier depends on the figure of merit of the tube and on the method of interstage coupling. However, even with the most perfect high-frequency compensation and the best available tubes, the largest value of η that can be achieved is about one per nanosecond. This means that the gain of a single stage with a rise time of 1 nsec will not exceed unity appreciably. Since, as noted in Section 4.4, the rise time of a cascade amplifier with identical stages increases in proportion to the square root of the number of stages, it is impossible to construct an amplifier with a rise time of the order of 1 nsec (corresponding to a bandwidth of a few hundred Mcps) and with an appreciable voltage gain (say 100) simply by cascading stages. Such an amplifier can be made, however,

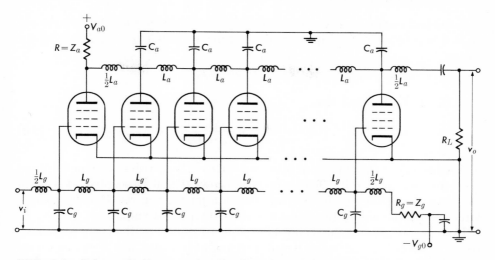

FIG. 6.4. Schematic diagram of a distributed amplifier. The delay line in the grid circuit is terminated in its characteristic impedance Z_g; the delay line in the anode circuit is terminated at the left in its characteristic impedance Z_a, at the right in a load resistance R_L.

by a different method of connecting tubes, as shown in Fig. 6.4. This type of amplifier is called a *distributed amplifier*, because the input and output capacities of the tubes are distributed along two lumped constant delay lines, one in the grid circuit and one in the anode circuit. The inductive elements of the lines are small coils between the grids and the anodes, chosen in such a way that the grid and the anode lines have the same delay per section:

$$\tau_d = 1/\sqrt{L_g C_g} = 1/\sqrt{L_a C_a}. \tag{6.6}$$

In this way, the mutual conductances of the tubes add, but not the spurious capacities that are distributed along the lines since their influence is compensated by the inductances. Thus, a total gain larger than unity can be obtained even though the gain per tube is smaller than unity.

A pulse applied to the grid line at the left propagates to the right and passes every grid consecutively, causing an anode current pulse in each tube. These current pulses divide into two equal components, those propagating to the right, which add with the proper timing, and those propagating to the left, which are completely absorbed in the resistor $R_a = Z_a = \sqrt{L_a/C_a}$ (= characteristic impedance of the anode line). The current propagating to the right reaches a load resistance R_L. It is sensible to choose $R_L = Z_g = \sqrt{L_g/C_g}$, the input resistance of an identical stage that is following next. In this case, the voltage gain for a stage with n tubes is

$$|A| = \frac{2Z_g}{Z_a + Z_g} \frac{n g_m Z_a}{2}. \tag{6.7}$$

A lumped constant delay line of the type used here has a cutoff frequency, $f_h \approx 1/\pi\sqrt{LC}$, corresponding to a rise time $\tau_r \approx 0.3/f_h \approx \sqrt{LC}$. Substituting

$$\tau_r = \sqrt{L_g C_g} = \sqrt{L_a C_a}$$

into Eq. (6.7), we find that

$$\eta = \frac{|A|}{\tau_r} \approx n\frac{g_m}{C_a + C_g}. \tag{6.8}$$

This value is just the number of tubes per stage of the distributed amplifier times the tube figure of merit. This expression shows that it is possible, at least in principle, to obtain any desired value of gain for a given rise time by using a large enough number of tubes in a one-stage distributed amplifier.

However, in general this is not the most economical method. It is actually better to cascade a number of distributed amplifier stages, and it can be shown that the total number of tubes required is minimal when the gain per stage is $|A| = \epsilon = 2.72$. Still, this number will often be considerable. For example, if we want to construct an amplifier with $|A| = 100$ and $\tau_r = 2$ nsec with 6AK5's [figure of merit $= 500\ \mu\mathrm{sec}^{-1}$], we will require at least 28 tubes.

6.3   HIGH-FREQUENCY TUNED AMPLIFIERS

The natural high-frequency limit of an RC-coupled amplifier imposed by the distributed capacity C_p can be very easily overcome simply by the connection of an inductance and a condenser in parallel with C_p, forming a resonant circuit as the anode or collector load. A variety of possible connections is shown in Fig. 6.5.

The tuned-amplifier circuit will operate over a band of frequencies centered about the resonant frequency of the LC-circuit, the bandwidth being determined

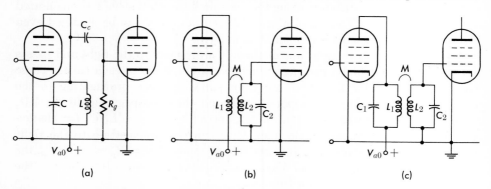

FIG. 6.5.   High-frequency tuned amplifiers. (a) Single-tuned circuit, (b) single-tuned circuit with transformer coupling, (c) double-tuned circuit with transformer coupling.

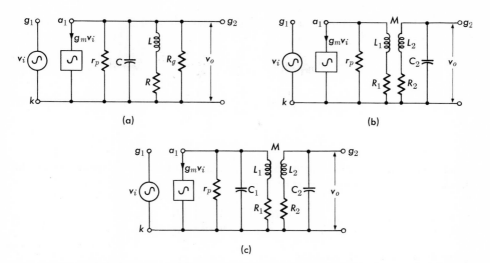

(a) (b)

(c)

FIG. 6.6. Equivalent circuits of tuned amplifiers. (a) Single-tuned circuit, (b) single-tuned with transformer coupling, (c) double-tuned with transformer coupling.

by the effective Q (for *quality*) of the load. The gain will also depend on the value of Q and, when coupled circuits are used, on the mutual inductance between the primary and secondary. Both of these parameters will influence the effective parallel impedance Z_{pe} across the output of the amplifier. In general, Z_{pe} will be a function of frequency and, by analogy with the RC-coupled amplifier, the small-signal gain of the circuit will be simply

$$A(\omega) \approx -g_m Z_{pe}(\omega). \tag{6.9}$$

Since g_m is fixed by the operating point of the amplifier tube or transistor, the gain depends only on the characteristics of the resonant coupling network. These can be readily derived from the equivalent circuits shown in Fig. 6.6.

6.3.1 Single-tuned circuit

In a single-tuned circuit, as shown in Fig. 6.6(a),

$$\frac{1}{Z_{pe}} = \frac{1}{r_p} + \frac{1}{R_g} + \frac{1}{Z_t}, \tag{6.10}$$

where Z_t is the impedance of the resonant "tank" circuit:

$$Z_t = \frac{(-j/\omega C)(R + j\omega L)}{R + j(\omega L - 1/\omega C)}, \tag{6.11}$$

in which C includes *all* the parallel capacities in the circuit and R is the coil resistance. It is convenient to define the three parameters:

$$\omega_0 = 2\pi f_0 = \frac{1}{\sqrt{LC}},\tag{6.12a}$$

$$Q = \frac{\omega_0 L}{R} = \frac{1}{R\omega_0 C} = \frac{1}{R}\sqrt{L/C},\tag{6.12b}$$

$$\delta = \frac{\omega}{\omega_0} - 1.\tag{6.12c}$$

Substituting these values into (6.11), we can express the impedance of the "tank" circuit in the reduced form

$$Z_t = \frac{RQ^2(1 + \delta - j/Q)}{1 + \delta + j\delta Q(2 + \delta)}.\tag{6.13}$$

At resonance, $\delta = 0$, so that

$$Z_{t_\text{res}} = RQ^2(1 - j/Q) \approx RQ^2 = \omega_0 LQ\tag{6.14}$$

for the usual case of practical importance, $Q \geq 10$. Combining (6.9), (6.10), and (6.14), we obtain

$$A_\text{res} = \frac{-g_m\omega_0 LQ}{1 + \omega_0 LQ/r_p + \omega_0 LQ/R_g}.\tag{6.15}$$

We can also define the effective Q of the whole circuit as

$$Q_e = \frac{Q}{1 + \omega_0 LQ/r_p + \omega_0 LQ/R_g}.\tag{6.16}$$

Then

$$A_\text{res} = -g_m\omega_0 LQ_e.\tag{6.17}$$

The complete expression for the gain as a function of frequency near resonance can readily be found by substitution of (6.13) into (6.10). For small values of the frequency deviation δ and high values of Q_e, this reduces to

$$A(\omega) = \frac{A_\text{res}}{(1 + j2\delta Q_e)},\tag{6.18}$$

with an amplitude

$$|A(\omega)| = \frac{|A_\text{res}|}{\sqrt{1 + (2\delta Q_e)^2}}\tag{6.19a}$$

and a phase angle

$$\phi = -\tan^{-1} 2\delta Q_e.\tag{6.19b}$$

The general form of Eq. (6.19) is shown in Fig. 6.7.

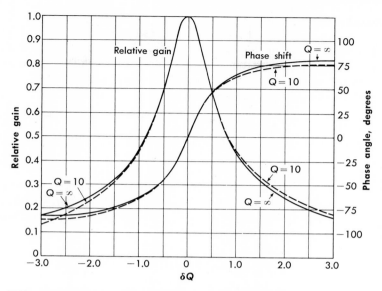

FIG. 6.7.   Relative gain and phase shift for single-tuned amplifier.

The bandwidth Δf between 3-db points, determined by the condition $2\,\delta Q_e = 1$, is evidently

$$\Delta f = f_0/Q_e. \tag{6.20}$$

6.3.2 Single-tuned transformer coupling

This circuit, shown in Fig. 6.6(b), is easily solved for the common case where the plate resistance r_p is much larger than the impedance of the transformer primary, $R_1 + j\omega L_1$. Then the gain is

$$A = \frac{-g_m M/C_2}{R_2 + j(\omega L_2 - 1/\omega C_2) + \omega^2 M^2/r_p}, \tag{6.21}$$

where M is the mutual inductance, and L_2, C_2, and R_2 are the inductance, capacity, and resistance, respectively, of the second tuned circuit. Defining $Q_2 = \omega_0 L_2/R_2$, we have

$$A_{\mathrm{res}} = \frac{-g_m \omega_0 M Q_2}{1 + \omega_0^2 M^2/r_p R_2} = -g_m \omega_0 M Q_e, \tag{6.22}$$

where $Q_e = Q_2/(1 + \omega_0^2 M^2/r_p R_2)$. In reduced form, as before, the frequency dependence of the gain is simply

$$A(\omega) = A_{\mathrm{res}}/(1 + j2\,\delta Q_e). \tag{6.23}$$

Thus Eqs. (6.17) and (6.18) are still valid with the new definitions of Q_e and A_{res}.

6.3.3 Double-tuned circuit

To simplify the analysis of this type of circuit, which is shown in Fig. 6.6(c), it is assumed that the plate resistance is large compared with the reactance of the primary tuning capacity C_1. For practical pentode amplifiers this is usually the case. Then the gain can be shown to be

$$A = -\frac{g_m M}{j\omega C_1 C_2} \frac{1}{[R_1 + j(\omega L_1 - 1/\omega C_1)][R_1 + j(\omega L_2 - 1/\omega C_2)] + \omega^2 M^2}.$$

(6.24)

Ordinarily both circuits are tuned to the same resonant frequency $\omega_0 = 1/\sqrt{L_1 C_1} = 1/\sqrt{L_2 C_2}$. Defining $Q_1 = \omega_0 L_1/R_1$ and $Q_2 = \omega_0 L_2/R_2$ and introducing the coefficient of coupling $k = M/\sqrt{L_1 L_2}$ of the primary and secondary circuits, we find, for the mid-band gain ($\omega = \omega_0$),

$$A_M = -\frac{j g_m k (Q_1 Q_2)^{3/2}\sqrt{R_1 R_2}}{1 + k^2 Q_1 Q_2}.$$

(6.25)

This expression has a maximum for

$$k = k_c = 1/\sqrt{Q_1 Q_2}.$$

(6.26)

When k has this value, the circuit is said to be *critically coupled*.

The higher the circuit Q's, the smaller the coupling needed for maximum gain. For $Q_1 = Q_2 = 100$, for example, $k_c = 0.01$, which means that the coils should be placed at some distance from each other to achieve critical coupling.

For high circuit Q's, the gain for frequencies near ω_0 is

$$A = \frac{A_m}{[1 - 4\delta^2 Q_1 Q_2/(1 + k^2 Q_1 Q_2)] + j[2\delta(Q_1 + Q_2)/(1 + k^2 Q_1 Q_2)]}.$$

(6.27)

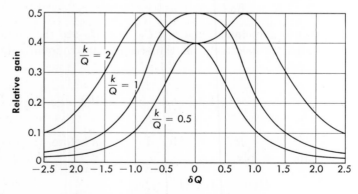

FIG. 6.8. Relative gain for double-tuned amplifier: $k/Q = 2$, overcoupled; $k/Q = 1$, critically coupled; $k/Q = 0.5$, undercoupled.

The absolute value of this expression can have more than one maximum since it contains a function in which δ^4 is the highest power of δ. A simple algebraic analysis shows that only one maximum occurs so long as the coefficient of coupling is kept below the value

$$k = k_t = \sqrt{\tfrac{1}{2}(1/Q_1^2 + 1/Q_2^2)}. \tag{6.28}$$

When k has this value, the circuit is said to be *transitionally coupled*. In this case, the amplifier has the flattest possible passband. For any increase of k above k_t, the passband exhibits two peaks.

A comparison of Eqs. (6.28) and (6.26) shows that $k_c = k_t$ if the Q's of the primary and secondary circuits are equal.

The frequency characteristic of an amplifier stage with double-tuned transformer coupling is shown in Fig. 6.8 for three different values of k/Q, assuming that $Q = Q_1 = Q_2$.

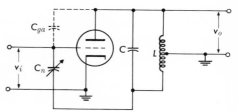

FIG. 6.9.   Neutralization of a triode amplifier by feedback of opposite phase signal to grid.

6.3.4   Use of triodes in high-frequency tuned amplifiers

In the preceding analysis, all the examples involved pentodes as the active elements. This choice was by no means arbitrary. Triodes generally have lower values of r_p and hence are less effective than pentodes in transformer-coupled circuits. However, a far more important limitation in the use of triodes stems from the large value of the parasitic capacity C_{ga} between anode and grid, which introduces feedback between input and output. At frequencies different from the resonant frequency of the tank circuit, the feedback through C_{ga} may become *regenerative* if it contains an in-phase component. If $|\beta A_0|$ becomes greater than unity, the circuit will oscillate. To overcome this problem, an additional small condenser can be connected between the grid and a point where the output signal is 180° out of phase with that at the anode, effectively canceling the signal fed back through C_{ga}. This procedure is called *neutralization* and is shown schematically in Fig. 6.9. Capacitive neutralization works well for narrow-band amplifiers, but it is difficult to achieve reliable stable operation for wide-band circuits. In most cases, use of pentodes affords a better solution.

However, as will be discussed in Chapter 10, triodes offer one distinct advantage over pentodes for amplifying very small signals; they introduce far less *noise* into the circuit. For cases where minimum-noise high-frequency amplifiers must be used, as in the input stages of high-sensitivity radio or television

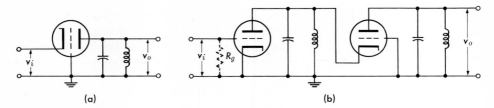

FIG. 6.10.   High-frequency triode amplifiers which require little or no neutralization (bias voltages not shown). (a) Grounded-grid amplifier, (b) cascode amplifier.

receivers, it may be essential to use triodes. There are two special triode circuits which are particularly adaptable to such use: the *grounded-grid amplifier* and the *cascode amplifier*, which are shown in Fig. 6.10.

The grounded-grid amplifier provides a high gain but a very low input impedance ($Z_i \approx 1/g_m$); thus it requires a matching transformer for connection to a high-impedance signal source. The cascode amplifier provides both a high gain and a high input impedance. In the cascode circuit the first triode acts as an ordinary grounded-cathode amplifier and the second, which forms the load for the first, as a grounded-grid amplifier; the voltage amplification between the grid and anode of the first tube is thus kept small, so that neutralization of C_{ga} is simple or unnecessary.

In the grounded-grid circuit, the grid screens the anode from the cathode; moreover, the loop gain $|\beta A_0|$ of a feedback loop from anode to cathode is always smaller than unity. Provided that the control grid is effectively grounded, no regeneration should occur in this type of circuit. It must be noted, however, that the effectiveness of the grounding may be impaired at very high frequencies because of the distributed inductance of the internal grid leads. Special tubes with low-impedance grid connections are available for grounded-grid vhf-amplifiers. The equivalent circuits for the cascode and grounded-grid amplifiers

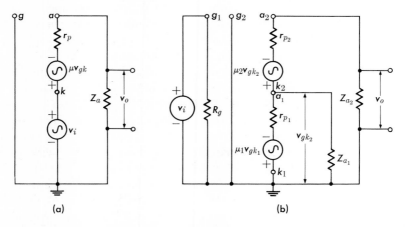

FIG. 6.11.   Equivalent circuits for (a) grounded grid amplifier, (b) cascode amplifier.

are shown in Fig. 6.11. From these we may readily determine the small-signal characteristics.

Grounded grid

Gain:
$$A = \frac{Z_a(\mu + 1)}{r_p + Z_a};$$

Input impedance: $Z_i = \dfrac{r_p + Z_a}{\mu + 1} \approx \dfrac{1}{g_m},$ for $r_p \gg Z_a, \mu \gg 1.$

$$(6.29)$$

Cascode

Gain:
$$A \approx \frac{-\mu_1(1 + \mu_2)Z_{a_2}}{(1 + \mu_1)r_{p_1} + r_{p_2} + Z_{a_2}}, \quad \text{for} \quad \frac{1}{g_{m_2}} \ll Z_{a_1},$$

$$\approx -g_m Z_{a_2}, \text{ for identical tubes, } \mu \gg 1,\ Z_a \ll (1 + \mu)r_p;$$

$$(6.30)$$

Input impedance: $Z_i \approx Z_g{}^*.$

From the form of (6.30) it is apparent that a cascode amplifier with identical tubes is equivalent to a pentode with a very high amplification factor $\mu' = \mu(\mu + 1)$ and a plate resistance $r_p' = (\mu + 2)r_p$. However, the cascode provides the low-noise characteristics of the triode, without neutralization, and is therefore ideally suited to applications in which pentodes or transistors would produce excessive noise.

6.4 LOW-FREQUENCY TUNED AMPLIFIERS

For some applications it is desirable to amplify only a very narrow band of frequencies centered about a relatively low frequency. For such uses, LC-circuits are often inadequate since it is difficult to achieve sufficiently high Q-values at

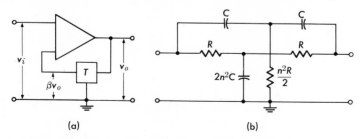

(a)　　　　　　　　　　　　　　　　(b)

FIG. 6.12. Low-frequency tuned amplifier with RC negative feedback circuit: (a) circuit arrangement with feedback network T; (b) twin-T feedback network.

---

* In the cascode circuit, Z_g is the effective *parallel* impedance in the grid-cathode circuit, usually that of a parallel LC-circuit. At very high frequencies the tube will offer an effective resistance parallel to this circuit caused by electron transit-time effects (see also Section 10.3).

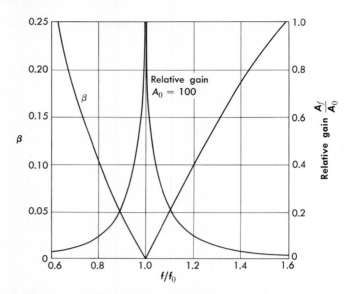

FIG. 6.13.   Feedback fraction and relative gain for a low-frequency tuned amplifier with twin-T feedback network; gain without feedback $A_0 = 100$.

low frequencies while maintaining a reasonable size of components. It is usually simpler to employ RC feedback networks, such as the twin-T circuit shown in Fig. 6.12. Here the network provides negative feedback at all frequencies *except* its balance frequency, so that the feedback characteristics and amplifier response are as shown in Fig. 6.13. For the twin-T feedback network, the balance frequency is

$$f_0 = 1/2\pi nRC, \qquad (6.31)$$

where n is as defined in the figure. The effective bandwidth depends on the gain, A_0, of the amplifier without feedback. For a high-gain amplifier, the effective Q of the circuit is $\approx A_0/4$ for $n = 1$ and $\approx A_0/5$ for $n = \frac{1}{2}$ or 2.

6.5   DIFFERENCE AMPLIFIERS

A difference amplifier has two inputs, to which separate signals v_{i_1} and v_{i_2} may be applied, and it may have either one or two outputs from which one or two signals, v_{o_1} and v_{o_2}, may be derived. In an ideal difference amplifier only the amplified difference of v_{i_1} and v_{i_2} appears at the output(s). If there are two output terminals, the signals at these terminals have opposite signs.

Commonly used difference-amplifier circuits are shown in Fig. 6.14. To a first approximation, the gain of either the tube or transistor circuit is approximately the same as that of a single-stage amplifier with the same anode or

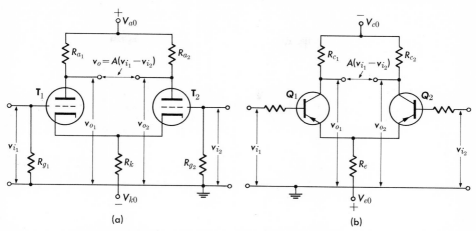

FIG. 6.14. Basic difference amplifier circuit. (a) With triodes, (b) with transistors.

collector resistor, if opposite signals, v_{i_1} and $v_{i_2} = -v_{i_1}$, are applied to the inputs:

$$A = v_{o_1}/v_{i_1} = v_{o_2}/v_{i_2} = -g_m R'_a \, [R'_a = R_a r_p/(R_a + r_p)]$$

for the triode circuit and

$$A \approx g_m^{(t)} R_c$$

for the transistor circuit (provided that $R_c \ll 1/h_{oe}$; $g_m^{(t)} = h_{fe}/h_{ie}$).

The output difference signal v_o becomes

$$v_o = v_{o_1} - v_{o_2} = A(v_{i_1} - v_{i_2}).$$

There will also be a residual signal at the output(s) if the two input signals have zero difference, that is, if $v_{i_1} = v_{i_2}$. This signal is termed the *common-mode* signal. The ratio of the desired output signal to this (undesired) common-mode signal is called the *common-mode rejection ratio* (F), which should be infinite in an ideal difference amplifier.

For equal input signals the inputs as well as the outputs may be tied together, and the two tubes or transistors may be replaced by one imaginary unit with a cathode (emitter) resistance $R_k(R_e)$, an anode (collector) resistance $\frac{1}{2}R_a(\frac{1}{2}R_c)$, and a mutual conductance $2g_m(2g_m^{(t)})$.

The gain of such a unit is

$$A_c \approx \frac{-R'_a g_m}{1 + 2g_m R_k} \qquad \text{(tube)}, \tag{6.32a}$$

$$A_c \approx \frac{-R_c g_m^{(t)}}{1 + 2g_m^{(t)} R_e} \qquad \text{(transistor)}. \tag{6.32b}$$

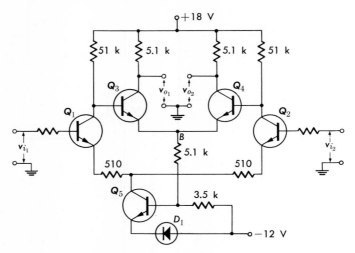

FIG. 6.15. Detailed circuit of a two-stage difference amplifier with common anode feedback (from General Electric Transistor Manual: $Q_1 - Q_2$ and $Q_3 - Q_4$-GE 2N2652 matched pairs; $Q_5 - D_1$-GE RA2B reference amplifier).

This is the common-mode gain; by definition the common-mode rejection ratio is

$$F = A/A_c = 1 + 2g_m R_k \qquad \text{(tube)}, \tag{6.33a}$$

$$F = A/A_c = 1 + 2g_m^{(t)} R_e \qquad \text{(transistor)}. \tag{6.33b}$$

Example. Consider a 12AX7 tube connected as in Fig. 6.14(a). Choose

$$V_{a0} = -V_{k0} = 300 \text{ V}, \qquad R_k = 150 \text{ k}\Omega,$$

and

$$R_{a_1} = R_{a_2} = 100 \text{ k}\Omega.$$

The choice of R_k determines the tube current; per section, we have $I_a \approx \frac{1}{2}V_{k0}/R_k = 1$ mA. From the tube data we find that $g_m \approx 1.4$ mA/V for this value of the anode current, and therefore $F \approx 420$. Practical values of F may be smaller than this because our tacit assumption that the tubes draw equal currents and that the tube current ratio is independent of the common-mode signal is never exactly fulfilled. We may try to achieve tube equality as well as possible by careful selection.

If much larger values of F are required, $R_k(R_e)$ may be replaced by a circuit or circuit element that represents a high effective resistance at a moderate voltage drop, for example a pentode, a triode with current feedback, or a transistor with current feedback.

Another very effective method of common-mode rejection is illustrated by the circuit shown in Fig. 6.15. This is a two-stage differential transistor amplifier in which the common-mode output signal from the second stage is applied to a reference amplifier (Q_5, D_1), which constitutes the emitter resistance of the first stage. Thus, the common-mode output signal is strongly fed back, while the desired differential output signal is not fed back because it leaves point B at a constant voltage.

This circuit will provide a common-mode rejection ratio $F \sim 10^5$. At the same time, the principle of common-mode feedback yields a large reduction of the temperature drift (see also Section 6.6.2).

In the circuits of Fig. 6.14 the signal can also be applied to only one of the inputs while the voltage at the other input is kept constant ($v_{i_2} = 0$). This is a widely used method for deriving two signals with opposite signs from a single input signal. Such signals are needed, for example, for symmetrical drive of the deflection plates of a cathode-ray tube.

Expressions for the output signals v_{o_1} and v_{o_2} are readily derived when we note that the same output signals would be obtained if opposite signals, $\frac{1}{2}v_{i_1}$ and $\frac{1}{2}v_{i_2} = -\frac{1}{2}v_{i_1}$, are supplied to $T_1(Q_1)$ and $T_2(Q_2)$ simultaneously with a common-mode signal, $\frac{1}{2}v_{i_1} = \frac{1}{2}v_{i_2}$. The total output voltages are

$$v_{o_1} = \tfrac{1}{2}Av_{i_1} + \tfrac{1}{2}A_cv_{i_1} = \tfrac{1}{2}Av_{i_1}(1 + 1/F) \tag{6.34a}$$

and

$$v_{o_2} = -\tfrac{1}{2}Av_{i_1} + \tfrac{1}{2}A_cv_{i_1} = -\tfrac{1}{2}Av_{i_1}(1 - 1/F). \tag{6.34b}$$

For infinitely large F, v_{o_1} and v_{o_2} have equal amplitudes and opposite sign. If F becomes smaller, v_{o_2} decreases while v_{o_1} increases; the circuit is no longer quite symmetrical. When the signal applied to $T_1(Q_1)$ is taken only from the output of $T_2(Q_2)$, the circuit is called a *cathode- (or emitter-) coupled amplifier*. In such amplifiers, the anode (collector) resistor of $T_1(Q_1)$ can be omitted (see Fig. 6.16). The gain of this circuit is readily derived from Eq. (6.34b), with $A = -g_mR'_{a_2}$ (or $= -g_m^{(t)}R_{c_2}$) and F taken from Eq. (6.33a) or (6.33b):

$$A = \frac{v_{o_2}}{v_{i_1}} = R'_{a_2}g_m \frac{R_kg_m}{1 + 2R_kg_m} \qquad \text{(tube)}, \tag{6.35a}$$

$$A \approx R_{c_2}g_m^{(t)} \frac{R_eg_m^{(t)}}{1 + 2R_eg_m^{(t)}} \qquad \text{(transistor)}. \tag{6.35b}$$

For values of R_kg_m (or $R_eg_m^{(t)}$) much larger than one, A approaches $\frac{1}{2}R'_{a_2}g_m$ (or $\frac{1}{2}R_{c_2}g_m^{(t)}$).

This type of amplifier provides good separation between input and output signals and no sign reversal. Its drift properties are much better than those of a single-tube amplifier stage (see also Section 6.6.2).

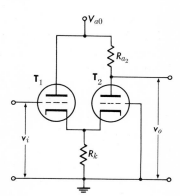

FIG. 6.16. Principle of cathode-coupled amplifier.

6.6   DIRECT-COUPLED AMPLIFIERS

6.6.1   Interstage coupling

For amplification at extremely low frequencies with a normal cascade vacuum-tube amplifier, the stages must be coupled by elements that will conduct a dc-current. The most obvious method, simply a direct-wire connection from the anode of each stage to the grid of the following stage, is not often used because the cathodes of the stages must then be at progressively higher dc-levels, which complicates the construction of a power supply for such an amplifier. Instead, the grid of the next stage is connected to the anode of the previous stage by a voltage divider, the bottom of which is returned to a negative voltage V_{g0}. The grid bias can be adjusted by a proper choice of the ratio R_1/R_2 or V_{g0}. Various arrangements are shown in Fig. 6.17. All cathodes can now be tied to the same base voltage, but the gain is reduced by a factor of $R_2/(R_1 + R_2)$, assuming that $(R_1 + R_2) \gg R_a$. To increase the effective value of R_2, this resistor can be replaced by a tube, as indicated in Fig. 6.17(b). The tube acts as a differential resistance, r_2, much larger than the resistance $R_2 \approx R_1 V_{g0}/V_{a0}$ of a normal resistor.

In some cases, R_1 is replaced by a special circuit element E of small differential resistance r_1, but providing a considerable voltage drop, as shown in Fig. 6.17(c). Such elements may be neon tubes or Zener diodes, for example. For proper operation, some current must be passed through these devices. A battery can also be used as the coupling element. Then R_2 must be omitted, and the anode signal is transmitted without attenuation. In using such special coupling elements, some care must be exercised because of extra noise that may be generated in them and because of possible drift of their operating voltages.

In transistor dc-amplifiers, direct connections between stages are frequently used. One example already encountered is the cascade emitter follower (Fig. 5.12), in which direct connections from the emitter of one stage to the base of the next stage are used.

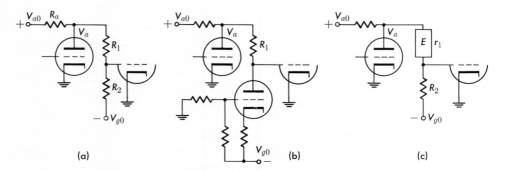

FIG. 6.17.   Some coupling methods for direct-coupled tube amplifiers.

Another possibility is shown in Fig. 6.18. Here
the combination of a pnp- and an npn-transistor
leads to a particularly simple circuit configuration.

Of course, the methods shown for tubes in
Fig. 6.17 can also be used for transistors.

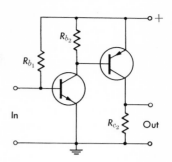

FIG. 6.18. Schematic of npn, pnp direct-coupled
two-stage amplifier.

6.6.2 Drift

In a sensitive dc-amplifier, the output voltage may show considerable changes
even when the input voltage is kept constant. Such *drift* is caused chiefly by
undesired current variations in the first stage. It should be kept small compared
with the desired output signal. To achieve this, special precautions must be
taken in all dc-amplifiers intended for input signals smaller than a few tenths
of a volt.

The following phenomena all contribute to drift: alteration and temperature
dependence of the characteristics of tubes and other components, fluctuations
of heater and supply voltages, and variations of the grid or base current. Changes
in heater voltage have a particularly deleterious influence; an increase of 10%
in the heater voltage of a tube with an indirectly heated cathode has the same
effect as a decrease in the negative grid bias by about 0.1 V. In a normal tube-
amplifier stage without feedback, such a change causes the anode current to
increase by 0.05 to 0.5 mA. A good, but not very economical, method of reducing
this source of drift is stabilization of the heater current.

Grid-current variations contribute to drift because they cause the voltage
drop across the grid resistor to vary. Since high values of the grid resistance are
often used, the grid current should be kept as small as possible. A negative grid
bias of at least about −1.5 V must be used to reduce the Edison current to a
negligible value.

The remaining leakage current can be kept small by use of low anode and
screen-grid voltages as well as a low anode current. It may also be advantageous
to reduce the heater voltage (e.g., to use 5 V instead of 6.3 V). Tubes for the
first stages of sensitive dc-amplifiers should have, in addition to a small grid
current, low microphonics and small low-frequency noise (so-called flicker
noise; see Chapter 10).

As we have already noted, in transistor circuits drift can result from the very
high sensitivity to temperature changes of the operating point, especially for
germanium transistors in the common-emitter configuration. This makes
transistors unsuitable for use in low-level dc-amplifiers unless special precautions
are taken. It has been found that the drift of a good transistor can be made

much smaller than that of a tube if its temperature is kept very constant. However, it is not so easy to obtain the required constancy in practice for a simple transistor cascade amplifier.

The drift of a dc-tube or transistor amplifier can also be reduced by *compensation*, i.e., by incorporation of an element with comparable drift properties as the amplifying element into the circuit in such a way that it counteracts the drift of the amplifying element. The most common method of compensation is the use of a *difference amplifier* (see Section 6.5) with pairs of tubes or transistors selected for about equal drift. In such amplifiers the drift acts as a common-mode signal, and therefore its influence on the output can be reduced by a large factor. In practice, drift reductions by a factor of up to about 100 are obtainable in vacuum-tube difference amplifiers, compared with single-ended stages. In a good amplifier of this type the residual drift, caused by independent changes of both tubes, should not depend on the heater voltage. An example of a stable dc-amplifier is shown in Fig. 6.19. The anode currents of the first stage are equalized by means of R_1. The 12AY7 used in this stage has been especially designed for use in small-signal difference amplifiers.

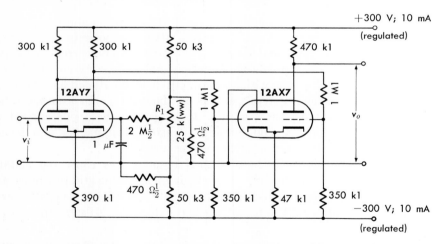

FIG. 6.19. Stable dc-amplifier (from R. W. Landee, D. C. Davis, and A. P. Albrecht, *Electronic Designers Handbook*, McGraw-Hill, 1957).

In spite of all precautions, the drift in tube amplifiers of the type just discussed cannot be made much smaller than a few tenths of a millivolt per hour. Much better results have been obtained with transistorized difference amplifiers. A good selection criterion for transistor pairs in such amplifiers is to choose units that have equal I_c at equal V_{eb}. We keep the temperature of the transistors of a pair equal by mounting them together in a copper block, for instance. For the amplifier circuit shown in Fig. 6.15, an equivalent drift input signal of 0.25 μV/°C is quoted.

6.6.3 Dc-amplifiers using dc-ac conversion

Another method of amplifying small, slowly varying voltages without introducing objectionable drift is by converting the "dc-signal" to an ac-signal with an amplitude proportional to that of the dc-signal. One way of doing this is with the aid of an electromechanical chopper. In essence, such a chopper is a single-pole double-throw switch, the arm of which is rapidly switched back and forth between two contacts when driven from an ac-source. A typical circuit for a chopper amplifier is shown in Fig. 6.20. In this circuit, the chopper arm periodically short-circuits the input signal applied through R to ground. Thus a square-wave voltage results at the input of the two-stage ac-amplifier at the base of transistor Q_1.

The output signal of this amplifier from the collector of Q_2 is applied to a low-pass filter, the input of which is periodically connected to ground by the chopper. The low-pass filter must suppress the ac-signal components at the chopper frequency. In this way a dc output signal v_o is produced that is proportional to the original dc input signal v_i and preserves its sign. The output circuit combined with the chopper constitutes a synchronous rectifier.

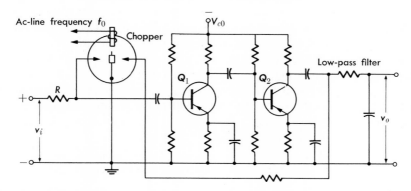

FIG. 6.20.   Chopper dc-amplifier. The grounded center contact converts the input dc to ac on one half-cycle and synchronously rectifies the output ac to dc on the other half-cycle.

The drift of mechanical-chopper amplifiers can be made extremely small; values of about a microvolt per day may be obtained without difficulty, while a drift of a few nanovolts per day can be achieved with a very carefully constructed chopper and associated circuit to minimize thermoelectric potentials.

A serious limitation of the chopper amplifier is its small bandwidth. The highest signal frequency that can be amplified will always be less than about half the chopper frequency, which for an electromechanical chopper cannot be made higher than a few hundred cps. Much higher frequencies can be obtained with transistor choppers. Such choppers are rapidly gaining acceptance; special low-drift transistors are available for them.

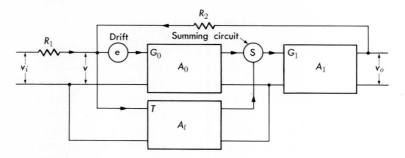

FIG. 6.21.   Block diagram of a chopper-stabilized dc-amplifier.

We can achieve a substantial reduction of drift in dc-feedback amplifiers by combining them with a chopper amplifier, for example in the manner indicated in Fig. 6.21. With such *chopper-stabilized* amplifiers, frequencies much higher than the chopper frequency can be handled. The chopper amplifier serves only to reduce slow variation due to drift; hence it must be capable of amplifying these low frequencies sufficiently. However, the higher-frequency components of the input signal are not amplified by the chopper amplifier.

The chopper-stabilized amplifier of Fig. 6.21 operates as follows: the dc-amplifier to be stabilized (block G_0) has a gain A_0 (>0). It is cascaded through a summing network S to a second dc-amplifier, G_1, with gain A_1 (<0). The sequence G_0, G_1 is fed back through R_2; a fraction, $[R_1/(R_1 + R_2)]v_o = \beta v_o$, of the output voltage is fed back to the input of G_0 ($\beta \ll 1$); T is a chopper amplifier with gain A_t (>0). Its output signal $A_t v$ is added to the output signal of G_0 in S and the sum is fed to G_1. The drift in G_0 is represented by a voltage source e in series with the input. If the total amplifier (G_0, G_1) is adjusted so that $v_o = 0$ when v_i and $e = 0$, then

$$v_o = A_1(A_0(v + e) + A_t v), \qquad (6.36)$$

and if $v_i = 0$, then

$$v = \beta v_o. \qquad (6.37)$$

Elimination of v from these two equations yields

$$v_o \approx -\frac{1}{\beta} \frac{A_0}{A_t + A_0} e, \qquad (6.38)$$

provided that $|\beta A_0 A_1| \gg 1$.

Next, assuming that an input signal v_i is applied while e is kept 0, we obtain

$$v_o \approx -\frac{1}{\beta} v_i. \qquad (6.39)$$

Obviously, this expression gives the gain to be expected for the composite feedback amplifier G_0, G_1.

A comparison of Eqs. (6.38) and (6.39) shows that the amplification of the equivalent drift voltage at the input is $A_0/(A_t + A_0)$ times smaller than that of an input-signal voltage. By making $A_t \gg A_0$, the influence of drift of the amplifier section G_0 can be made as small as we wish. However, A_0 must be made sufficiently large to ensure that the minimum signal at the input of G_1 is much larger than the equivalent drift voltage of this second amplifier section, which has not been taken into account. The lower limit of the drift of a chopper-stabilized amplifier is set by the drift of the chopper amplifier T; its influence is not reduced in the circuit just discussed. Chopper-stabilized dc-amplifiers are frequently used in analog computers, and for this application they have been developed to a high degree of perfection.*

6.7 POWER AMPLIFIERS

At the final stages of most electronic apparatus it inevitably becomes necessary to do something useful with the signals which have been processed by the circuit. This may involve driving a loudspeaker, deflecting an electron beam in a cathode-ray tube, delivering energy to an antenna, or driving a meter or a motor. In all these, the output circuit must deliver *power* to the ultimate load. If the total amount of power to be delivered is somewhat less than that ordinarily dissipated internally in the final tubes or transistors, the power stage may simply be a husky version of a standard voltage amplifier, with the load coupled to the anode or collector circuit, either directly for a high-impedance load or through a cathode or emitter follower for a low-impedance load. However, in many cases the circuit must provide relatively large amounts of power to the load, and special power amplifier circuits can provide far greater over-all efficiency and better linearity.

Power amplifiers almost always employ an output transformer in the final anode or collector circuit, for two good reasons:

1. If the resistance of the transformer primary is small, there is little dc voltage drop between the power supply and the anode or collector. Thus this element can operate with large voltage swings. In addition, little dc-power is wasted in heating the load resistor when there is no input signal.

2. By varying the ratio of primary to secondary turns in the transformer, the internal resistance of the final stage can be matched to that of the load to ensure maximum power transfer.

6.7.1 Efficiency

If the load is properly matched, the efficiency of the circuit, defined as the percentile ratio of the signal power delivered to the load to the dc-power taken from the power supply, depends on the operating point chosen for the amplifier.

---

* For detailed circuits, see G. A. Korn and T. M. Korn, *Electronic Analog Computers*, McGraw-Hill, 1956.

Ignoring the power required for the heaters and previous stages, the maximum efficiency of the final amplifier stage itself is readily calculated* as shown below.

1. Class A

$$\eta_{\max} = 25 \frac{V_{a\max} - V_{a\min}}{V_{a0}} \text{ percent,} \qquad (6.40)$$

where $V_{a\max} - V_{a\min}$ is the peak-to-peak voltage swing at the anode or collector and V_{a0} is the supply voltage. Clearly $\eta_{\max}$ must be less than 50%, and is usually much less, since the peak-to-peak voltage swing cannot exceed twice the supply voltage without driving the tube out of Class A operation. For reasonably linear operation, efficiency values of $\eta \approx 10\text{--}20\%$ are common.

2. Class B

$$\eta_{\max} = 78.5 \frac{V_{a\max}}{V_{a0}} \text{ percent,} \qquad (6.41)$$

where $V_{a\max}$ is the peak value of the voltage swing at the anode or collector, and must be less than the supply voltage V_{a0}. The improvement in efficiency over Class A operation is traceable to the fact that the stage is biased just to cutoff and therefore dissipates no power with no input signal.

3. Class C. Calculation of the efficiency of a Class-C power amplifier requires detailed graphical analysis, since the operation is extremely nonlinear under the conditions where the tube or transistor is driven from far beyond cutoff to the forward conduction region. Because of the large distortion introduced, such amplifiers are useful only with tuned anode or collector circuits. The efficiency is then

$$\eta_{\max} = 100 \frac{V_{s\,\mathrm{rms}} I_{s\,\mathrm{rms}}}{V_{a0} I_{a0}} \text{ percent.} \qquad (6.42)$$

The product $V_{s\,\mathrm{rms}} I_{s\,\mathrm{rms}}$ is the rms signal power delivered to the load, while $V_{a0} I_{a0}$ is the dc-power taken from the power supply. If the tuned load has a very high Q, the rms signal power can equal the dc-power, so that theoretically the Class-C amplifier can achieve an efficiency of 100%. In practice, such amplifiers can provide efficiencies of 90% or even slightly higher; therefore they are very commonly used for power amplifiers in radio and television transmitters.

Since both Class-B and Class-C power amplifiers ordinarily draw grid current, the previous *driver* stage must also be a power amplifier, and the losses in this stage should be included in estimating the over-all circuit efficiency.

---

* These derivations can be found in many standard texts, for example, S. Seely, *Radio Electronics*, Chapters 8, 10, McGraw-Hill, 1956.

6.7.2   Distortion in audio-frequency power amplifiers

As a general rule, the distortion in the signal delivered to the load increases with increasing efficiency of the final power-amplifier stage. Indeed, as noted, for Class-C operation, the distortion is so pronounced that a tuned circuit or other filter must be used to remove undesired components; such amplifiers are therefore unsuitable for broad-band audiofrequency applications.

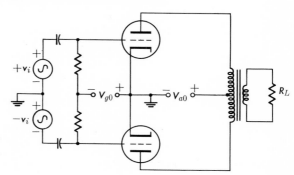

FIG. 6.22. Push-pull amplifier circuit used to minimize even-harmonic distortion.

The distortion introduced by large voltage swings in Class A, AB, or B amplifiers can be minimized by use of the special circuit called a *push-pull* amplifier, shown schematically in Fig. 6.22. The two anodes or collectors are connected to opposite ends of the center-tapped output transformer, and the two inputs are fed with signals of equal magnitude but of opposite phase. The output of each amplifier will contain distortion terms (compare with Eq. 5.6):

$$v_{o_1} = A'_{1_0}(v_{i_1}) + A'_{2_0}(v_{i_1})^2 + A'_{3_0}(v_{i_1})^3 + \cdots,$$

$$v_{o_2} = A'_{1_0}(v_{i_2}) + A'_{2_0}(v_{i_2})^2 + A'_{3_0}(v_{i_2})^3 \cdots$$

$$(6.43)$$

The voltage across the transformer primary, v_o, will now be equal to the difference $v_{o_1} - v_{o_2}$. If $v_{i_1} - v_{i_2} = v_i$, and the amplifiers are exactly matched so that $A'_{1_0} = A'_{1_0}$, $A'_{2_0} = A'_{2_0}$, etc., then

$$v_o = 2(A_{1_0}v_i + A_{3_0}v_i^3 + \cdots). \qquad (6.44)$$

All even harmonic-distortion terms cancel in the output.

The operation may be optimized by the selection of tubes or transistors and an operating point which provide minimum third- and fifth-order distortions; even though the even-order distortion terms may then be quite severe, these cancel in the output. The performance may be further improved by use of negative feedback.

To provide the proper balanced input signals, the push-pull amplifier must be driven by a *phase-inverter* circuit. Some typical phase inverters are shown in

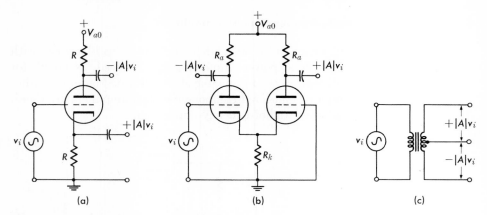

FIG. 6.23. Phase inverters (bias voltages not shown). (a) Inverter using equal resistors in cathode and anode leads, (b) balanced arrangement based on difference amplifier, (c) transformer with center-tapped secondary.

Fig. 6.23. The simplest circuit, shown in Fig. 6.23(a), is a feedback amplifier with equal resistors in the anode and cathode leads. This circuit, while it provides equal signal amplitudes at the two outputs when unloaded, has a lower output impedance at the cathode than at the anode terminal; hence, it will deliver unequal signals to the next stage if the input impedance of this stage is not very high. When this is a problem, the difference-amplifier balanced phase inverter of Fig. 6.23(b) can be used. If the phase inverter must deliver power to the final amplifier, a transformer may be required, as in Fig. 6.23(c).

A special transistor push-pull circuit arrangement which requires only a single-ended unbalanced input can be designed by use of both pnp- and npn-transistors in the configuration shown in Fig. 6.24(a), called a *complementary symmetry* amplifier. This circuit has no vacuum-tube counterpart since it depends, for its operation, on the fact that the current from emitter to collector in pnp-transistors flows in the opposite direction to that in npn-transistors. The two transistors are actually driven in parallel as emitter followers; therefore, no phase inverter is needed. When the transistors are operated near cutoff for high efficiency, the resistor R_i will be small compared with R_b and hence does not materially increase the input resistance. This resistor can therefore be made a potentiometer, as shown, to improve the balance. In this amplifier there is no dc-current flowing through the load R_L; hence, an output transformer does not have to be used unless needed to match impedance for optimum power transfer. Since power transistors have low output impedances as emitter followers, this circuit can be used for directly driving low-impedance loads such as the voice coils of loudspeakers.

There are two major disadvantages to the complementary symmetry amplifier. First, as shown in Fig. 6.24(a), two separate collector power supplies are required. More important, for "high fidelity" applications, the two transistors must have identical gain characteristics to achieve exact cancellation of the

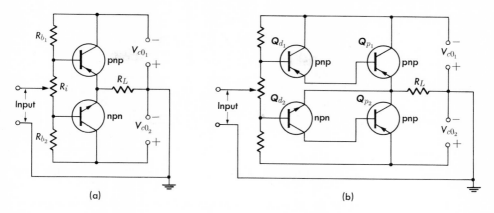

FIG. 6.24. Transistor power amplifiers which operate with an unbalanced input.
(a) Complementary symmetry amplifier using matched pnp and npn final transistors,
(b) quasi-complementary amplifier using final power transistors of the same type.

even-order distortion terms. Since, as discussed in Chapter 3, pnp- and npn-transistors are usually constructed by quite different methods, it is frequently difficult to find properly matched pairs for use in a complementary symmetry power amplifier. Another circuit which utilizes the principle of the complementary symmetry amplifier but employs power transistors of the same type is the quasi-complementary circuit shown in Fig. 6.24(b). In this arrangement the inputs to the power transistors Q_{p_1} and Q_{p_2} are in series rather than in parallel and form the load for the complementary symmetry driver pair Q_{d_1}, Q_{d_2}. Since the driver circuit need deliver only small power to the final amplifier, Q_{d_1} and Q_{d_2} need not be closely matched. Some imbalance in the operation can be expected with this circuit since one of the final power transistors, Q_{p_1}, is connected as an emitter follower and the other, Q_{p_2}, as a common-emitter amplifier; therefore the two will have very different input impedances, as seen from the driver. However, since the complementary symmetry driver has a very low output impedance, the imbalance is small.

PROBLEMS

6.1   Design a two-stage video amplifier, using 6AK5 pentodes, to provide maximum gain over a frequency band ranging from 50 cps to 5 Mcps. Assume that in addition to the interelectrode capacities listed in Table 6.1, there is an additional 15 pF of wiring capacity between stages. Take a value of $m = 0.5$ (see Fig. 6.1). Specify values for all components and calculate the approximate gain of the amplifier.

6.2   In Fig. 6.25, the "tank" circuit in the anode lead has an inductance $L = 300\ \mu\text{H}$ with $Q = 50$, tuned to resonance at $f = 1$ Mcps. Assume that for the pentode $r_p = 1\ \text{M}\Omega$ and $g_m = 2.5\ \text{mA/V}$. Find the gain at resonance and the bandwidth for $R_L = \infty$ and $R_L = 40\ \text{k}\Omega$.

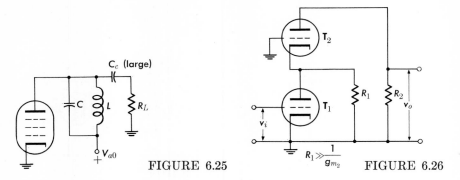

FIGURE 6.25   FIGURE 6.26

6.3   Derive expressions for the input and output impedances and the voltage gain of a grounded-grid amplifier.

6.4   Derive an expression for the voltage gain of the circuit shown in Fig. 6.26 (bias voltages omitted for simplicity).

6.5   The diagram in Fig. 6.27 shows the circuit of a "reflex" amplifier, in which a single active element is used simultaneously as a tuned high-frequency amplifier and a broad-band low-frequency amplifier. (Such circuits are sometimes used in inexpensive radio receivers to economize on components; the low-frequency input is then the detected audio-signal voltage which has been derived by a detector from the high-frequency output and "reflected" back to the input—hence the name.)   The high frequency in the above circuit is 500 kcps and the maximum low frequency is 5 kcps. Discuss how both signals can be amplified but kept separate by appropriate choice of C_1, C_2, L_1, and L_2.

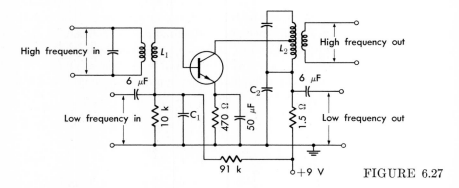

FIGURE 6.27

6.6   Show that with the circuit in Fig. 6.28 an output-signal voltage with a frequency precisely twice that of the input signal is obtained, i.e., that the circuit behaves as a *frequency doubler*. Discuss the general requirements of such a circuit, the required bias levels, additional methods for suppressing undesired voltages, etc., which might be used to optimize the performance as a frequency doubler. (This circuit, with the input signals applied in opposite phase and the outputs in phase is sometimes called a "push-push" amplifier.)

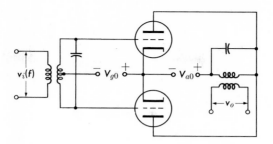

FIGURE 6.28

6.7 The circuit shown in Fig. 6.29, frequently called a *balanced modulator*, has identical tubes, T_1 and T_2. Suppose that v_{i_1} is a low-frequency signal of frequency $f_1 = 100$ cps to 10 kcps, while v_{i_2} is a high-frequency signal of fixed frequency $f_2 = 1$ Mcps. Show that the output signal contains only components of frequency $f_2 - f_1$ and $f_2 + f_1$. (Assume that the condenser C is effectively a short circuit at frequency f_2 and an open circuit at frequency f_1.)

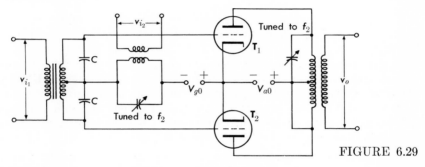

FIGURE 6.29

6.8 The circuit shown in Fig. 6.30 is a constant-gain driver for a push-pull power amplifier, used in a servosystem. The condenser C is tuned to resonate the transformer primary at the operating frequency. Discuss the operation of the circuit semiquantitatively, and show that the current gain $i_{c_1}/i_s \approx -i_{c_2}/i_s \approx R_e/R_f$.

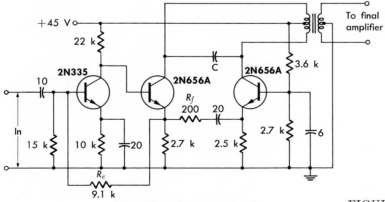

Note: All condensers are in μF.

FIGURE 6.30

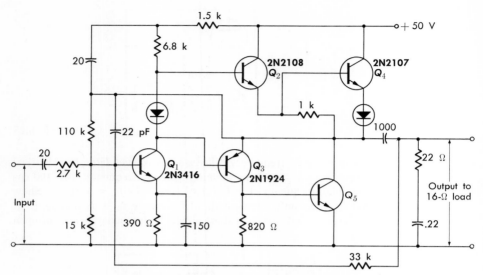

Note: All C's are in μF unless labeled otherwise.

FIGURE 6.31

6.9   The diagram in Fig. 6.31 shows the circuit for an 8-W "high fidelity" audio amplifier for directly driving a 16-Ω voice coil of a loudspeaker from the silicon power transistors Q_4 and Q_5. Discuss the operation of the various parts of the circuit semiquantitatively, isolating the feedback loops. Estimate the gain, bandwidth, and output impedance of the amplifier for typical audio transistors. (The diodes in the circuit of Q_1 and Q_4 are to establish bias levels; ignore their role in this analysis.)

6.10   The circuit in Fig. 6.32 is that of a "high fidelity" preamplifier for an input signal derived from a tape recorder. Transistor Q_4 serves as the collector load of Q_1 and stabilizes the circuit operation over a wide range in ambient temperature. Discuss semiquantitatively the functions of other components in the circuit. Find an approximate value for the midfrequency gain with the level adjust set at maximum output.

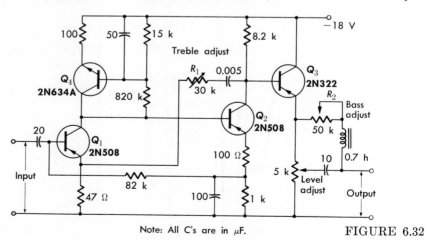

Note: All C's are in μF.

FIGURE 6.32

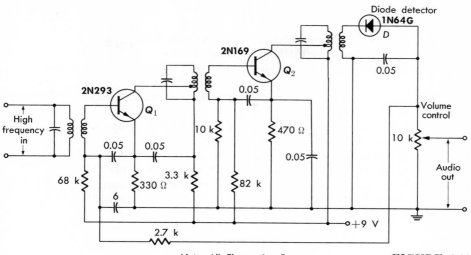

Note: All C's are in μF.   FIGURE 6.33

(Assume typical pnp audio transistors, $h_{fe} \approx 50$.)   Find the effect of varying the treble adjust control R_1 and the bass adjust control R_2 on the high- and low-frequency response.

6.11   In radio receivers it is usually desirable to adjust the amplifier gain to produce a constant audio output signal independent of the magnitude of the high-frequency radio "carrier" input signal, so that the listener does not have to readjust the volume control when switching in different stations of greatly differing signal strength.   For this purpose a simple "AGC" (automatic gain control) circuit, like the one shown in Fig. 6.33, is frequently used.

Analyze the feedback in the circuit qualitatively.   Assuming that without feedback, each tuned high-frequency amplifier would provide a voltage gain of 100, determine the gain of the first stage as a function of emitter current if the response of the amplifier is as shown in Fig. 6.34.   (Assume that all the condensers of capacity 0.05 μF or greater are effective short circuits at the "carrier" frequency, and that the LC "tank" circuits in the collectors of Q_1 and Q_2 are tuned to resonance.   Assume that the dc-voltage at the detector D is equal to the amplitude of the high-frequency input signal to D.

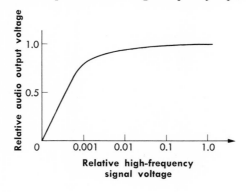

FIGURE 6.34

REFERENCES

Alley, C. L., and K. W. Atwood, *Electronic Engineering*, Wiley, 1962.

Cattermole, K. W., *Transistor Circuits*, Heywood, 1959.

Cooke-Yarborough, E. H., *An Introduction to Transistor Circuits*, Oliver and Boyd, 1957.

Landee, R. W., D. C. Davis, and A. P. Albrecht, *Electronic Designers Handbook*, McGraw-Hill, 1957, Chapter 3.

Ryder, J. D., *Engineering Electronics*, McGraw-Hill, 1957, Chapters 4–8.

Shea, R. F., *Transistor Applications*, Wiley, 1964.

Terman, F. E., *Radio Engineers Handbook*, McGraw-Hill, 1943, Section 5.

Valley, G. E., and H. Wallman, *Vacuum Tube Amplifiers*, McGraw-Hill, 1948.

Vasseur, J. P., *Properties and Applications of Transistors*, Pergamon, 1964.

Walston, J. A., and J. R. Miller, *Transistor Circuit Design*, McGraw-Hill, 1963.

Chapter 7

POWER SUPPLIES

7.1 GENERAL CONSIDERATIONS

All electronic circuits (except simple diode detectors) require at least one power supply for their operation. This must provide the dc voltage and current for the anode or collector circuits and, for tubes, the power needed to heat the cathodes to their operating temperature. The simplest power supply is just a battery and, for some purposes, particularly in portable equipment, batteries can provide efficient, though short-lived, power sources. Since transistor circuits require no heater power and operate at low voltage levels, they are particularly adaptable to battery supplies. However, for most circuits, batteries (even the rechargeable variety) are far too expensive and massive to be considered for continuous use, and it is more efficient to use electronic power supplies, which operate from the available power lines. The power supply must convert power at the line voltage and frequency, commonly 110–120 V rms at 60 cps,* to the levels required by the circuit. In tube circuits, the heaters can usually be operated on ac-voltage, either through a suitable step-down transformer or (provided all the heaters operate on the same current) through connection of the heaters in series across the line, with a series "ballast" resistor, if it is required to make the sum of the voltage drops equal to the line voltage. (This technique is commonly used in inexpensive home radio and TV sets.) The primary function of the power supply is to provide the required dc voltages and currents as efficiently as possible, by converting the ac line voltage to a smooth, constant dc-voltage. For this function, the supply generally includes one or more transformers, rectifier circuits, smoothing filters and, for critical applications, regulator circuits. In this chapter we shall consider in some detail the functions and limitations of each of these circuit components.

---

* Sometimes the line power is provided by a local generator. In this case it is usually advantageous to use higher line frequencies (500–2000 cps) since this can result in substantial reductions in size and weight of transformers and inductors, a fact of particular importance in airborne equipment.

A. Power transformer. A power supply usually contains a transformer with separate primary and secondary windings, which serves to

1. transform the line voltage to a suitable value,

2. insulate the output terminals of the supply from the line,

3. prevent the introduction of noise from the line into the voltages delivered by the supply. For this purpose a static shield is often provided between the primary and secondary windings of the transformer; this shield must be grounded.

Joule heat is developed in the transformer windings, eddy current and hysteresis heat in the core. In 60-cps supplies, power losses in the windings are usually the principal limitation. The power that can be delivered by a transformer depends on the maximum allowable temperature. If a temperature of 60°C is permitted, and cooling is by natural convection of air at room temperature, we can use the following rough empirical rule to determine the required transformer size:

> rms primary voltage times rms primary current (V $\times$ A) at maximum load = 0.64 $\times$ (square of the area of the cross section of the cores of the transformer leg(s) that carry windings, in cm^2).

Current is usually delivered by the transformer in pulses, the duration of which depends on the particular rectifier circuit used. The shorter the pulses, the higher the rms secondary current and, therefore, the higher the power losses at a given value of the average output current. Power supplies with a condenser-input filter (see Figs. 7.1 through 7.4), to which the current is delivered in short bursts, therefore have a smaller efficiency than those with a choke input filter (Fig. 7.10), in which the current flows much more evenly.

The power transformer frequently also includes separate secondary windings to provide ac heater power. This load must be included in determining the proper transformer size.

B. Rectifiers. The transformed ac-voltage is rectified by circuit elements that conduct more current in one direction than in the other. An ideal rectifier diode has no resistance at all in one direction and infinitely high resistance in the other. The more the rectifier diodes deviate from this ideal, the more power is dissipated in them, and the smaller their efficiency. The following types of diodes are used in power rectifiers.

1. *High-vacuum diodes.* The current-voltage relation of these diodes essentially follows the space-charge law, which implies that the anode current increases only gradually with voltage (see Section 2.4). Therefore, the voltage drop across such rectifiers may become rather large, and they are relatively inefficient, particularly for providing low dc-voltages. However, high-vacuum diodes have the advantages of high peak-inverse-voltage ratings and relative immunity from temperature and radiation. They are most useful for high-voltage, low-current supplies. Normal double high-vacuum rectifier diodes can deliver dc-currents of

up to about 300 mA. This current may be increased by putting more diodes in parallel, but usually more efficient rectifying devices would be preferred for large currents. It is good practice to allow the cathodes of rectifier tubes to reach their normal working temperature before any load is applied, for the oxide cathode may be damaged otherwise (see Section 2.6.3). For directly heated cathodes, the delay in switching on the load should be about 5 sec; for indirectly heated cathodes, about 20 sec. At normal cathode temperatures, high-vacuum rectifiers can stand heavy current overloads of short duration very well.

2. *Hot-cathode gas-filled diodes.* As discussed in Section 2.14, an arc discharge is formed in these tubes as soon as the positive anode voltage exceeds 10 to 20 V. Thus, a high current can be drawn at a low voltage drop, making the efficiency of gas-filled diodes considerably higher than that of high-vacuum diodes. However, they are much more susceptible to damage by overloading and have smaller peak-inverse-voltage ratings. As soon as the saturation emission of the cathode is exceeded, the voltage drop in the tube increases, leading to rapid destruction of the cathode. Rectifiers with gas-filled tubes must therefore be treated much more carefully than those with high-vacuum tubes. Usually, a choke-input filter is used to avoid high peak currents (see Section 7.5). In addition, a time-delay relay is often incorporated to ensure that the load is not switched on until a few minutes after the heaters are turned on. Special care must be taken when mercury-vapor rectifiers are used for the first time or after a tube has received a mechanical shock. Then the tube should be run with only the filament on for about half an hour. In addition to limitations in the allowable forward current, a limit must also be observed for the maximum reverse anode voltage. Above this voltage, the tube may arc through in the reverse direction; the resulting gas discharge will lead to a rapid destruction of the cathode. The operating temperature of mercury-vapor rectifiers should be maintained between about 20°C and 60°C; at lower temperatures the vapor pressure becomes too small and the normal arc voltage therefore too high, while at higher temperatures the peak-inverse breakdown voltage becomes too low because of excessive vapor pressure. Tubes with a noble-gas filling have much wider temperature limits.

3. *Metallic rectifiers.* Metallic rectifiers (see Section 3.2.3) have a number of advantages over tubes: they require no heater power nor warm-up time prior to use; they are mechanically rugged; they have long operational lives (tens of thousands of hours if temperature limits are not exceeded); they have relatively small forward-voltage drops and thus are fairly efficient; they can withstand substantial peak currents so long as the average forward current is kept within rated limits (without cooling plates, 30–60 mA/cm^2 of electrode area; with cooling, 40–80 mA/cm^2); they are relatively inexpensive. Their chief disadvantage is in their rather low peak-inverse-voltage ratings, about 20–40 V per cell. Usually several cells are stacked in series to increase the maximum allowable reverse voltage. Selenium rectifiers are always preferable to the older copper-oxide variety.

4. *Germanium and silicon junction diodes.* The principle of operation of these devices has been extensively discussed in Chapter 3. They have excellent rectifying efficiency; silicon diodes in particular have a high conductivity in the forward direction and a very small conductivity in the reverse direction. They can stand very high current densities, up to 1 A/mm² of electrode area when properly cooled. Therefore they can be much smaller than selenium rectifiers. Maximum permissible operating temperatures and reverse voltages must be strictly observed for junction diodes. Peak-inverse-voltage ratings as high as 1 kV have been achieved for silicon diodes, and this can be increased by connecting diodes in series.

Like metallic rectifiers, junction diodes require no warm-up period. At present, junction diodes offer the best combination of characteristics for nearly all power-supply applications, except for supplies which must furnish exceptionally high voltages or operate in highly unusual environments, or for cases where the slight additional cost of junction diodes is a dominant factor.

C. Smoothing filters. The unfiltered output of a rectifier is a highly distorted signal which contains a large proportion of ac-*ripple* in addition to the desired dc-voltage. The unwanted ac-components can be eliminated by smoothing filters. There are two general classes of such filters: condenser-input filters, in which the output of the rectifier is first impressed across a fairly large condenser, and choke-input filters, in which an inductance is connected between the rectifier and the first filter condenser. These circuits will be discussed in the next sections.

7.2 RECTIFIER CIRCUITS WITH CONDENSER-INPUT FILTERS

Some typical rectifier circuits which employ condenser-input filters are shown in Figs. 7.1 through 7.4. Only the first filter condenser is indicated; the effect of additional filter components will be discussed in Section 7.4. In the circuit diagrams, for simplicity the rectifier diodes are indicated by the symbol ▬◀▬ . The arrow, giving the direction of positive current flow, represents the anode. When tubes are used as rectifiers, heater voltages must be supplied, of course. For small supplies (up to about 50 VA), the heater voltage is usually taken from a separate winding on the high-voltage transformer. For larger supplies it is often advisable to use a separate heater transformer to provide for switching on the heater before turning on the high voltage.

The rms-value of the ac-voltage to be rectified will be denoted by V_s, the peak value by $V_s^{(0)} = V_s\sqrt{2}$.

7.2.1   Half-wave rectifiers

These simple rectifier circuits, shown in Fig. 7.1, are used chiefly when only a little power is required (e.g., in cathode-ray tube supplies). In the steady state, the charge that flows from the condenser C into the load is replaced once per cycle through the diode.

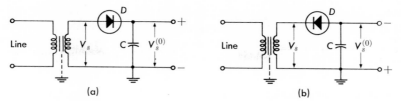

FIG. 7.1. Half-wave rectifiers with condenser across output. (a) Positive output voltage, (b) negative output voltage.

The ratio of the peak to the average current, which determines the losses in the rectifier and transformer as well as the ripple voltage, is higher for a half-wave rectifier than for a full-wave rectifier, in which the condenser is recharged twice per cycle. Furthermore, in the half-wave circuit, current always flows through the transformer winding in the same direction, causing magnetization of the iron core, reduction of the transformer inductance, and therefore a further rise in transformer losses.

If one of the output terminals must be grounded, it is advisable to do it as indicated in Fig. 7.1, with the rectifier always in the ungrounded leg. In this way, the maximum voltage between ground and the top of the secondary winding will be only $V_s^{(0)}$. By grounding the positive terminal in Fig. 7.1(a) or the negative terminal in Fig. 7.1(b), the maximum voltage would become $2V_s^{(0)}$, placing higher demands on the insulation between the transformer winding and the grounded core.

7.2.2 Full-wave rectifiers

The most common full-wave circuit is shown in Fig. 7.2(a); now the condenser C is recharged twice per cycle, alternately from the top and bottom half of the transformer secondary winding, through rectifiers D_1 or D_2. If the transformer secondary does not have a center tap, the bridge circuit of Fig. 7.2(b) can be used. In this case, C is also recharged twice per cycle; as soon as the voltage across the secondary rises above the voltage across C, current will flow through D_1 to C to D_4 if the top of the secondary is positive with respect to the bottom,

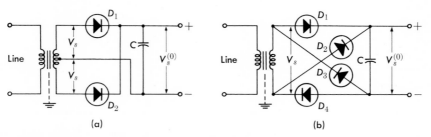

FIG. 7.2. Full-wave rectifiers with condenser across output. (a) Normal circuit with center-tapped transformer, (b) full-wave bridge circuit.

or through D_2 to C to D_3 on the other half cycle. For either of the full-wave circuits in Fig. 7.2, the maximum reverse voltage across each of the diodes is only $V_s^{(0)}$, whereas for all the other circuits of Figs. 7.1 through 7.4 it is $2V_s^{(0)}$. This should be taken into account for selection of rectifier diodes.

7.2.3 Voltage multiplication

Figure 7.3(a) shows the circuit of a voltage doubler, derived by connecting two half-wave rectifiers fed from a single common transformer winding in series. With this circuit, a dc-voltage of $2V_s^{(0)}$ can be obtained (for example, 10 kV for $V_s = 3550$ V). Current flows in both directions through the secondary winding; therefore, the transformer is used to better advantage than in a half-wave rectifier.

When either the positive or negative terminal is grounded, the insulation of one side of the secondary winding must be capable of withstanding a voltage of $2V_s^{(0)}$ with respect to ground. The voltage-doubler circuit shown in Fig. 7.3(b) can be considered as consisting of two full-wave rectifiers operating from one center-tapped winding, with the outputs connected in series. This circuit can be used to good advantage when voltages of $V_s^{(0)}$ and $2V_s^{(0)}$ are both needed.

In Fig. 7.4 two cascade rectifier circuits are illustrated. If one end of the secondary winding is grounded, insulation requirements are lower than for the

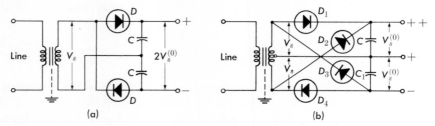

FIG. 7.3. Voltage doubler rectifiers. (a) Half-wave, (b) full-wave.

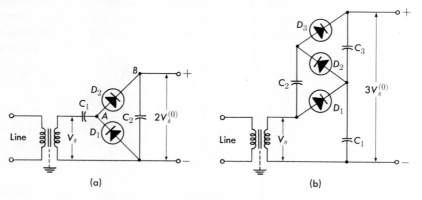

FIG. 7.4. (a) Cascade doubler, (b) cascade tripler.

previous circuits. The circuits shown deliver a positive voltage with respect to ground; a negative voltage can be obtained by reversing all the diodes. The operation of these circuits in the absence of any load can be most simply understood by considering that the condensers $C_1, C_2 \ldots$ are charged to dc-voltages of such magnitude that the diodes $D_1, D_2 \ldots$ need not deliver any current while, at the same time, there must be identical ac-voltages at both terminals of each condenser. These two conditions mean that in the circuit of Fig. 7.4(a), for instance, the voltage at point A must go up and down between 0 and $2V_s^{(0)}$. If D_2 never carries any current, the voltage at point B of C_2 must be equal to the maximum voltage at point A, that is $2V_s^{(0)}$. The output voltage therefore is $2V_s^{(0)}$.

With additional rectifiers and condensers, the voltage can in principle be multiplied by any factor; each stage of the cascade increases the output voltage by an amount $V_s^{(0)}$. Large cascade rectifiers with twenty or more stages are sometimes used to generate voltages of up to a few million volts for nuclear accelerators. The internal resistance R_i of such a cascade rectifier rises rapidly with the number of stages (m). If all the condensers except C_1 are equal, and $\frac{1}{2}C_1 = C_2 = C_3 = \cdots = C$, the internal resistance is approximately

$$R_i \approx \tfrac{2}{3}m^3/fC, \qquad f = \text{line frequency,} \tag{7.1}$$

which is valid for large m.

7.3 ELECTRIC CHARACTERISTICS OF RECTIFIERS WITH CONDENSER-INPUT FILTERS

7.3.1 Output voltage drop under load

If a rectifier with an input filter condenser C is loaded by a resistance R_L, the dc-output current I_o through this resistance will tend to discharge C. It will be recharged every time one of the rectifier diodes conducts, through a series resistance R_g, which consists of the sum of the average forward resistance R_d of one rectifier, the resistance R_s of the part of the transformer secondary winding that delivers current through the rectifier, and the transformed primary resistance $T_1^2 R_p$ (T_1 is the transformer voltage ratio V_s/V_p and R_p is the resistance in the primary circuit). If the load resistance R_L is much larger than R_g, C will be charged almost to the peak value $V_s^{(0)}$ of the secondary voltage; if, moreover, the time constant CR_L is large compared with the duration of one period of the ac supply voltage, the charging current will be delivered in pulses very much shorter than one period. Under these conditions, the voltage V_C across the condenser looks like that shown in Fig. 7.5(a). Between two charging current pulses the condenser voltage drops by an amount

$$\Delta V_C = -\Delta Q/C \approx -I_o T/nC = -I_o/nfC.$$

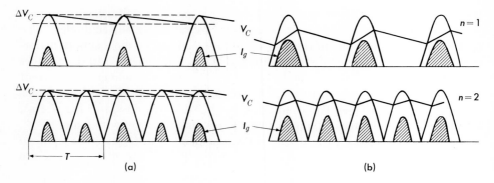

FIG. 7.5. Voltage across input filter condenser (V_C) and current pulses (I_g) in the rectifier diodes of a half-wave ($n = 1$) and full-wave ($n = 2$) rectifier with condenser-input filter, (a) for a small load, (b) for a heavier load.

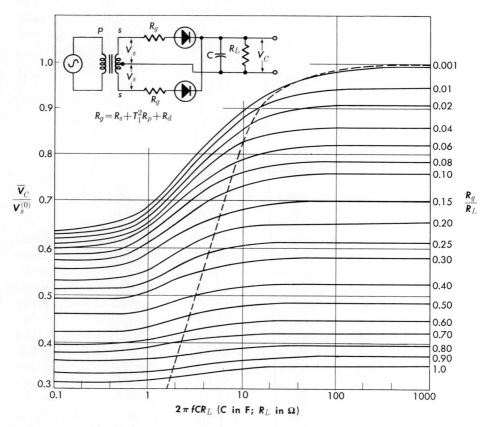

FIG. 7.6. Average condenser voltage ($\overline{V}_C$) for a full-wave rectifier, shown as a fraction of the peak voltage $V_s^{(0)}$ across one-half the transformer secondary, as a function of various parameters.

(ΔQ is the charge lost by C between two pulses; I_o is the dc output current; $T = 1/f$ is the period of the ac-voltage; $n = 1$ for half-wave rectifiers; $n = 2$ for full-wave rectifiers.) The average voltage drop, which is just one half of the total drop ΔV_C, is then

$$\overline{\Delta V_C} \approx -I_o/2nfC. \tag{7.2}$$

For 60-cps supplies, (7.2) can be written as $\overline{\Delta V_C} \approx -8.3 I_o/nC$ V if C is measured in microfarads and I_o in milliamperes.

For heavier loads, when R_L is no longer large compared with R_g and C is no longer charged to $V_s^{(0)}$, charging current flows during a larger part of each cycle (cf. Fig. 7.5b). The calculation of V_C now becomes rather complicated.* The curves of Fig. 7.6 give the results of such a calculation for a full-wave rectifier. The dashed curve represents Eq. (7.2). It is clear that (7.2) is valid only for small loads ($R_g/R_L < 0.001$) and for a sufficiently large time constant $CR_L (>2T)$. Figure 7.6 is very useful for evaluating the performance of power supplies. In order for the resistance $R_g = R_s + T_1^2 R_p + R_d$ to be determined, besides R_s and R_p (which can be easily measured), the average diode resistance R_d must be known. This is given in Fig. 7.7 for a few common high-vacuum diode rectifiers. Note that R_d is a function of the average output current as well as of the size of the input filter condenser.

If the rectifiers are gas-filled diodes, they would tend to operate with a small constant voltage drop (5–20 V) when the tube conducts, independent of the value of I_o, but actually such tubes would never be used with a condenser-input filter because of the high-peak currents required. Metallic rectifiers and junction diodes have much smaller values of R_d than vacuum diodes, because the forward current increases exponentially with voltage in semiconductor diodes. In fact, these devices are similar to gas tubes in that they operate with almost a constant voltage drop across the rectifier: 1–3 V for metallic rectifiers, 0.5–2 V for junction

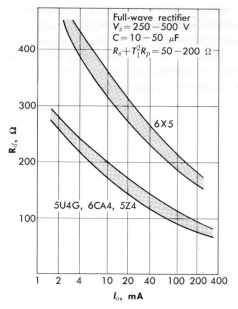

FIG. 7.7. Average value of the resistance, R_d, for one-half of some representative high-vacuum diode rectifiers as a function of the dc-current, I_o, for a full-wave rectifier.

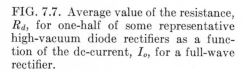

---

* See Q. H. Schade, Proc. Inst. Radio Engrs. **31** (1943), 341.

diodes. This small drop must be subtracted from $V_s^{(0)}$ for estimation of the value of V_C and, to a good approximation, we can assume that $R_g \approx T_1^2 R_p + R_s$.

7.3.2   Ripple voltage

As seen in Fig. 7.5, the ripple voltage across the input filter condenser has a saw-tooth shape, with a frequency f for half-wave rectifiers and $2f$ for full-wave rectifiers. Under the same conditions where Eq. (7.2) is valid, the peak-to-peak ripple voltage is just $|\Delta V_C|$ and is

$$\tilde{V}_C \approx I_o/nfC. \qquad (7.3)$$

A more detailed analysis shows that the actual peak-to-peak ripple voltage does not deviate much from Eq. (7.3) even for heavier loads, where (7.2) is no longer valid. For $CR_L > 1/f$ and $R_g/R_L < 0.1$, which is almost always true in practice, the deviation is less than 20%. Thus the range in I_o over which (7.3) may be used to estimate the ripple voltage is far greater than that for which the decrease in dc output voltage is given by (7.2).

7.3.3   Peak-to-average current ratio in transformer and rectifier diodes

At a fixed value of the average output current, the width of the pulses charging the input filter condenser C decreases (and therefore the peak-to-average current ratio increases) as R_g is made smaller or C is made larger. In practice, the peak-to-average current ratio of a fully loaded full-wave rectifier lies between 4 and 7 (for one half the transformer and one rectifier). The minimum possible value is π. In order not to exceed the maximum peak-current rating of a particular rectifier diode, for each given value of $R_s + T_1^2 R_p$ a certain maximum value of C must be observed. Such data are often given in tube manuals. For metallic or junction diodes it is often recommended that a resistor of at least $2/I_{omax}$ ohms (I_{omax} is the maximum average diode current in amperes) be placed in series with each diode to limit the peak forward current if $R_s + T_1^2 R_p$ is small.

7.4   FILTERS

If the ripple at the input condenser C is too large for the rectifier to be used directly to furnish dc-voltage to the circuit, additional filter sections can be added, following C. The two simplest possibilities, the LC- and RC-filter, are shown in Fig. 7.8.

Such filters should give the maximum possible ripple reduction at the smallest possible dc voltage drop. In this respect, the LC-filter is better than the RC-filter, because the ac-impedance of the choke Z_{ch}, which determines the reduction of the ripple voltage, can be made much larger than its dc-resistance R_{ch},

which introduces a drop, I_oR_{ch}, in the dc output voltage. For an RC-filter, the
dc- and ac-resistance values are, of course, equal. Still, RC-filters are frequently
used because of their smaller dimensions, weight, and cost.

In practice, we use large chokes and condensers, so that $\omega L \gg 1/\omega C'$ or
$R \gg 1/\omega C'$ ($\omega/2\pi$ is the frequency of the first harmonic of the ripple voltage).
Then the amplitude of the first harmonic is reduced to a fraction, $(1/\omega C')/\omega L = 1/\omega^2 C'L$ by a single-stage LC-filter and to a fraction $(1/\omega C')/R = 1/\omega RC'$, by a
single-stage RC-filter. Combining this with (7.3), which gives the peak-to-peak
ripple voltage across the input filter capacitor C, we find, for the peak-to-peak
value of the first harmonic after the filter,

$$LC\text{-filter:} \quad \tilde{V}_{rf} \approx 0.017 \, \frac{I_o}{n^3 f^3 LCC'} \text{ V,} \tag{7.4}$$

$$RC\text{-filter:} \quad \tilde{V}_{rf} \approx 0.11 \, \frac{I_o}{n^2 f^2 RCC'} \text{ V,} \tag{7.5}$$

where $f =$ line frequency in cps; I_o is in amp, L in henries, C and C' in farads,
R in ohms; $n = 1$ for half-wave, $n = 2$ for full-wave rectifiers. In these expressions, the fact that the ratio of the amplitudes of the first harmonic and the total
ripple voltage across C is about 0.7 has been taken into account. Higher harmonics of the ripple voltage are attenuated much more; at the filter output
they are quite negligible compared with the first harmonic. A ripple at the line
frequency is attenuated four times less than a ripple at twice the line frequency
in an LC-filter, two times less in an RC-filter. It is therefore important to construct full-wave rectifiers with the two halves as symmetrical as possible, for
otherwise a ripple at the line frequency may become predominant at the filter
output. Generally C and C' are chosen equal; in this way the product CC' in
Eqs. (7.4) and (7.5) is a maximum for a given sum $C + C'$, which determines
the total size of the two capacitors. If insufficient filtering is achieved after
one stage, additional LC- or RC-sections may be added after the first. For each
LC-section, $\tilde{V}_{rf}$ is reduced by an additional factor of $1/(2\pi nf)^2 LC$, and for each
RC-stage, by a factor of $1/(2\pi nf RC)$.

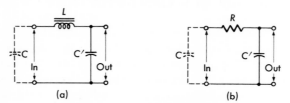

FIG. 7.8. LC- and RC-filters.

Iron cores are invariably used in low-frequency filter chokes. The inductance
of such a choke decreases when a dc-current is passed through it, due to saturation of the core. A gradual saturation can be achieved if the core is provided
with an air gap. Often, power must be supplied to various parts of a circuit

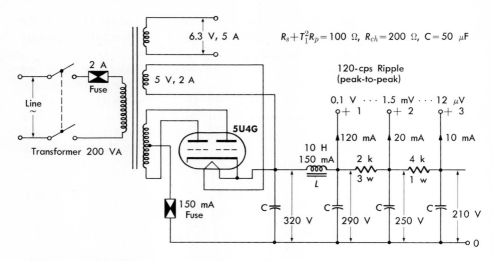

FIG. 7.9. Full-wave power supply with cascaded filters. The indicated output voltages are obtained at various points in the filter chain for the current loads shown.

which have different sensitivities to ripple voltage. In such cases it is advantageous to use a number of filters in cascade. An example of such an arrangement is shown in Fig. 7.9. In this circuit there are three outputs, 1, 2, and 3, supplying progressively lower currents at progressively lower ripple voltages. Such a supply is suitable for feeding an amplifier with several stages in cascade; the most sensitive stage should be connected to output 3, the next stage to output 2, and the final stage to output 1. This method has the additional advantage that the influence of the final stage current on the supply voltage of the previous stages, which may lead to regeneration (motorboating), is strongly reduced since the power-supply leads to each stage are decoupled from one another through the RC-filter networks.

7.5 FULL-WAVE RECTIFIER WITH CHOKE-INPUT FILTER

In the full-wave rectifier circuit shown in Fig. 7.10, the rectifier output is connected to the load R_L directly through a choke; there is no condenser across the input to the filter. The omission of this single component radically changes the character of the circuit. The operation can be best understood if we assume first that the inductance of the choke is infinitely large. If this were true, then the total current delivered through the choke would have to be constant in time since for any dI/dt, the back voltage, $-L \, dI/dt$, opposing the change would be infinitely large. The currents I_1 and I_2, flowing through each rectifier in turn during each half cycle of the line voltage, would be ideal rectangular pulses in that the total current through L would be perfectly constant. The voltage drop across each rectifier, V_d, would then be a constant (at constant current), determinable from the I vs. V characteristics of the rectifier. The voltage V_{ch} at the choke input would exactly follow the voltage at that half of the secondary winding which was delivering current; if the line voltage is a pure sine wave, V_{ch} must then be a double rectified sinusoidal voltage $|V_s^{(0)} \sin \omega t|$ less the dc-drop across the rectifier:

$$V_{ch} = |V_s^{(0)} \sin \omega t| - V_d. \tag{7.6}$$

In a real circuit, of course, L is finite, but the essential behavior of the circuit is closely analogous to the ideal case. If the dc-voltage drop in the choke is negligible, the dc output voltage of a real rectifier, V_o, with a choke-input filter, is to a good approximation the same as that of the ideal circuit, equal simply to the average value of V_{ch} in (7.6):

$$V_o = 2V_s^{(0)}/\pi - V_d. \tag{7.7}$$

Note that in this approximation, V_o is independent of the load current I_o except through the dependence of V_d (and the IR-drop in the choke and transformer) on I_o; with hot-cathode gas-filled rectifiers, V_d would also be essentially independent of I_o. A rectifier with a choke-input filter can thus furnish a dc output voltage which depends only slightly on the current; such a supply is termed *well regulated.*

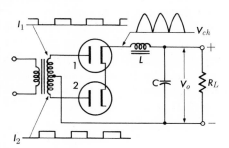

FIG. 7.10. Full-wave rectifier with a choke-input filter.

The ratio of the peak-to-average current in each rectifier is only 2 for the ideal choke-input circuit, so that the transformer losses are far less than with a condenser-input filter. On the whole, the choke-input circuit is thus considerably more efficient and clearly indicated when large dc-power must be provided. However, the circuit also has its obvious disadvantages. For one thing, from (7.7) we see that the output voltage is reduced by about a factor of $2/\pi$ relative to that of the condenser-input circuit. In addition, since L is not infinite and there are only two reactive components in the choke-input filter, the output ripple voltage will be higher for the choke-input filter than for a condenser-input filter. We can easily calculate the output ripple voltage by considering the attenuation of the fundamental ac-component of V_o through the actual LC-circuit. Since we have a full-wave rectifier, the fundamental frequency is

$2f$, twice the line frequency f; hence, the filter will attenuate the ac-signal by a factor of about

$$\frac{1/\omega C}{\omega L} = \frac{1}{(2\pi)^2(2f)^2 LC} = \frac{1}{16\pi^2 f^2 LC}.$$

Since the peak-to-peak value of the fundamental component of V_o at a frequency $2f$ is $8V_s^{(0)}/3\pi$, the peak-to-peak ripple voltage at the output is

$$\tilde{V}_{rf} \approx V_s^{(0)}/6\pi^3 f^2 LC; \tag{7.8}$$

for $f = 60$ cps, the ripple is approximately

$$\tilde{V}_{rf} \approx 1.6\, V_s^{(0)}/LC \text{ volts}, \qquad L \text{ in henries, } C \text{ in microfarads.} \tag{7.9}$$

In this approximation, the output ripple voltage is independent of I_o.

The choke-input filter can be used *only* under conditions where the current through L can be maintained approximately constant, as in a full-wave rectifier. The circuit is thus completely inappropriate for a half-wave rectifier, where the current *must* go to zero each cycle when the rectifier is cut off. This would have the effect of causing a large dI/dt, resulting in large high-frequency ac-voltages at the choke that tend to arc back across the rectifier, increase the ac-ripple as well as the output voltage, and spoil the good regulation. Even with a full-wave rectifier, the choke-input circuit will not behave properly if the current through the choke actually goes to zero. This can occur if the peak value of the ac-current through the actual finite choke is greater than the dc-current I_o; if this happens, the current through L will be periodically interrupted and the circuit will no longer approximate the ideal case. If I_o goes to zero, the circuit must, in fact, behave like a condenser-input filter, and V_C must rise toward $V_s^{(0)}$. The peak ac-current through L at the frequency $2f$ will be $4V_s^{(0)}/(3\pi Z_{ch})$ or approximately

$$I_r \approx V_s^{(0)}/(3\pi 2fL). \tag{7.10}$$

Since $I_o = V_C/R_L \approx 2V_s^{(0)}/\pi R_L$, the condition for stability, $I_o > I_r$, requires that

$$L \geq R_L/6\pi f. \tag{7.11}$$

For $f = 60$ cps, R_L should not exceed 1141 ohms per henry of inductance in the input choke.

In practical supplies, condition (7.11) is frequently maintained by two devices. First, a special choke is used for the input inductance, an iron-core choke with a very narrow air gap called a "swinging choke," which saturates at small dc-current, so that L increases rapidly as I_o decreases (or R_L increases). Second, a fixed minimum internal load is provided by use of a *bleeder* resistor across the output, so that even with the circuit load completely disconnected, R_L will never be smaller than required by (7.11), and the output voltage will never rise to excessive values.

7.6 VOLTAGE REGULATION

For many applications, power supplies are needed with an output voltage that remains as constant as possible under variations of input voltage and load current and also when the input voltage and load are kept constant. The performance of such a regulated supply may be characterized by the following quantities.

1. *The regulation factor* δ, defined as the ratio of a small relative change, $\Delta V_i/V_i$, of the input voltage and the resulting relative change, $\Delta V_o/V_o$, of the output voltage (at constant output current):

$$\delta = \frac{\Delta V_i/V_i}{\Delta V_o/V_o}.$$
(7.12)

2. *The internal resistance* R_i, defined as the ratio of a small voltage change impressed on the output and the resulting current change ΔI_o of the current (at constant input voltage):

$$R_i = -\Delta V_o/\Delta I_o.$$
(7.13)

The minus sign indicates that R_i must be taken positive when the output voltage decreases for increasing output current, and vice versa.

3. *The drift*, i.e. slow changes in the output voltage for constant V_i and load. The drift is governed by the quality of the components and by the care taken in the construction of the supply. An important factor of component quality with respect to drift is the constancy with changes of temperature.

   Generally, drift cannot be specified by one single figure; in most cases there are different constituents of the total drift, each with its own time constant. Usually the drift is quite a bit larger during the warm-up period of an instrument, which may amount to as much as one or two hours. The warm-up period and the maximum drift during a definite time interval after warm-up are often given as separate data for commercially built power supplies.

7.6.1 Voltage regulators with cold-cathode gas-discharge tubes

The regulation characteristics of a power supply can be improved considerably if a gas-discharge tube is connected across the output, as shown in Fig. 7.11. Consider the voltage V_o across the terminals of the cold-cathode gas-filled diode connected through a resistor R_v to a variable input voltage V_i (Fig. 7.11a). If V_i starts increasing from 0, the output voltage V_o between the electrodes of the diode will behave as indicated in Fig. 7.11(b). At first, V_o will rise at the same rate as V_i. When V_i reaches the starting voltage, V_{b0}, of the gas discharge, the tube suddenly starts conducting, and V_o drops by 10 to 30 V to the operating voltage V_b of the tube. The tube is now in its glow-discharge region (cf. Section 2.14). When V_i is increased further, V_o remains almost constant while the glow

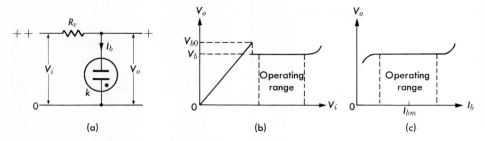

FIG. 7.11. Voltage regulation with a cold-cathode gas diode. (a) Circuit arrangement, (b) V_o vs. V_i characteristic with increasing voltage—the tube fires when $V_o = V_{b0}$, and then V_o drops to the value V_b, (c) V_o vs. I_b characteristic after tube is fired—the tube is usually biased to the current I_{bm}.

discharge spreads over the cathode surface of the tube. The tube current is now $I_b = (V_i - V_b)/R_v$. After the cathode surface is completely covered by the glow discharge, V_o will start rising again if V_i is increased still further. The tube should never be operated in this region because its life would then be seriously reduced by sputtering of the cathode. The operating range for good voltage regulation is indicated in Fig. 7.11(b) and (c). In practice, the limits of this range correspond to tube currents differing by a factor of 2 to 10 from minimum to maximum values. Within the operating range, the output voltage V_o still increases slightly with I_b; this dependence may be characterized by an internal tube resistance $R_i' = \Delta V_o/\Delta I_b$. Good regulator tubes have small values of R_i' and of the drift in the operating voltage V_b. Internal-resistance values for some commonly used tubes are given in Table 7.1.

TABLE 7.1

Characteristics of Some Gas-Filled Regulator Tubes

Type	V_{b0}, V	V_b, V	I_{bm}, mA	R_i', Ω
5651A*	107	85.5	2.5	270
0B2	115	108	17	40
0A2	156	150	17	80

* Voltage-reference tube.

The regulation factor of the circuit of Fig. 7.11(a) can easily be derived with the aid of Fig. 7.12. In Fig. 7.12(b) the diode is replaced by a voltage source V_b in series with a resistance R_i'. The fixed voltage V_b has no influence on voltage changes and therefore may be omitted when the regulation factor is calculated. The circuit then reduces to that of Fig. 7.12(c).

A change ΔV_i of the input voltage produces an output-voltage change $\Delta V_o = [R_s/(R_s + R_v)]\Delta V_i$ (R_s is the equivalent value of R_i' and R_L in parallel).

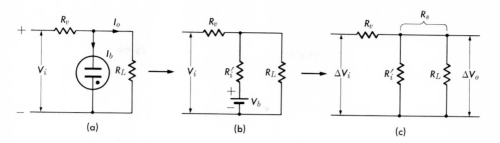

FIG. 7.12. Equivalent circuits for calculation of the regulation factor.

The regulation factor therefore is

$$\delta = \frac{\Delta V_i/V_i}{\Delta V_o/V_o} = \frac{V_o}{V_i}\frac{R_v + R_s}{R_s}. \tag{7.14}$$

In practice, usually $R_L \gg R_i'$, and $R_v \gg R_i'$; then (7.14) reduces to

$$\delta \approx \frac{V_o}{V_i}\frac{R_v}{R_i'}. \tag{7.15}$$

For $R_v \gg R_i'$, the internal resistance of the regulator is about equal to that of the tube:

$$R_i \approx R_i', \tag{7.16}$$

which can be easily verified.

For the proper operation of regulators by use of gas diodes, the following rules must be observed.

1. The diode current must be adjusted to the middle of its operating range ($I_b \approx I_{bm}$) by the correct choice of R_v.

2. The load current must not exceed I_{bm} by too large a factor, for otherwise δ will become too small (since R_v must be made small). Also, a small relative change of I_o may cause the tube to shift out of its operating current range.

3. To ensure that the starting voltage V_{b0} of the glow discharge is reached, V_i must be sufficiently larger than V_o: $V_i > V_{b0}(R_L + R_v)/R_L$.

EXAMPLE. Given a 5651A tube with $V_{b0} = 105$ V, $V_b = 85$ V, $R_i' = 270\ \Omega$, $I_{bm} = 2.5$ mA, determine
(i) R_v and δ for $I_o = 2.5$ mA, $V_i = 300$ V,
(ii) the minimum possible V_i and resulting values of R_v and δ for $I_o = 2.5$ mA.

Solution

(i)
$$R_v = \frac{V_i - V_o}{I_o + I_{bm}} = \frac{300 - 85}{5} \approx 43\ \text{k}\Omega$$

(heat developed in R_v: $W = (I_o + I_{bm})^2 R_v = 5^2 \cdot 43 \cdot 10^{-3} \approx 1$ W; take a 2-W composition resistor for R_v). Now,

$$\delta = \frac{V_o}{V_i} \frac{R_v}{R_i'} = \frac{85}{300} \cdot \frac{43}{0.27} \approx 46$$

(i.e., a 10% change of V_i gives a 0.2% change of V_o).

(ii) $$R_v = \frac{V_i - V_o}{I_o + I_{bm}};$$

$$V_i > \frac{V_{bo}(R_L + R_v)}{R_L} = \frac{V_{bo}[R_L + (V_i - V_o)/(I_o + I_{bm})]}{R_L};$$

$$V_i > V_{bo} \frac{[(I_o + I_{bm})R_L - V_o]}{[(I_o + I_{bm})R_L - V_{bo}]} = \frac{105(170 - 85)}{(170 - 105)} \approx 137 \text{ V}.$$

Take $V_i = 145$ V; then R_v must be 12 kΩ, and we obtain $\delta = 26$.

If V_i is very much larger than V_o and if the load current is small, the regulation factor approaches its maximum possible value, $\delta_{max} \approx V_o/(I_b R_i')$ (for a 5651A, $\delta_{max} \approx 120$). We can obtain larger regulation factors by cascading two or more regulator stages. An example of this is shown in Fig. 7.13.

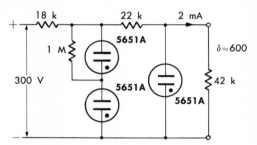

FIG. 7.13.   Cascade regulator with neon tubes.

The drift of the operating voltage V_b sets a limit to the maximum useful value of the regulation factor. For ordinary neon tubes this drift may amount to as much as 1 V in 24 hr. Special-voltage reference tubes like the 5651A have a much smaller drift; selected tubes show drifts of the order of 0.1 V/1000 hr.

Such exceptional performance can be obtained only when the ambient temperature is kept reasonably constant; for instance, the 5651A has a temperature coefficient of the operating voltage of about -4 mV/°C. Voltage regulators with gas diodes are used mainly when the load currents are small (at most about 50 mA) and when the load is reasonably constant.

7.6.2   Regulators with Zener diodes

As we have seen in Section 3.3.2, when the reverse voltage across a silicon-junction diode exceeds a certain sharply defined value, the *Zener voltage* (V_z), the reverse current suddenly increases very rapidly, and the internal resistance may drop from some megohms to a few ohms for a voltage change of only a few tenths of a volt. A silicon diode operating in this region is called a Zener diode. Such a diode, connected through a resistor R_v to a reverse voltage $V_i > V_z$, behaves like a voltage source with an output voltage V_o which depends very little on V_i, $V_o \approx V_z$. Its performance is analogous to that of a gas diode; however, Zener diodes can be made for much lower operating voltages. Zener diodes with operating voltage ranging from less than one volt to over a thousand volts are commercially available. The maximum current in a Zener diode is determined by the permissible power dissipation W_{max}, and therefore is inversely proportional to V_z for types with the same W_{max}. High-power Zener diodes for voltages under 10 V may carry currents of up to some tens of amperes.

Since V_z is somewhat temperature-dependent (temperature coefficients lie in the range of $\pm 0.1\%$ per °C), the temperature must be kept constant if very stable output voltages are required. The drift of V_z at constant temperature is very small; good voltage regulators with a Zener diode in a thermostat can be used as standard voltage reference sources. The magnitude of the temperature coefficient of the Zener voltage depends on the current through the diode. In favorable cases, the temperature coefficient may go through zero for a normal value of the current. The Zener voltage can then be made insensitive to temperature variation by a proper adjustment of the current.

7.6.3 Electronic voltage regulators

With more sophisticated electronic regulators, high regulation factors can be obtained together with very low internal resistances, for widely different voltages and loads. Electronic voltage regulation is usually obtained by a negative-feedback amplifier circuit feeding back a fraction βV_o of the output voltage. This fraction is compared with a highly constant reference voltage V_{ref} and the difference $(\beta V_o - V_{ref})$ is employed after amplification to counteract any deviation of βV_o from the value V_{ref}. Thus V_o is kept approximately equal to V_{ref}/β. Such a feedback circuit is a special case of a feedback dc-amplifier. Its gain $A \approx 1/\beta$; the input signal is the constant voltage V_{ref} (Fig. 7.14a).

The amplifier is fed by an unstabilized voltage V_i from an unregulated power supply. The output voltage V_o can be controlled by the amplified difference voltage $V_r = A_0(\beta V_o - V_{ref})$ in different ways. Usually V_r is applied to the control grid of a series tube or to the base of a series transistor through which the current flows from the unregulated source to the regulated output; this is called a *series regulator* (Fig. 7.14b). In another arrangement, a variable load controlled by V_r can be put in parallel with the external load; this case is termed *shunt regulation* (Fig. 7.14c). The second method is used only when the external load is approximately constant; otherwise, if the external load is switched off, the shunt must dissipate the maximum available output power. Favorable characteristics can sometimes be obtained by a combination of shunt and series regulations. As an example of the operation of an electronic regulator, we shall derive the expressions for the regulation factor and internal resistance

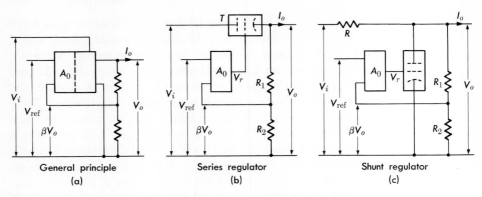

FIG. 7.14. Electronic voltage regulation. (a) General principle, (b) series regulator, (c) shunt regulator.

of a typical series regulator circuit in which regulator tubes T (Fig. 7.14b) are used in series with the input. The series tube T, characterized by its mutual conductance g_m and its amplification factor μ, has an anode voltage V_i, a control-grid voltage $V_r +$ a constant, and a cathode voltage V_o. If V_i changes by an amount ΔV_i, the effective control voltage of T changes by

$$\Delta V_{ec} = \Delta V_r - \Delta V_o + \frac{\Delta V_i - \Delta V_o}{\mu}$$

$$= -\left(-\beta A_0 + 1 + \frac{1}{\mu}\right)\Delta V_o + \frac{\Delta V_i}{\mu} \qquad (7.17)$$

and its anode current therefore changes by

$$\Delta I_a = g_m \Delta V_{ec} = -g_m\left(-\beta A_0 + 1 + \frac{1}{\mu}\right)\Delta V_o + \frac{\Delta V_i}{\mu}. \qquad (7.18)$$

Neglecting the fraction of the current I_a flowing through the voltage divider (R_1, R_2), we can write

$$\Delta I_a = \Delta V_o/R_L, \qquad (7.19)$$

where R_L is the load resistance. From Eqs. (7.18) and (7.19), a relation between ΔI_a and ΔV_o is easily derived. For $g_m R_L \gg 1$ and $|\beta A_0| \gg 1$ (which is always true in practical cases), we find for the regulation factor

$$\delta = \frac{\Delta V_i/V_i}{\Delta V_o/V_o} \approx \frac{V_o}{V_i}\mu\beta|A_0|. \qquad (7.20)$$

A voltage change ΔV_o impressed at the output of the regulator causes the effective control voltage of T to change by $\Delta V_{ec} \approx -|A_0|\beta\,\Delta V_o - \Delta V_o,^*$ so

---

* We assume that the source of V_i has negligible internal resistance.

that I_o changes by $\Delta I_o = g_m \Delta V_{ec} \approx -g_m \beta |A_0| \Delta V_o$. The internal resistance of the regulator is therefore

$$R_i = -\frac{\Delta V_o}{\Delta I_o} \approx \frac{1}{g_m \beta |A_0|}. \tag{7.21}$$

Simple regulator circuits, in which a difference amplifier with only one tube is used, are capable of regulation factors of about 100 and have an internal resistance of a few ohms. If the difference amplifier contains two stages, regulation factors in excess of 1000 can be obtained. Such high values make sense only when the drift is very small as a result of the use of high-quality components and careful construction.

There is certainly nothing unique about choosing a vacuum tube for the series regulator element. This element could as easily be a power transistor of sufficient rating to carry the full output current. In the following, we shall discuss two typical electronically regulated power supplies, one using all vacuum tubes in the amplifier and series regulator, and the second employing all semiconductor devices.

EXAMPLE 1. *Regulated tube supply.* The complete circuit of a vacuum-tube power supply with series regulation is given in Fig. 7.15. The output voltage is variable from 200 to 300 V; currents of up to 100 mA can be delivered. In this circuit, the reference voltage V_{ref} is developed at the cathode of the amplifier tube T_2 by a neon tube T_1 fed from the regulated voltage through R_5 and R_6. The control grid of T_2 carries a fraction, $[R_2/(R_1 + R_2)]V_o$, of the output voltage. The difference between this voltage and V_{ref} is amplified in T_2 and applied to the control grids of the two series regulator tubes T_3 and T_4 in parallel. When V_o decreases, these grids become more positive, causing the series tubes to deliver more current, thus counteracting the decrease of V_o. An increase of V_o is counteracted in the same way. The output voltage can be varied with the aid of the potentiometer R_3, which controls the ratio $\beta = R_2/(R_1 + R_2)$.

To derive values of the regulation factor and the internal resistance with the aid of Eqs. (7.20) and (7.21), we should first note some peculiarities in the circuit. In the first place, the 220-kΩ anode resistor R_a of T_2 is connected to the *unregulated* supply so that sufficient current can be passed through T_2 at all times, no matter what the output voltage setting. If R_a were connected to the regulated output, the voltage across R_a would equal only the negative control-grid voltage of the series regulator tube, which is small for heavy loads. Then T_2 would be very nearly cut off and the amplifier gain would become too small. However, because of the connection of R_a to V_i, variations of V_i reach the control grids of the series regulator tubes with very little attenuation. This causes a reduction in the effective amplification factor of the series tubes to about 1. Further, the effective mutual conductance of the series tubes is actually reduced to about 1 mA/V because of the internal resistance of the unregulated

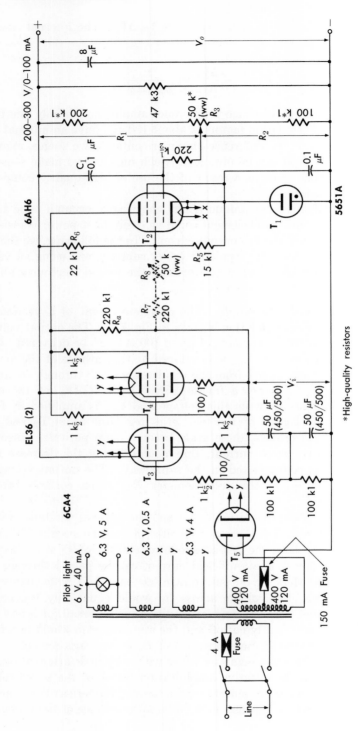

FIG. 7.15. Complete circuit of an electronically regulated power supply using vacuum tubes.

supply. On top of this, the gain of T_2 is about 30% less than its expected value $R_a g_{m_2} \approx 200$, because the neon tube T_1 in its cathode lead represents a resistance of about 300 ohms (cf. Section 5.1). If all these effects are taken into account, Eq. (7.20) gives $\delta \sim 30$, while from (7.21) we know that $R_i \approx 20\,\Omega$, in reasonable agreement with the values measured for this circuit.

Compensation. If the screen grid of T_2 is also connected to the unregulated supply voltage V_i through a suitably chosen resistance (R_7, R_8), the undesirable influence of V_i on the control-grid voltage of the series tubes can be compensated. In this way, a much higher regulation factor (about 200) and a much smaller internal resistance (about 3 Ω) can be obtained. With a small degree of over-compensation, an infinitely large regulation factor can in principle be realized. However, this would be the case only for one particular value of the load and one particular value of V_i, since compensation depends on variable parameters such as the mutual conductance of the tubes. Because these parameters depend not only on the operating point but also on time, compensation must always be combined with a sufficient amount of negative feedback.

Ripple. The ripple voltage at the output reaches the control grid of T_2 directly through C_1 and therefore is reduced by a factor of 2 to 3 more than the slow fluctuations of V_o, which must reach T_2 through the voltage divider R_1, R_2. For the circuit of Fig. 7.15, a peak-to-peak ripple voltage of 90 mV has been measured without compensation; with compensation, the ripple is reduced to 15 mV ($V_o = 300$ V, $I_o = 100$ mA).

Drift. This can be caused in the first place by the temperature-dependence of the resistors in the voltage divider (R_1, R_2). High-quality temperature-compensated resistors should be used here. As already noted, temperature will also influence the operating voltage of the neon tube T_1. For this reason T_1 must be kept away from components which dissipate much heat. Another source of drift is the influence of the cathode temperature of T_2 on its anode current at constant electrode voltages. This source of drift becomes apparent particularly after sudden changes of the line voltage. Because the cathode temperature adjusts itself rather slowly to a new value after such a jump, the output voltage also requires some time for readjustment. In most cases, this effect causes a regulator circuit *without* compensation to have a considerably *better* regulation against slow changes of line voltage than expected. In more refined regulator circuits, the contribution of this source of drift is greatly reduced by use of a special difference amplifier (see Section 6.5) with a double triode: fluctuations in the temperature of the cathode of T_2 cause changes in the anode currents of the two halves of the double triode which are largely suppressed in the output signal.

Operating range. There are several factors which limit the maximum output current and voltage: mainly the maximum allowable dissipation of the series tubes, and also the fact that T_2, T_3, and T_4 may draw grid current, thus leading to a sharp drop in the loop gain. For excessive loads, for instance, T_3

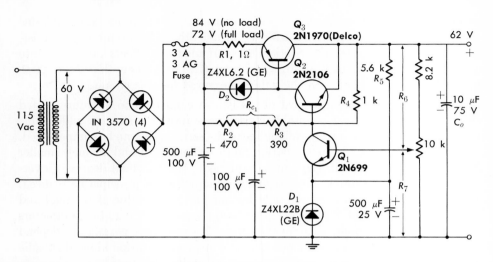

FIG. 7.16. Complete circuit of an electronically regulated power supply using semi-conductor components (from General Electric Transistor Manual, 1964, p. 228).

and T_4 will draw grid current because otherwise they cannot deliver the large current required. Then V_o rapidly drops when the load increases further. In this case, T_2 is cut off, and a small amount of grid current, limited only by R_a, will be drawn in T_3 and T_4. For a higher preset value of V_o, this condition is reached for a smaller overload; for output voltages above 300 V, the normal full-load current of 100 mA can no longer be delivered. For output voltages below 200 V, trouble is first experienced for *small* loads, since now the anode current of T_2 cannot be made large enough to cause a sufficient voltage drop in R_a to bring the series tubes sufficiently close to cutoff. A small control-grid current will then flow in T_2, and V_o cannot decrease any further.

EXAMPLE 2. *Regulated transistor supply.* Transistor power supplies are usually designed to deliver larger currents at lower voltages than their tube counterparts. The complete circuit of a transistor supply with series regulation is shown in Fig. 7.16. It is capable of delivering currents of up to 2 A at output voltages of from 45 to 65 V. We shall analyze its operation, which is in many respects similar to that of the tube circuit just discussed. The main differences are caused by the fact that the transistors operate as current amplifiers rather than voltage amplifiers.

A reference voltage, $V_{ref} = 22$ V, is developed across the Zener diode D_1 inserted in the emitter lead of the npn difference amplifier Q_1. At the base of Q_1 a fraction βV_o of the output voltage appears, determined by the voltage divider R_6, R_7. The divider current is made large compared with the base current I_{b_1} of Q_1, so that changes of I_{b_1} will have little influence on the feedback fraction. The base-emitter voltage difference $V_{be_1} = \beta V_o - V_{ref}$ of Q_1 determines the collector current I_{c_1}. Any small change ΔV_{be_1} of this difference causes a change of collector current:

$$\Delta I_{c_1} \approx \Delta V_{be_1}(h_{fe_1}/h_{ie_1}) = \Delta V_{be_1}g_{m_1}, \qquad (7.22)$$

where g_{m_1} is the *transconductance* of Q_1.

Equation (7.22) is readily verified by comparison with Eqs. (3.24) and (3.25) of Section 3.5.3.

The dc collector current I_{c_1} flows through the series combination $R_2 + R_3$ $(= R_{c_1})$ together with the base current I_{b_2} of Q_2 (generally $I_{b_2} \ll I_{c_1}$). From the circuit we see that

$$(I_{b_2} + I_{c_1})R_{c_1} \approx V_i - V_o \qquad (7.23)$$

if we neglect the small base-emitter voltage difference of Q_2.

The tandem arrangement of the npn-transistor Q_2 and the pnp power transistor Q_3 (Darlington connection) constitutes the series regulator. It is simply a current amplifier consisting of two directly coupled common-emitter stages in cascade. We denote its current gain $\Delta I_{c_3}/\Delta I_{b_2}$ by $A_{I(2,3)}$.

Expressions for internal resistance and regulation factor analogous to those for tube regulators can now be easily derived.

From (7.22) and (7.23) we see that a change ΔV_o of the output voltage results in a change, $\Delta I_{c_3} = -A_{I(2,3)}(h_{fe_1}/h_{ie_1})\beta\,\Delta V_o$, in the collector current of the series regulator transistor Q_3. Since for all except very small loads, we may neglect the fraction of I_{c_3} through R_5, R_6, and R_7 as well as the contribution of the emitter current of Q_2 to the output current, we may replace I_{c_3} with I_o, and obtain, for the internal resistance,

$$R_i = -\frac{\Delta V_o}{\Delta I_o} = \frac{1}{g_{m_1}A_{I(2,3)}\beta}. \qquad (7.24)$$

This expression closely resembles Eq. (7.21), derived for a tube circuit. Indeed, the quantity $g_m|A_0|$ for the tube circuit and the quantity $g_{m_1}A_{I(2,3)}$ for the transistor circuit both represent the ratio of the regulator element current and the input voltage to the difference amplifier.

To evaluate the internal resistance, we must know $A_{I(2,3)}$. If the voltage across Q_3 would remain constant for varying loads, we would simply have $A_{I(2,3)} = h_{fe_2}h_{fe_3} = A_{I(2,3)}^{(0)}$, the product of the current transfer ratios of the two transistors. However, $A_{I(2,3)}$ is considerably less than this value here for the same reason that it is in the tube circuit: the collector resistor, $R_{c_1} = R_2 + R_3$, of the difference amplifier is connected to the unregulated input voltage V_i, the source of which has a significant internal resistance R_{ii}. This causes a negative feedback to the base of Q_2 through R_{c_1}. The resulting current gain is

$$A_{I(2,3)} = \frac{A_{I(2,3)}^{(0)}}{1 + (R_{ii}/R_{c_1})A_{I(2,3)}^{(0)}}. \qquad (7.25)$$

From the data for the transistors Q_2 and Q_3 we find that $A_{I(2,3)}^{(0)} > 600$. Combining this with a measured value, $R_{ii} \approx 6\,\Omega$, for the internal resistance of the unregulated supply, and $R_{c_1} = 860\,\Omega$, we calculate $120 < A_{I(2,3)} < 160$. The transconductance g_{m_1} of Q_1 depends rather strongly on the current passed through it, which is determined by the load current. We use an average value $g_{m_1} \sim 0.1\,\text{A/V}$. Inserting these values and $\beta = 0.3$ into Eq. (7.24), we find for the internal resistance $R_i \approx 0.2\,\Omega$. Measured values range from 0.1–0.5 Ω.

An expression for the regulation factor can be written by analogy with Eq. (7.20), which gives the result for a tube circuit. We have only to replace $\mu|A_0|$ by the appropriate expression for a transistor circuit. In principle, $\mu|A_0|$ is that ratio of (opposite) changes of V_i and V_{be_1} for which I_{c_3} remains constant. This quantity is largely determined again by the direct influence of V_i on I_{b_2} through R_{c_1}. The circuit operates to keep V_o, and therefore $I_o \approx I_{c_3}$, constant when V_i is changed. For this reason, the influence of V_i on I_{b_2} must be compensated by a change of I_{c_1}: $-\Delta I_{c_1} \approx \Delta V_i/R_{c_1}$. When this is combined with Eq. (7.22), we see at once that $-\Delta V_i/\Delta V_{be_1} \approx R_{c_1}g_{m_1}$, so that Eq. (7.20) now looks like

$$\delta \approx (V_o/V_i)\beta R_{c_1}g_{m_1}. \tag{7.26}$$

With the circuit parameters just quoted, we obtain $\delta \approx 50$, in good agreement with the measured value.

The direct supply of the base current I_{b_2} of Q_2 from the unregulated input results in a considerable reduction of δ as well as a rather large increase of the internal resistance R_i. The use of a separate Zener-regulated supply in series with V_o to provide a constant voltage source for I_{b_2} gives an important improvement in performance. This, however, must be weighed against the increased complexity of the circuit.

An indispensable feature of all transistor supplies is an adequate overload protection. A transistor is so much more rapidly destroyed by overload than a tube that normal fuses, while offering sufficient protection in tube circuits, are too slow to give a good enough protection in transistor circuits.

In the circuit of Fig. 7.16, overload protection is achieved with the resistor $R_1 = 1\,\Omega$ in combination with the Zener diode D_2. For a load current larger than 5 A, the voltage drop in R_1 would exceed the Zener voltage of D_2, cutting off transistor Q_3. Therefore, the maximum load current is limited to about 5 A. At this current, the 3-A fuse will blow before Q_3 is damaged, even when the output is completely short-circuited. More refined methods of overload protection have been devised, some of them involving transistor switching circuits capable of switching off the series element very rapidly as soon as a certain preset load current is exceeded.

The number of cascaded transistors needed in the series regulator is determined by the maximum load current to be delivered. In the circuit just discussed, at least two transistors, Q_2 and Q_3, are required, since the maximum load current is about 200 times the maximum base current that can be delivered to Q_2

$(I_{b_2 \text{ max}} \approx (V_i - V_o)/R_{c_1} \approx 10 \text{ mA}, \ I_{c_3 \text{ max}} \approx 2 \text{ A})$. Estimated dc current transfer ratios for Q_2 and Q_3 are $h_{FE(2)} = 25$, $h_{FE(3)} = 15$; their product, $I_{c_3}/I_{b_2} = h_{FE(2)}h_{FE(3)} = 375$, exceeds the required value by a wide enough margin.

At zero load ($I_{c_3} \approx 11 \text{ mA}$, flowing into R_5 and $R_6 + R_7$), I_{b_2} will be quite small, so that almost all of the current through R_{c_1} will flow into the collector of Q_1. For

$$h_{FE(1)} = 50 \quad \text{and} \quad I_{c_1} \approx (V_i^{(0)} - V_o)/R_{c_1} = 13 \text{ mA},$$

we then have $I_{b_1} = 0.26 \text{ mA}$, which is small compared with the current through the voltage divider R_6, R_7, as was required in the beginning.

Stability of the feedback loop is of more concern in transistor regulators than in tube regulators because of the intrinsic phase shifts in the transistors. For this reason, transistor types with rather high cutoff frequencies have been chosen for Q_1 and Q_2. Further, a shunt capacitor C_o across the output reduces the loop gain to below unity at frequencies where the total phase shift in the loop exceeds 180°.

7.6.4 Electronic current regulation

It is clear that any method for electronic voltage regulation also provides current regulation so long as the load resistance remains constant. However, there are often requirements for regulating the current in a resistance, for example in a copper-wound magnet coil, in which the resistance depends rather strongly on temperature. In such cases, current-feedback circuits must be used. Usually, a small, very constant resistor, R_1, is inserted in series with the load for this purpose; the voltage V_1 across R_1 is then compared with a highly constant reference voltage V_{ref}. The difference between these two voltages is amplified as before, and the amplified signal is used to control all or part of the current through the load.

For practical reasons, V_1 must be kept small, frequently of the order of 1 V, in many cases. To achieve a sufficient stability of the output current, the difference amplifier must have a very low drift. Since drifts smaller than about 1 mV are hard to obtain with tube or transistor dc-amplifiers, the small dc voltage difference, $V_1 - V_{\text{ref}}$, is often converted into an ac-voltage with the aid of an electromechanical chopper of the type described in Section 6.6.3. The voltages V_1 and V_{ref} are applied to the two stationary chopper contacts, between which the chopper arm moves rapidly. Thus, at the arm there appears a square-wave ac-voltage, which can be amplified in an ac-amplifier. In this way, the drift, now caused chiefly by contact potential changes in the chopper, can be reduced to below 1 μV. After amplification, the ac-voltage is rectified in a phase-sensitive detector (see Problem 7.13). At the output of this detector, a dc-voltage appears, proportional to the voltage difference, $V_1 - V_{\text{ref}}$, and

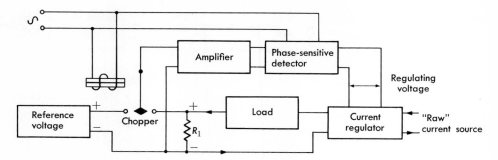

FIG. 7.17. Block diagram for a current regulator in which a chopper amplifier is incorporated to minimize drift.

conserving the sign of this difference. In addition to the amplified ac-voltage, a reference ac-voltage must be supplied to such a detector. This may be derived from the ac-supply driving the chopper. A block diagram of such a current regulator with a chopper amplifier is shown in Fig. 7.17. In favorable cases, currents may be kept constant within 0.001% with such regulators.

PROBLEMS

7.1   A transformer of negligible internal resistance applies a sinusoidal voltage $V_s = 100 \sin 120\pi t$ V through a rectifier diode D to a load resistor R_L, which varies from 1 kΩ to 2 kΩ (Fig. 7.18). Consider that the diode is (a) a typical high-vacuum rectifier, (b) a gas-filled rectifier with a breakdown and maintaining voltage of 15 V, (c) a typical silicon pn-junction rectifier. For each case, estimate

   (1)   the dc-current through the load,
   (2)   the dc voltage drop across the rectifier,
   (3)   the rms ac-current through the load,
   (4)   the ripple factor,
   (5)   the change in dc-voltage across the load as R_L is varied.

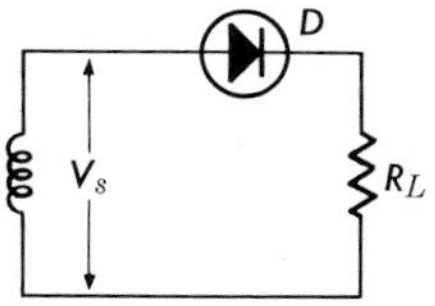

FIGURE 7.18

7.2   The peak inverse breakdown voltage of a silicon diode is 1 kV. What is the maximum dc-voltage which can be delivered to a load when such diodes are connected in

   (a)   a half-wave rectifier circuit,
   (b)   a full-wave rectifier circuit,
   (c)   a full-wave bridge rectifier circuit,
   (d)   a full-wave voltage-doubler circuit,
   (e)   a half-wave voltage-tripler circuit?

7.3   An inexpensive battery charger for a 12.6-V battery is constructed as shown in Fig. 7.19. The open-circuit secondary voltage $V_s = 40 \sin 120\pi t$ V. The transformer secondary has a resistance $R_s = 2\,\Omega$. The diode has 1-Ω forward resistance.

   (a)   What setting of the variable resistor R will keep the peak diode current below 5 A if the battery voltage $V_b = 11$ V?

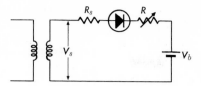

FIGURE 7.19

(b) What is the maximum dc-current delivered to the battery under the conditions of (a)?

(c) What is the total rms-power drawn from the line?

7.4 A transformer of negligible internal resistance, which furnishes a secondary voltage of $V_s = 350$ V rms either side of the center tap, is connected through two halves of a 5U4-G rectifier tube in the full-wave rectifier circuit shown in Fig. 7.20, Here $C_1 = C_2 = C_3 = 16\,\mu\text{F}$; $L_1 = L_2 = 15$ H, 100 Ω.

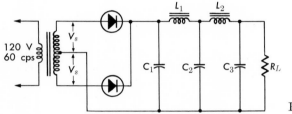

FIGURE 7.20

(a) Calculate the dc-voltage and ac ripple voltage across the load R_L for $R_L = 3$ kΩ and 6 kΩ.

(b) Repeat (a) for the same circuit, but with C_1 removed.

(c) Find the minimum value of R_L which will give reasonable regulation for both (a) and (b).

7.5 With the circuit for Problem 7.4 (b) (C_1 removed), find a value for V_s such that the supply will provide a dc-voltage of 300 V at a current of 100 mA to R_L. Assume that the rectifier is a 5U4-G, as before, but now assume that the transformer secondary introduces a resistance of 50 Ω in either leg. Find the ac ripple voltage across the load. Suppose that L_1 is a "swinging" choke with an inductance of 15 H at 100 mA but a higher inductance at low current; find a value for the minimum load resistance ("bleeder" resistance) that must always be connected across the output to avoid diode cutoff if the maximum value of L_1 is 40 H.

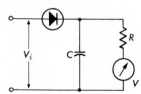

FIGURE 7.21

7.6 A peak voltmeter circuit is made by connecting a dc-voltmeter, rectifier, and condenser as shown in Fig. 7.21. Assume that the input V_i is a sinusoidal voltage and that the forward resistance of the diode is negligible. What is the minimum frequency for which the meter will read a value within 5% of the peak input voltage?

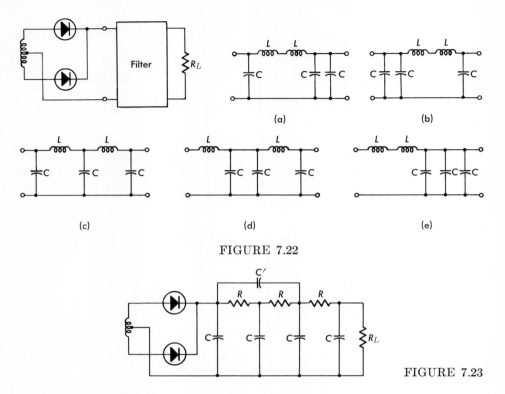

FIGURE 7.22

FIGURE 7.23

7.7 A full-wave rectifier circuit is constructed, as shown in Fig. 7.22, from a transformer which provides 300 V rms on either side of the center tap. The rectifier output is to be filtered before being connected across the load $R_L = 5$ kΩ. The five possible filter arrangements (a) through (e) all use two identical chokes, $L = 20$ H, and three identical condensers, $C = 20\,\mu$F. Ignoring any dc-drops in the transformer, rectifiers, or chokes, compare the relative dc output voltages and ac ripple voltages across the load for the different filter arrangements.

7.8 In the power supply filter shown in Fig. 7.23, the three resistors R are equal and much smaller than the load resistor R_L. The four condensers C are equal. Find a value for the parallel condenser C' which will produce minimum ripple across the load.

7.9 Figure 7.24 is a diagram of a three-phase full-wave rectifier. Assume that the open-circuit secondary voltage V_s across each leg of the secondary has an rms-value of 350 V and a frequency of 60 cps, with 120° phase shift between adjacent legs, that each secondary winding has a resistance of 10 Ω and that the diodes are silicon rectifiers with a forward resistance of 5 Ω. Find the dc-voltage and ac ripple voltage across the 500-Ω load.

7.10 The diagram in Fig. 7.25 shows a variable-voltage power supply with silicon-controlled rectifiers (SCR). Explain qualitatively the operation of the circuit. Estimate the range in dc output voltage obtainable across R_L if $V_s = 200$ V rms, $R_2 = R_3 = 100$ kΩ, $C = 10\,\mu$F, $R_1 = 0$–500 kΩ. Ignore any possible effects due to current drawn through the protective resistors R by the SCR gates and to drops across the SCR's or in the transformer.

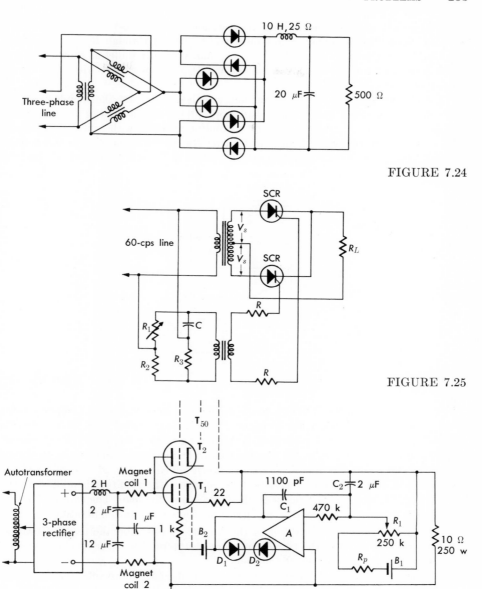

FIGURE 7.24

FIGURE 7.25

FIGURE 7.26

7.11   Figure 7.26 shows the arrangement of components for a regulated power supply to provide current to a magnet used for nuclear magnetic-resonance experiments, which require a magnetic field stable to one part in 10^5. The supply furnishes a voltage of 0–2 kV (depending on the setting of the autotransformer) at a current of 0–3 A. The regulating current range is adjusted by the 40-turn potentiometer R_1. The reference voltage battery B_1 is a 20.05-V mercury cell in a thermostatically controlled box; R_p is a preset current-limiting resistor; and B_2 is a 33-V bias battery. A is a chopper-stabilized amplifier, whose output is connected through B_2 to the grids of 50 regulator triodes T1, . . . , T50, which are connected in parallel as shown; D_1 is a Zener diode with a 10-V breakdown voltage and D_2 is a Zener diode with a 2-V breakdown voltage.

Describe the operation of the circuit and calculate values for the open-loop gain of the chopper-stabilized amplifier A and appropriate characteristics for the series regulator tubes T1, . . . , T50 to provide adequate regulation with expected variations in line voltage of 10% and changes in load resistance due to heating of the magnet of 2%. Discuss the role of the Zener diodes, D_1 and D_2, and condensers C_1 and C_2.

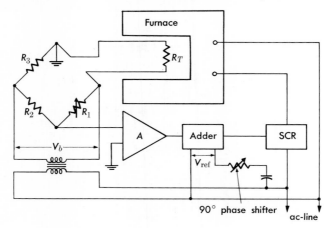

FIGURE 7.27

7.12   The diagram in Fig. 7.27 represents a schematic arrangement of components for a temperature-control circuit for a furnace. A change in temperature of the furnace causes a change in electrical resistance of the sensing resistor R_T, which in turn causes an imbalance of the ac-bridge, so that a signal of line frequency appears at the input to the amplifier A. The amplified signal is then added to a fixed reference voltage V_{ref}, which is 90° out of phase with the line voltage. The resultant is applied to the gate of an SCR which is in series with the furnace and the line. The current through the furnace is thereby varied to compensate for the change in temperature.

(a) Discuss the general operation of the circuit, showing how the temperature can be set initially and how the circuit can compensate for either increases or decreases in furnace temperature from the set point.

(b) Formulate a practical design for such a circuit, specifying values for the bridge components, R_1, R_2, and R_3, and the bridge voltage V_b, the reference voltage V_{ref}, the amplifier gain A, and the SCR characteristics, for the following conditions.

Furnace power required: 100 V rms at 10 A at 1000°C.

Line voltage: 120 V rms ± 10%.

R_T: platinum resistor, 50 Ω at room temperature, temperature coefficient of resistance 0.004/°C.

Temperature set range: 100°C to 1000°C.

Temperature control: fluctuations less than ±1°C at any temperature.

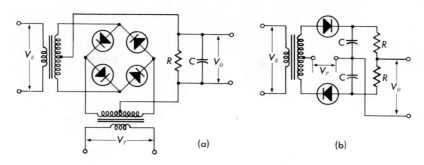

FIGURE 7.28

7.13   Figure 7.28 shows two examples of a very useful and important circuit, usually called a *phase-sensitive detector*, or *lock-in detector*. The function of the circuit is to provide a dc output voltage, V_o, which is proportional to the amplitude of the input signal voltage V_s, if V_s is of the same frequency as the reference signal V_r. The dc output voltage is also proportional to cos ϕ, ϕ being the phase angle between V_r and V_s. Phase reversal thus leads to reversal of the sign of the output voltage, whence the circuit derives its name.   Such circuits are particularly useful where the signal V_s may be accompanied by unwanted noise and interference signals, since only those components of the signal which satisfy the proper phase relationships will appear at the output. Analyze the behavior of each of the circuits shown (a) when V_s and V_r are of the same frequency but are different in phase and (b) when they are of slightly different frequency.   Show how the output voltage depends on the magnitude of V_r and the time constant RC (steady-state solution only).

REFERENCES

Arguimbau, L. B., *Vacuum Tube Circuits*, Wiley, 1956.

Elmore, W. C., and M. Sands, *Electronics*, McGraw-Hill, 1949, Chapter 7.

Landee, R. W., D. C. Davis, and A. P. Albrecht, *Electronic Designers Handbook*, McGraw-Hill, 1957, Chapter 15.

Terman, F. E., *Radio Engineers Handbook*, McGraw-Hill, 1943, Section 8.

Chapter 8

OSCILLATORS

8.1 GENERAL CONSIDERATIONS

This chapter deals with methods for generating signals of essentially sinusoidal wave shape and widely different frequencies. The operation of circuits used for this purpose generally involves one of the following two principles:

1. *Positive feedback in an amplifier (gain A_0) through a frequency-selective feedback network (response function β).* In Section 5.1 the general condition $\beta A_0 = +1$ was derived for regeneration in such a circuit. Since the type of feedback network used here in its general form has four terminals, two for the input signal and two for the output signal, it is commonly called a four-terminal network, and the oscillator circuit may be designated a *four-terminal oscillator*. (In practice one of the output terminals is usually common to one of the input terminals.)

2. *Regeneration of a tuned circuit by incorporation of a circuit element or circuit representing a negative resistance.* Such a circuit element can be used either in parallel or in series with the oscillating circuit, with only two connections needed between the negative-resistance element and the tuned circuit; hence, this type of oscillator is frequently called a *two-terminal oscillator*.

The construction of the feedback network or tuned circuit and the choice of the active circuit elements are determined by the frequency range in which the oscillator is intended to work. Suitable choices are surveyed in Fig. 8.1. The upper frequency limit of the indicated ranges is determined by factors of a fundamental nature (e.g., electron transit time in tubes, self-inductance of leads); the lower frequency limit is usually determined by considerations of a practical nature (e.g., the size of the components).

An oscillator circuit frequently has special requirements dictated by its intended use, which may have an important bearing on the choice of an optimal circuit. They include (a) frequency stability, (b) amplitude stability (at fixed frequency and with variable frequency), and (c) freedom from nonlinear distortion. For example, oscillators intended for measuring the frequency character-

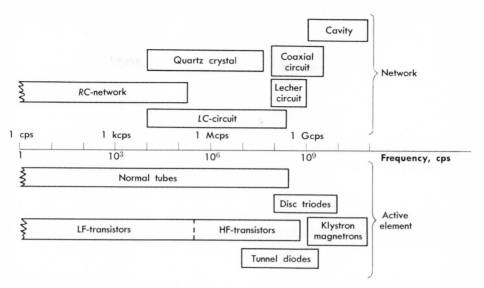

FIG. 8.1.   Preferred choices of circuit elements for oscillators operating in various frequency ranges.

istics of amplifiers must meet strict requirements regarding (b) and (c), while oscillators intended for use in radio transmitters must primarily have excellent frequency stability.

8.2 LOW-FREQUENCY OSCILLATORS

8.2.1 *RC-oscillators.*

These circuits consist of positive feedback amplifiers with a feedback network constructed of resistive and capacitive elements.

A. Phase-shift oscillators with a single amplifier stage. Two examples of this type of circuit are shown in Fig. 8.2; in both, networks consisting of three RC-sections are used. The oscillator shown in Fig. 8.2(a) contains three *integrating* sections, each of which produces a phase lag. The following assumptions are made.

1. $b \gg 1$, that is, each subsequent RC-section does not appreciably influence the previous section.

2. The value of the anode resistance satisfies the relation $R_o = R_a r_p/(R_a + r_p) = R$ (where r_p is the internal tube resistance), and hence the sections $R_o - C$, $bR - C/b$, and $b^2 R - C/b^2$ give equal phase shifts. The tube current and the output voltage of the network will be in phase if the phase lag per section is 60°; this is the case for a frequency, f_0, for which $\tan^{-1}(2\pi f_0 RC) = 60°$, so that

$$f_0 = \sqrt{3}/2\pi RC. \tag{8.1}$$

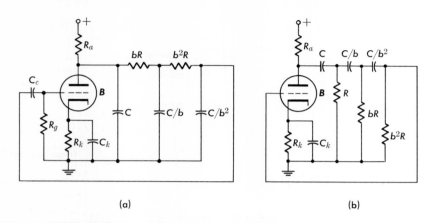

(a)   (b)

FIG. 8.2.   Phase shift oscillators (a) with "integrating" phase shift networks, (b) with "differentiating" phase shift networks.

3. The coupling network $C_c R_g$ does not produce a phase shift at frequency f_0; hence there is positive feedback at that frequency. Since each RC-section attenuates the signal by a factor of 2, the amplification must be larger than 8,

$$|A_0| > 8, \tag{8.2}$$

for the circuit to oscillate. If one or more of these assumptions are invalid, Eqs. (8.1) and (8.2) will become more complicated, but the principle remains exactly the same; oscillation will occur when the total phase shift adds to 180° if the amplifier gain exceeds the network attenuation factor.

The circuit of Fig. 8.2(b) contains three *differentiating* RC-sections, each of which produces a phase lead. Again, if we make the simplifying assumptions that

1. $b \gg 1$,

2. the anode resistance R_a is much smaller than the impedance of the RC-network connected to it,

3. the input impedance of the tube is large compared with $b^2 R$,

then expressions completely analogous to (8.1) and (8.2) are obtained for the operating frequency and the minimum gain required for oscillations:

$$f_0 = 1/2\pi RC\sqrt{3}, \tag{8.3}$$

$$|A_0| > 8. \tag{8.4}$$

The circuits just described are not very suitable for variable-frequency oscillators, because three resistors or three capacitors must be changed simultaneously to obtain good frequency control over a wide range. Therefore, these oscillators are used mostly in fixed-frequency applications. The signal amplitude

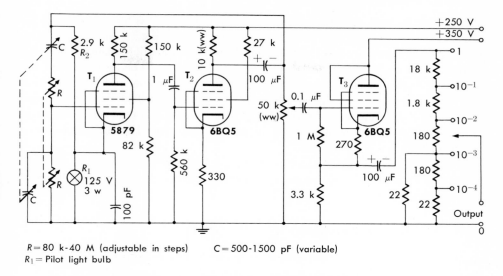

R = 80 k-40 M (adjustable in steps)   C = 500-1500 pF (variable)
R_1 = Pilot light bulb

FIG. 8.3. RC-oscillator with a frequency range of 3 cps to 35 kcps.

is determined by the grid bias on the tube. Since the amplitude is limited by grid current, the signal will have a rather large nonlinear distortion, which, however, can be reduced by inclusion of a bypassed cathode resistance R_k.

The design considerations for phase-shift oscillators with transistors are quite similar to those for tube oscillators, but because of the low input resistance of a transistor, it is more difficult to fulfill the condition $b \gg 1$.

B. Wien-bridge RC-oscillator A practical example of a widely used RC-oscillator circuit which generates a sinusoidal signal with small distortion over a large frequency range is shown in Fig. 8.3. In this oscillator, an amplifier with two phase-inverting tubes T_1 and T_2 is used; therefore, in this case the feedback network should give *zero* phase shift at the oscillation frequency. This network consists of one arm of a *Wien bridge* consisting of two equal resistors (R) and two equal capacitors (C), as shown in the figure. This network has zero phase shift at a frequency

$$f_0 = 1/2\pi RC. \tag{8.5}$$

Moreover, at this frequency the attenuation factor of the filter reaches its minimum value of 3. (The phase shift also goes to 0 for $f \to 0$ and $f \to \infty$; in these cases, though, the attenuation is infinite.) Equation (8.5) is exact only if the amplifier itself does not produce any phase shift in the frequency range to be covered. The amplifier phase characteristic can be improved by negative feedback; in the circuit shown in Fig. 8.3, this feedback is provided by the voltage divider R_2, R_1.

The linearity of the amplifier is also improved by negative feedback so long as no grid current flows. To prevent grid current, the amplitude of the generated signal must be kept sufficiently small. We can achieve this by choosing for R_1 a resistor with a high positive temperature coefficient, e.g., a small light bulb. For increasing amplitude of the generated ac-voltage, the resistance R_1 will increase, and with it the amount of negative feedback. The amplitude of the generated voltage will thereby adjust itself to such a value that the condition $\beta A_0 = +1$ is precisely fulfilled while the amplifier is still in its linear range. A constant-amplitude output signal over a large frequency range is also obtained in this way, with a low-impedance output derived from the cathode-follower circuit of tube T_3.

Continuous frequency control is provided by two equal, ganged variable capacitors C, and stepwise frequency control by a switch that selects different pairs of resistors R.

8.2.2 Beat-frequency oscillators

Another method for generating sine waves with a large continuously variable frequency range is the *beat-frequency* oscillator shown schematically in Fig. 8.4. This circuit consists of two oscillators, Osc 1 and Osc 2; one is operated at a fixed frequency, the other one is variable. The oscillators generate sine waves with frequencies ω_1 and ω_2, both high in comparison with the highest frequency that the beat-frequency oscillator should deliver. The oscillator signals are mixed in a mixer M, at the output of which a signal proportional to the *product* of the input voltages appears (among others). [In principle, any nonlinear circuit element can be used in such a *multiplicative mixer;* in practice, a hexode or heptode is often employed.]

Since, from trigonometry,

$$2 \cos \omega_1 t \cos \omega_2 t = \cos (\omega_1 + \omega_2)t + \cos (\omega_1 - \omega_2)t,$$

the product of the two signals contains a component of frequency $|\omega_1 - \omega_2|$, the beat frequency. This is the signal we want. We eliminate unwanted components (those with frequencies ω_1, ω_2, $2\omega_1$, $2\omega_2$, and $\omega_1 + \omega_2$) by passing the total output signal from the mixer through a low-pass filter F. After this, the desired beat-frequency component may be amplified in a linear amplifier A.

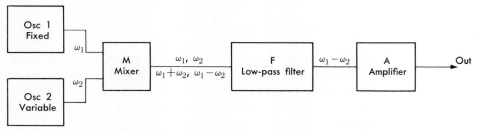

FIG. 8.4. Block diagram of a beat-frequency oscillator.

To obtain signals of good frequency stability, expecially at very low frequencies, Osc 1 and Osc 2 must be highly stable. They must also be very well isolated electrically, for otherwise they may have a tendency to lock in, especially for small differences $\omega_1 - \omega_2$. (That is, they start oscillating at exactly the same frequency. This phenomenon is also called *pulling*.)

8.2.3 Sine-wave generation by distortion of a triangular sawtooth

It is difficult to construct good *RC*- or beat-frequency oscillators for very low frequencies (i.e., lower than 1 cps), which will directly generate a sinusoidal signal with small distortion. Sine waves with a very long period (up to 1000 sec) can be obtained by the shaping of other wave forms that can more easily be generated at very low frequencies. A suitable wave form is the triangular saw-tooth, which we may obtain by integrating a square wave (see Section 9.2.4). Such a triangular wave may be applied to a system of diodes with different biases, as shown in Fig. 8.5.

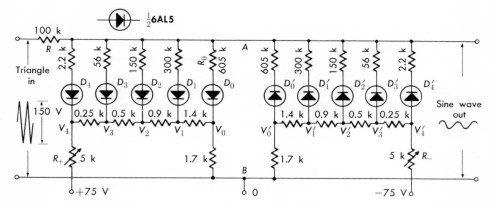

FIG. 8.5. Diode network for generating very-low-frequency sinusoidal signals by distortion of a triangular sawtooth voltage.

When the voltage at A rises above a certain value, V_0, D_0 starts conducting. From this moment on the combination (R, R_0) acts as a voltage divider, allowing only a fraction, $R_0/(R_0 + R)$, of any further increment of the input voltage to reach the output. As the input voltage rises further, diodes D_1, D_2, etc., biased at voltages $\cdots > V_2 > V_1 > V_0$, start conducting. Every time the input voltage exceeds one of these biases, the rise of the output voltage becomes slower. The curvature of the diode characteristics rounds off sudden kinks in the output voltage. By a careful adjustment of the variable resistor R_+ and the fixed resistors R_0, $R_1 \ldots$, the positive half of the output voltage can be made to approximate a sine wave within 1%; likewise, a careful adjustment of R_- takes care of the negative half of the sine wave. This method of "modeling" wave shapes with the aid of biased diodes is also applied in function generators, which are frequently used in electronic analog computers.*

8.3   HIGH-FREQUENCY OSCILLATORS

In this section we shall restrict our attention mainly to a (rather brief) treatment of conventional oscillators with either a tuned LC-circuit or a quartz crystal. Such oscillators are suitable in a frequency range extending from a few kcps to a few hundred Mcps.

For frequencies above a few hundred kcps, LC-oscillators replace RC-oscillators since spurious capacities set an upper limit to the operating frequency of RC-feedback networks. In LC-oscillators, these capacities are of course also present, but there they form part of the capacity of the circuit; in this case, their adverse influence starts at much higher frequencies, at about 100 Mcps. At such high frequencies the *quality* (usually designated as the *circuit Q*) of a normal LC-circuit, consisting of a separate coil and condenser, becomes so low that it does not oscillate readily, and the frequency generated is not very constant. Much higher values of Q can be obtained at these frequencies by use of circuits with distributed capacitance and inductance, such as Lecher circuits or coaxial circuits, while at still higher frequencies (> 1000 Mcps) resonant cavities are used. At such frequencies conventional tubes do not work properly because of the inductance of their internal leads and, more fundamentally, because the transit time of the electrons, especially in the cathode-to-grid space, becomes comparable to the period of the generated signal. Still higher frequencies may be attained by use of special tubes (disk triodes) and with other devices, like *klystrons, magnetrons,* and *traveling wave tubes,* which operate on entirely different principles. The operation of these devices depends primarily on the same transit-time effects that set a limitation to the use of conventional tubes. Microwave signals with frequencies of over 100,000 Mcps can be generated with these special devices. Such microwave oscillators are used in radar and microwave television links; they also have important applications in physics, especially atomic and solid-state physics. Further information can be found in many references.†

8.3.1   Four-terminal LC-oscillators

In these oscillators, a feedback network consisting of inductances and condensers is used, effectively connected between the anode and grid of the oscillator tube

---

* See G. A. Korn and T. M. Korn, *Electronic Analog Computers*, McGraw-Hill, 1956, pp. 290–299.
† See, for example, the following: G. G. Montgomery, R. H. Dicke, and E. M. Purcell, *Principles of Microwave Circuits*, McGraw-Hill, 1948; H. A. Atwater, *Introduction to Microwave Theory*, McGraw-Hill, 1962; E. L. Ginzton, *Microwave Measurements*, McGraw-Hill, 1957; A. F. Harvey, *Microwave Engineering*, Academic Press, 1963.

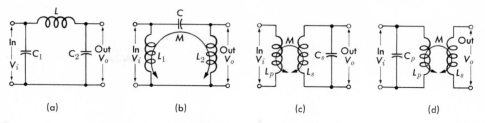

FIG. 8.6. Four-terminal networks for LC-oscillators.

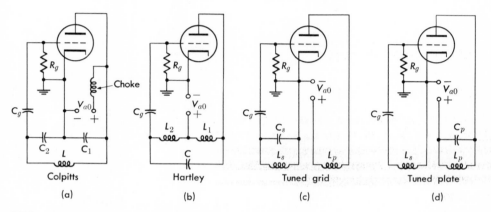

FIG. 8.7. Basic circuit arrangements for LC-oscillators with the four-terminal networks shown in Fig. 8.6.

(or the collector and base of the oscillator transistor). The required positive feedback is obtained when the input current (i.e., the anode or collector current) is in phase with the output voltage of the four-terminal network.* In most cases this condition is fulfilled only at one value of the frequency, and usually this frequency deviates only very slightly from the resonant frequency of the four-terminal network. Some commonly used feedback networks are shown in Fig. 8.6. Network (a) has a resonant frequency $\omega_{\text{res}} = 1/\sqrt{LC}$, with $C = C_1C_2/(C_1 + C_2)$; the input-output voltage ratio at this frequency is $v_o/v_i = -C_1/C_2$. Network (b) has a resonant frequency $\omega_{\text{res}} = 1/\sqrt{LC}$, with $L = L_1 + L_2 + 2M$ (M is the coefficient of mutual induction); at this frequency, $v_o/v_i = -(L_2 + M)/(L_1 + M)$. In parts (c) and (d) examples are given of networks with tuned transformers; for (c), $\omega_{\text{res}} = 1/\sqrt{L_sC_s}$ and $v_o/v_i = -L_s/M$, while for (d), $\omega_{\text{res}} = 1/\sqrt{L_pC_p}$ and $v_o/v_i = -M/L_p$. Basic oscillator circuits using these networks are shown in Fig. 8.7. Which of these circuits is preferable depends mainly on rather trivial practical matters. For instance, if the oscillator must be tuned with a variable condenser of which one set of plates is grounded, circuit (c) is preferred; the Colpitts circuit of Fig.

---

* This is true only when the transit time of the charge carriers can be neglected.

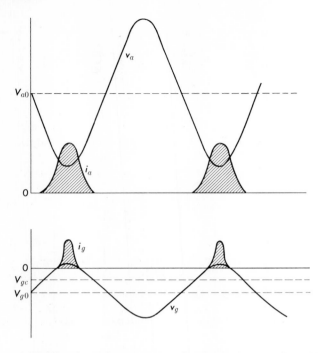

FIG. 8.8. Grid and anode currents and voltages in an *LC*-oscillator.

8.7(a) has the advantage of simple coil construction. All the oscillators employ a grid condenser C_g and a grid resistor R_g to provide automatic adjustment of the grid bias. At the moment the oscillator is switched on, the grid voltage is zero; the mutual conductance therefore is high, and the loop amplification $\beta A_0 \gg +1$. The amplitude of the generated signal therefore rises rapidly until the ac-anode signal reaches an amplitude only a little smaller than the supply voltage V_{a0}. At the grid the voltage is comprised of two terms, the output ac-voltage of the feedback network transmitted through C_g and a negative dc-voltage, V_{g0}, resulting from grid current. Grid current, flowing at the peaks of the ac-grid voltage, recharges C_g in exactly the same way as in a half-wave rectifier. During the rest of each period, C_g discharges through R_g. The time constant $C_g R_g$ is made large compared with the period T of the oscillator frequency (for example, $C_g R_g > 10T$). This time constant should not be made too large, however, since a very large value may lead to periodic interruption of the oscillation (*superregenerative* behavior). Usually, the dc bias V_{g0} is larger than the cutoff voltage V_{gc} of the tube; the tube therefore is operated in Class C_2 (see Section 4.2.1). Anode current flows in short pulses, just when the anode voltage is at its minimum value. The general behavior of the grid and anode voltages and currents is shown in Fig. 8.8.

A convenient method for deriving signals from oscillators of the types shown in Fig. 8.7 is by inductive coupling of an output coil to the oscillator coil. When the oscillator is loaded in this or any other way, the ac anode and grid voltages decrease, and therefore the negative grid bias V_{g0} decreases. Anode current then flows during a larger part of a cycle, and the average anode current increases.

Clearly, the sine wave at the anode will often show appreciable nonlinear distortion, because it is developed by a current delivered in short pulses. The higher the quality of the LC-circuit (circuit Q), the lower the distortion. Since Q decreases when the oscillator is loaded, oscillators for pure sine waves should be loaded as little as possible.

Frequency stability. It is often important to keep the influence of changes in temperature, supply voltages, and load on the oscillator frequency as small as possible. Therefore, we need to understand the way in which these quantities influence the frequency.

1. *Temperature dependence of the resonant frequency of the circuit.* Changes in resonant frequency can occur due to thermal expansion of materials used for coils and condensers with rising temperature. Coils should therefore be wound on ceramic forms with a small coefficient of expansion, and the wire should be tightly stretched during winding. Commonly, insulating material in variable condensers is made of ceramic for the same reason. Low temperature-coefficient fixed condensers use mainly mica as a dielectric, with the electrodes formed by vacuum deposition on either side of the mica. To keep the heat dissipated in the LC-circuit low, the oscillator input power is chosen as small as possible; in addition, the circuit components should be thermally shielded from parts that generate heat, especially the tubes. In general, ceramic condensers should be avoided in tuned circuits for high-stability oscillators because the (negative) temperature coefficient of a ceramic dielectric is often quite large. In some cases, however, a small ceramic condenser can be used to compensate the influence on the frequency of other circuit components with positive temperature coefficients. Such a compensating condenser may be placed in parallel with the main tuning condenser (see Fig. 8.10).

2. *Influence of the tube.* The oscillator frequency may be affected by various tube parameters, especially the internal tube capacities and the internal resistance of the grid and anode. These parameters, in turn, depend on the heater and anode voltages. Since the internal tube capacities are in parallel with the input and output of the feedback network, it is clear that variations of these capacities must influence the oscillator frequency. The influence on the frequency of changes of the internal tube resistances can be understood if we imagine that these resistances are present across the input and output of the four terminal networks of Fig. 8.6. Such resistances will influence the phase relation between the input current and output voltage; in particular, for the resistively loaded circuit, the frequency at which these two quantities are in phase will be different from that for the unloaded circuit. This difference will be smaller as the Q of the LC-circuit (including the loading by the tube) becomes higher. (A phase shift $\Delta\phi$ be-

tween output voltage and input current and a small relative change $\Delta\omega/\omega$ of the resonance frequency are related by $\Delta\phi = -2Q\,\Delta\omega/\omega$, provided that $Q \gg 1$.)

The tube resistances loading the LC-circuit can be transformed into one effective resistance R in parallel. If we assume that the circuit Q is entirely determined by this resistance, then $Q = R\sqrt{C/L}$. From this relation, we see that a circuit with a high C/L ratio should be used. The influence of changes of the tube capacities is also smaller as C/L is made larger.

The effective circuit Q can be further increased if we connect the tube between taps on the tuned circuit. In this way, the transformed resistance R across the circuit is increased while the transformed capacitance is decreased. The circuit of a capacitively tapped Colpitts oscillator is shown in Fig. 8.9. This circuit is commonly called the *Clapp oscillator*. Characteristically, C_1 and C_2 are made five times larger than C_3.

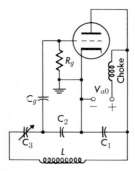

FIG. 8.9. Circuit diagram of the Clapp oscillator.

3. *Influence of the load.* When an oscillator is loaded, its frequency may change because resistance, capacitance, or inductance is coupled into the tuned circuit and because the operating point of the tube shifts. To counteract these effects, a second stage, which effectively isolates the load from the oscillator, is often inserted. This stage itself should present a small and constant load to the oscillator. For one thing, it should not be allowed to draw grid current. Rather good isolation between load and oscillator can also be achieved in the electron-coupled oscillator circuit (ECO), in which only one tube is used. An example of this is shown in Fig. 8.10. In this circuit a pentode is used, its screen grid acting as the oscillator anode.

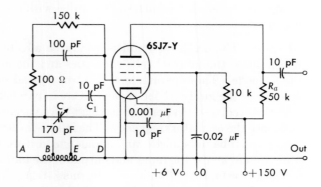

FIG. 8.10. Circuit of an electron-coupled oscillator with good frequency stability (range 2 to 4 Mcps); C_1 is a special ceramic condenser which provides temperature compensation for the LC-circuit. The grid is tapped at point B and the cathode at point E on the coil (the winding ratios are $N_{BD}/N_{AD} = 0.4$ and $N_{ED}/N_{AD} = 0.15$).

This oscillator circuit can be compared with that of Fig. 8.7(b). One difference is that here the screen grid, instead of the cathode, is grounded for high frequencies. Further, the grid is tapped on the coil to reduce the influence of changes in the tube parameters on the oscillator frequency. The load is coupled to the anode of the tube. Since a pentode with a high amplification factor is used, the oscillator current will depend only very slightly on the anode load; further, the screen grid, which is bypassed to ground for signal frequencies, provides a good capacitive separation between the load and the oscillator. If a sine wave is required at the output, the anode resistor should be replaced by a second tuned circuit. This circuit can also be tuned to some harmonic of the fundamental oscillator frequency; the circuit then acts as a *frequency multiplier*.

8.3.2   Crystal oscillators

Very high frequency stability can be obtained with oscillators in which the frequency is determined by a mechanically vibrating element. Such oscillators are invariably for fixed-frequency operation; their frequency can at best be varied by an extremely small amount. At low frequencies an electrically driven tuning fork is sometimes used as the frequency determining element; at higher frequencies (some kcps to about 100 Mcps), quartz crystal plates are used almost exclusively as the vibrating element. Quartz crystals are piezoelectric; i.e., an electric field gives rise to a mechanical deformation of the crystal. Conversely, a mechanical deformation of the crystal creates opposite charges on the crystal

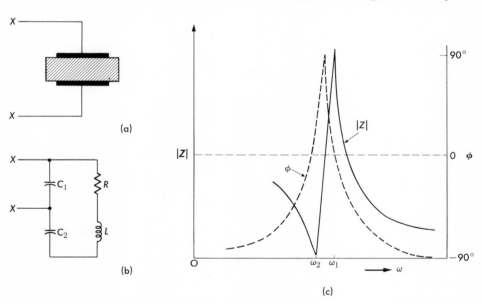

FIG. 8.11. (a) Quartz crystal plate and (b) its equivalent circuit. (c) Magnitude and phase angle of the impedance of the crystal near resonance.

faces, allowing energy to be transferred from the crystal into an electronic circuit. Since the damping of a well-mounted quartz crystal is extremely small, the mechanical resonance is very sharp. Electrically, a quartz crystal between metal electrodes (often these are vacuum evaporated onto the quartz) is equivalent to a tuned circuit with very high Q ($\sim 10^5$). The equivalent circuit is shown in Fig. 8.11(b).

The capacity C_1 (this is the real electrostatic capacity between the electrodes if the crystal does not vibrate) is much larger than C_2 (the capacity which represents the elasticity of the crystal). In practice we may have $C_1/C_2 \sim 100$. This high ratio implies extremely loose coupling between the tuned circuit and the other parts of the oscillator circuit. The equivalent circuit has two resonant frequencies: parallel resonance is found for a frequency $\omega_1 = 1/\sqrt{LC}$ with $C = C_1 C_2/(C_1 + C_2)$, series resonance for a frequency $\omega_2 = 1/\sqrt{LC_2}$. Since $C_1/C_2 \gg 1$, these frequencies lie very close together.

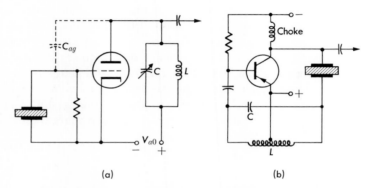

(a)   (b)

FIG. 8.12. Examples of crystal-oscillator circuits.

The frequency dependence of the magnitude and the phase angle of the impedance between the points X is given in Fig. 8.11(c). Two basic crystal-oscillator circuits are shown in Fig. 8.12. In the circuit of Fig. 8.12(a), energy is supplied to the crystal through the anode-to-grid capacitance C_{ag} of the oscillator triode (if a pentode is used as the oscillator tube, C_{ag} must often be increased by an external capacitor). The tuned circuit in the anode should be adjusted in such a way that both the anode circuit and the equivalent crystal circuit behave inductively at the frequency of oscillation, for only then can a zero phase shift between the tube current and the feedback voltage be obtained. The circuit will oscillate at a frequency very slightly lower than ω_1 in Fig. 8.11(c).

In Fig. 8.12(b), a transistor oscillator is shown which resembles the Hartley circuit of Fig. 8.7(b). However, the collector is coupled to the LC-circuit not through a bypass capacitor but, rather, through the crystal. Since the impedance of the crystal is low only very close to its series resonant frequency ω_2 the circuit will oscillate close to that frequency. For a more extensive treatment of these and other crystal oscillators and of the properties of quartz crystals, the reader is referred to the literature.*

8.3.3 Two-terminal oscillators

Only two examples will be mentioned here of oscillators incorporating negative-resistance circuit elements for undamping LC-circuits. We have already encountered both of these circuit elements. The first is a tetrode adjusted to the anomalous part of its I_a vs. V_a characteristic, where the anode current decreases with increasing anode voltage due to secondary-emission effects (see Fig. 2.23). In this region the plate resistance of the tetrode is negative. A tuned circuit in the anode lead of a tetrode operating in this region will be undamped, and the circuit may oscillate. This circuit, called the *dynatron oscillator*, is rarely used today.

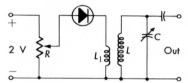

FIG. 8.13. Principle of a two-terminal oscillator using a tunnel diode.

However, the other negative-resistance circuit element we have treated, the tunnel diode, is currently widely used in two-terminal oscillator circuits; the principle of such an oscillator is shown in Fig. 8.13. With a (low resistance) potentiometer, the tunnel-diode forward voltage is adjusted to its maximum negative internal resistance. This negative resistance, coupled by means of L_1 into the LC-circuit, undamps this circuit, and will cause it to oscillate at its resonant frequency $\omega_r = 1/\sqrt{LC}$ if its Q-value is large enough. Frequencies of up to thousands of Mcps have been generated with tunnel-diode oscillators.†

PROBLEMS

8.1 For the circuit shown in Fig. 8.14, $L = 400 \,\mu\text{H}$, $C = 1000 \,\text{pF}$, $g_m = 1.5 \,\text{mA/V}$, $r_p = 30 \,\text{k}\Omega$. Ignoring the effects of coil losses and of the grid-bias network $R_g C_g$, find
  (a) the minimum value of R for which the circuit will oscillate,
  (b) the approximate frequency of oscillation.

8.2 Two identical triodes are connected in the oscillator circuit shown in Fig. 8.15. Assuming that the coupling condensers C_c and the grid resistors R_g are large, and

---

* See, for example, the following: F. E. Terman, *Radio Engineers Handbook*, Chapters 14 and 15, McGraw-Hill, 1943; R. W. Landee, D. C. Davis, and A. P. Albrecht, *Electronic Designers Handbook*, Chapter 6, McGraw-Hill, 1957.
† F. Sterzer and D. E. Nelson, "Tunnel-diode Microwave Oscillators," *Proc. Inst. Radio Engrs.* **49**, 744–753 (1961).

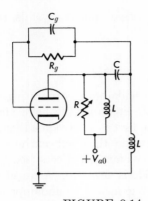

FIGURE 8.14

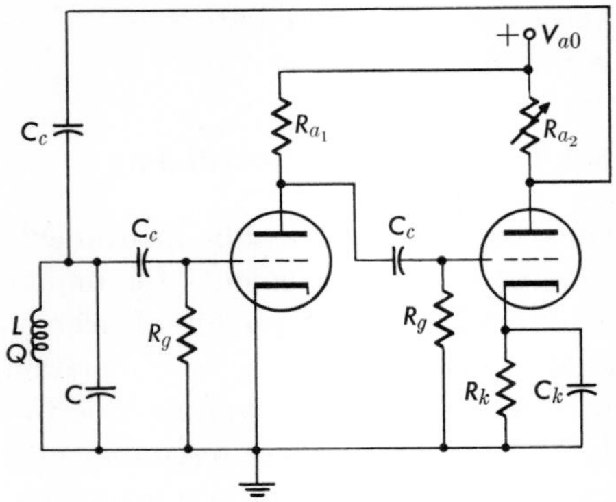

FIGURE 8.15

taking into account the effects of the finite Q of the inductance, input, and output impedances of the tubes, find

(a) the value for R_{a_2} at which oscillation will just begin,
(b) the approximate frequency of oscillation.

8.3 For the transistor Hartley-oscillator circuit shown in
Fig. 8.16, find

(a) the oscillation frequency,
(b) the approximate signal amplitude across the "tank"
circuit. Assume that C_c is large compared with C and that
$L_1 + L_2$ are not coupled.

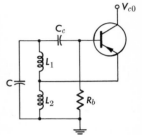

FIGURE 8.16

8.4 (a) Find the oscillation frequency of the circuit shown in Fig. 8.17.
(b) Derive an expression for the amplitude of the output signal at either cathode.

8.5 For the Wien-bridge oscillator shown in Fig. 8.18, $R_1 = R_2 = 10 \text{ k}\Omega$, $R_{a_1} = 50 \text{ k}\Omega$, $R_g = r_{p_1} = r_{p_2} = 1 \text{ M}\Omega$; $g_{m_1} = g_{m_2} = 0.5 \text{ mA/V}$; $C_1 = C_2$; $C_c = 1 \mu\text{F}$.
Find the frequency of oscillation and the output signal amplitude as a function of
C_1 and R_{a_2}. (Note that saturation may occur, resulting in a nonsinusoidal output.)

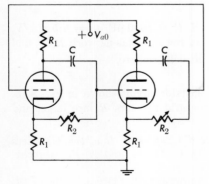

FIGURE 8.17

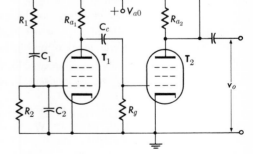

FIGURE 8.18

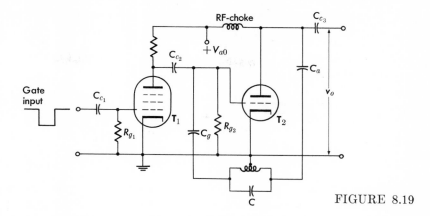

FIGURE 8.19

8.6   The diagram in Fig. 8.19 shows the arrangement of a *gated* or *clamped* oscillator circuit. T_1 is normally conducting at zero grid bias, its anode loading the grid-cathode circuit of T_2. When a negative square pulse is applied to the input, T_1 is driven past cutoff. Discuss the operation of the circuit, and derive a semiquantitative relationship for the buildup and decay of oscillations in the circuit of T_2 as a function of the parameters of the circuit of T_1, when T_1 is conducting and when it is cut off. (Do not attempt an exact solution.)

8.7   The circuit shown in Fig. 8.20 is a schematic diagram of a dc-to-ac *inverter*, useful for transforming a small dc-voltage to a high ac-voltage. A rectifier can be added to the output to provide a high dc-voltage, for example, for use in a portable electronic flashlamp for photography. Discuss qualitatively the general principles of operation of the circuit, including the role of the protective diodes D_1 and D_2. Consider the effects of saturation of the transformer core on the output wave shape. (Do not attempt an exact solution.)

8.8   Figure 8.21 shows the circuit of a simple code-practice oscillator. Discuss the operation of the circuit and find an approximate expression for the frequency as a function of the setting of the tone control.

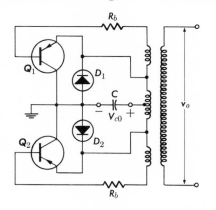

FIGURE 8.20

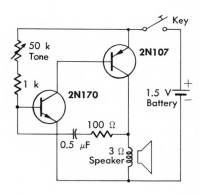

FIGURE 8.21

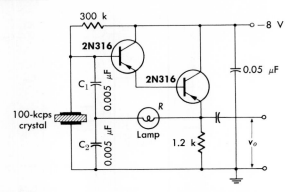

FIGURE 8.22

8.9   Figure 8.22 shows the circuit of a stabilized 100-kcps crystal oscillator.   The crystal oscillates in the positive-reactance mode very slightly above its series resonant frequency.   Discuss qualitatively the operation of the circuit and the stabilizing effect of the condensers C_1 and C_2 and the change in resistance of the lamp R on the frequency stability of the output with changes in transistor characteristics.   (Do not attempt an exact solution.)

REFERENCES

Chance, B., *et al.*, *Waveforms*, Radiation Laboratory Series **19,** McGraw-Hill, 1949.

Chow, W. F., *Principles of Tunnel Diode Circuits*, Wiley, 1964.

Landee, R. W., D. C. Davis, and A. P. Albrecht, *Electronic Designer's Handbook*, McGraw-Hill, 1957, Chapter 6.

Strauss, L., *Wave Generation and Shaping*, McGraw-Hill, 1960, Chapters 14 and 15.

Terman, F. E., *Radio Engineer's Handbook*, McGraw-Hill, 1943, Chapter 6.

Chapter 9

PULSE CIRCUITS

9.1 GENERAL CONSIDERATIONS

In the previous chapters we were concerned chiefly with a particular class of electronic circuits which are often designated as *linear* circuits, although this is surely a semantic oversimplification. Our oscillator circuits were designed to produce pure, simple sinusoidal signals, and our amplifier circuits were intended to enhance these signals and transform them to various impedance levels with a minimum of distortion. The quality of our circuits could be implicitly described in terms of some measure of their *fidelity*, the extent to which the shape of the output signal was a faithful linear replica of the input. As we have seen, such linear circuits are basic to a wide variety of applications in communications and control as well as to other areas of technology.

In this chapter we shall introduce a new class of circuits, which are basic to another area of applications, particularly those in which *time*, rather than shape, is the most important signal characteristic. Such circuits are sometimes called *nonlinear, digital, logical* or, since they most often employ signals of short duration, *pulse* circuits. They are fundamental in computer or switching applications, in nuclear detectors and counters, in radar, and in other fields. Since in these applications the detailed signal shape is often of little relevance, we frequently operate tubes and transistors over their full dynamic range, from cutoff to saturation, so that they behave more like binary on-off switches than linear amplifiers. In such applications, the small-signal linear-circuit analysis techniques, which were essential for consideration of amplifier circuits, are frequently irrelevant, and we are more concerned with the effects of the circuit parameters on the timing of the signals. In a large number of important cases, the analysis reduces to a simple consideration of the effects occurring in various equivalent *RC*-circuits as the signal changes level. Thus we shall begin by a review of the response of typical *RC*-circuits to rectangular voltage changes. In later sections, we shall see how to combine these passive circuit elements with active components, tubes and transistors, to make a variety of useful and interesting circuits.

9.2 RESPONSE OF *RC*-CIRCUITS

9.2.1 Step response of a series *RC*-circuit

Consider the simple circuit of Fig. 9.1. Suppose that the switch is closed at time $t = 0$. Then, from the familiar result for the charging of a condenser through a series resistor, the voltage across the condenser, V_C, is apparently

$$V_C = V_0(1 - \epsilon^{-t/RC}) \tag{9.1}$$

and, since $V_C + V_R = V_0$, then

$$V_R = V_0 \epsilon^{-t/RC}. \tag{9.2}$$

In a time $t = RC$, the condenser voltage has risen to a fraction $(1 - 1/\epsilon) \approx 63\%$ of its eventual value, while the voltage across the resistor has fallen by the same fraction. The fact that our circuit employed a battery and switch has no particular relevance to the solution; the battery served merely to define a voltage V_0, and the switch a time $t = 0$. Thus, Eqs. (9.1) and (9.2) are apparently valid for any series RC-circuit in which a voltage change V_0 occurs at time $t = 0$, whatever the actual mechanism.

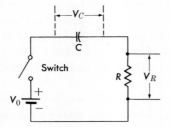

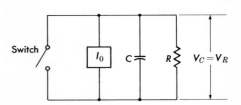

FIG. 9.1. Circuit for charging a condenser through a resistor. The switch is closed at time $t = 0$.

FIG. 9.2. Circuit for charging a parallel *RC*-circuit from a current source; the switch is opened at time $t = 0$.

In many cases, the signal source delivers a current rather than a voltage. In this case we must consider the circuit of Fig. 9.2, where a current I_o is applied at time $t = 0$ to the parallel combination of a resistor and a condenser by opening switch S. The relevant expressions for the currents through C and R are now

$$I_C = I_0 \epsilon^{-t/RC} \tag{9.3}$$

$$I_R = I_0(1 - \epsilon^{-t/RC}) \tag{9.4}$$

The voltage across R and C is, of course,

$$V_R = V_C = I_0 R(1 - \epsilon^{-t/RC}) \tag{9.5}$$

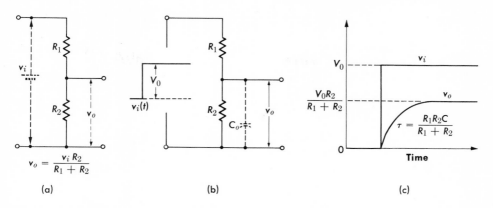

FIG. 9.3. Simple attenuator (a) for a dc-voltage input, (b) showing step-input voltage and output capacity, (c) rise-time distortion in output due to C_o, for step input.

9.2.2 Attenuator circuits

The simplest way of reducing the magnitude of a signal voltage is with a voltage divider, as shown in Fig. 9.3(a); here $v_o = v_i R_2/(R_1 + R_2)$. However, as shown in Fig. 9.3(b), there will actually always be some parasitic capacity C_o across the output terminals; hence, the output voltage v_o will not exactly follow a sudden step in the input voltage v_i, since C_o must first charge through the parallel combination of R_1 and R_2. Therefore, the output voltage will follow the exponential curve shown in Fig. 9.3(c), rising with a time constant $R_1 R_2 C_o/(R_1 + R_2)$.

To overcome this limitation, attenuators for pulse circuits are almost always constructed in the manner shown in Fig. 9.4(a) with a variable condenser $C_1 = C_o R_2/R_1$ in parallel with the input resistor. The value of C_o may be deliberately increased from its parasitic value to make the response of the attenuator less sensitive to changes in leads, etc., and to raise the required value of C_1 to a practical one. Since with C_1 properly adjusted, $R_1 C_1 = R_2 C_o$, the compensated attenuator behaves like a balanced ac-bridge, and no current flows in the wire joining the center of the two resistors to the center of the two condensers. The input signal is then reduced in magnitude by a factor of $R_2/(R_1 + R_2)$ with no distortion. In many practical attenuators, for example on oscilloscope probes, C_1 is made continuously variable and may be adjusted if we connect the attenuator to a known rectangular signal. When C_1 is correctly adjusted, as in Fig. 9.4(a), the output signal will be rectangular. When C_1 is too small, as in Fig. 9.4(b), there will be rise-time distortion, and if C_1 is too large, as in Fig. 9.4(c), there will be droop distortion.

Since the proper value of C_1 is fixed by the value of C_o and the ratio R_2/R_1, the divider, R_1, R_2, cannot be a continuously variable tapped resistor, as in a linear-circuit amplitude control. Instead, a switchable stepwise attenuator

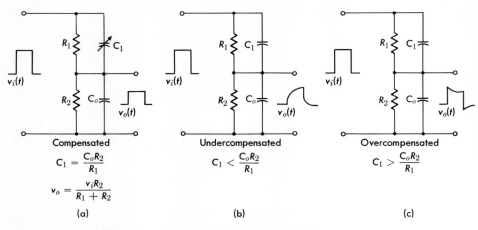

FIG. 9.4.   Compensated attenuator (a) properly adjusted, (b) C_1 too small, (c) C_1 too large.

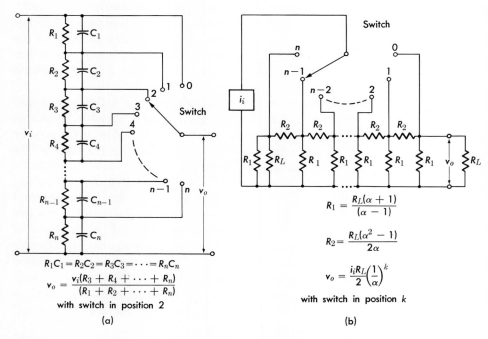

FIG. 9.5.   Stepwise variable attenuators. (a) RC-compensated, (b) ladder attenuator to provide constant input impedance for current source.

must be used, as shown in Fig. 9.5(a). Another method for signal attenuation
is use of the *ladder* attenuator shown in Fig. 9.5(b). If the attenuator input is
connected to a source which delivers a signal *current* i_i, and the resistors R_1
and R_2 are chosen so that

$$R_1 = R_L(\alpha + 1)/(\alpha - 1) \tag{9.6}$$

and

$$R_2 = R_L(\alpha^2 - 1)/2\alpha, \tag{9.7}$$

then the output voltage will be reduced by a factor of α for each step of the
switch. With a ladder attenuator, the input and output impedances are independent of the amount of attenuation.

9.2.3   Differentiator circuits

If a rectangular voltage signal is applied to the simple high-pass *RC*-circuit of
Fig. 9.6(a), each sudden rise or fall of the input voltage produces a peak in the
output voltage, a positive peak if v_i increases and a negative peak if v_i decreases.
Since the output corresponds roughly to the time derivative of the input, such
a circuit is often called a *differentiator*. The duration of the peaks is determined
by the *RC*-time constant since, for a single rectangular pulse of duration T,

$$
\begin{aligned}
v_o &= 0 &&\text{before the pulse} \quad (t < 0), \\
v_o &= V_0\epsilon^{-t/RC} &&\text{during the pulse} \quad (0 \leq t < T), \\
v_o &= V_0\epsilon^{-t/RC}(1 - \epsilon^{T/RC}) &&\text{after the pulse} \quad (t \geq T).
\end{aligned}
\tag{9.8}
$$

If $RC \ll T$, the positive and negative pulses are very short compared with the
duration of the input pulse, and the name differentiator is rather appropriate.

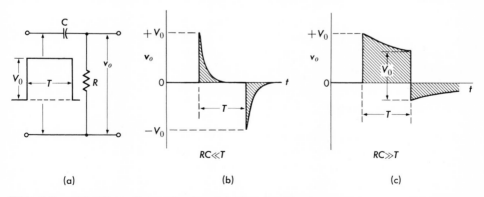

FIG. 9.6.   *RC*-differentiator circuit. (a) Circuit, (b) output for time constant small
compared to pulse width; (c) output for time constant large compared to pulse width.

However, even if the input voltage rises infinitely fast, the output signal can never exceed V_0; therefore, the circuit is not a true differentiator. Moreover, if the input rectangular pulse has an exponential rise time τ_s which is not negligible compared with the time constant $\tau = RC$ of the differentiator (as is usually the case), the height of the peaks will be less than the value given by Eq. (9.8), and will depend on the ratio τ/τ_s. This effect is illustrated in Fig. 9.7, where the relative output peak amplitude is shown as a function of τ/τ_s, on the assumption that the input signal rises and falls exponentially with a rise time τ_s.

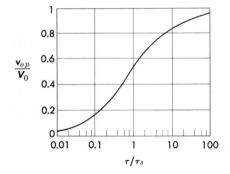

FIG. 9.7. Peak voltage at the output of an RC-differentiator circuit as a function of the ratio of the differentiator time constant $\tau = RC$ and the rise time τ_s of a transient at the input.

It is important to realize that no matter what the value of RC and no matter what the input signal, the *average voltage across the output resistor R must be identically zero*. This result (frequently overlooked even in "professional" circuit designs) arises from the fact that a condenser must, of course, behave like an open circuit to a dc-voltage. Therefore, in passing through even one differentiator circuit, the *average* value of the signal voltage becomes zero, and if useful information was contained before in the average value of the signal, it is now lost. This information can be restored by use of nonlinear *clamping* circuits, also called *dc-restorers*, which will be described in Section 9.4.

The simple high-pass RC-circuit can, at best, produce an output signal which is a crude approximation to the true derivative of the input signal. If a more exact derivative function is required, more complex circuits, such as the operational differentiator described in Sec. 5.9, may be used.

9.2.4 Integrator circuits

If a rectangular signal voltage is applied to the input of the simple low-pass RC-circuit of Fig. 9.8, where the positions of the resistor and condenser are just reversed from those in the differentiator circuit of Fig. 9.6, the output voltage will rise and fall only slowly, approximately as the time integral of the input signal; hence the name *integrator* circuit. The solutions for this circuit may be found immediately from those of the differentiator circuit. Since the sum of the voltage drops across R and C must equal the input voltage, it is clear that

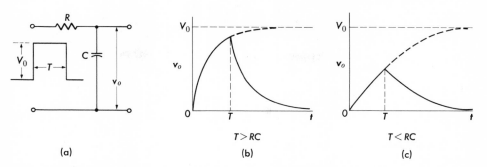

FIG. 9.8. *RC*-integrator circuit. (a) Circuit, (b) output for time constant less than pulse width, (c) output for time constant greater than pulse width.

for the integrator,

$$v_o = 0 \qquad\qquad\qquad\qquad \text{before the pulse} \quad (t < 0),$$
$$v_o = V_0(1 - \epsilon^{-t/RC}) \qquad\qquad \text{during the pulse} \quad (0 \le t < T), \qquad (9.9)$$
$$v_o = V_0\epsilon^{-t/RC}(\epsilon^{T/RC} - 1) \qquad \text{after the pulse} \quad (t \ge T).$$

For many applications, integrating circuits are required to deliver a voltage which increases linearly with time so long as the input pulse persists (the linear time-base sweep voltage for a cathode-ray oscilloscope is only one of many important practical cases). In principle, the simple network shown in Fig. 9.8 permits us to achieve such a true "integral" to any desired degree of precision. Since $v_o = V_0(1 - \epsilon^{-t/RC})$ during the pulse, by expanding the exponential in a power series and setting $RC = \tau$, we obtain

$$v_o = \frac{V_0 t}{\tau}\left(1 - \frac{t}{2\tau} + \cdots\right). \qquad (9.10)$$

When the output voltage has risen to a fraction t/τ of V_0, the second-order term causes a departure by a fraction $\tfrac{1}{2}t/\tau$ from linearity. In practical terms, if we wanted a linear output voltage of a peak value of 20 V, linear to within 1%, we would require an input pulse of peak value $V_0 = 1000$ V while, for 0.1% linearity, we would need $V_0 = 10{,}000$ V! Thus, while the simple *RC*-integrator is suitable "in principle" for deriving a linear time-base voltage, it is impractical for high orders of linearity. The difficulty in the simple *RC*-circuit is immediately apparent; the current charging the condenser varies with time because it is proportional to $V_0 - v_o$. If the charging current can be maintained constant, the voltage across the condenser will rise linearly with time. One simple arrangement is shown in Fig. 9.9. Here the resistor R is effectively replaced by the plate resistance r_p of a pentode, which is gated on at the control grid to start discharging the condenser. The discharge current through the tube is almost independent of the anode voltage of the pentode (cf. Section 2.9.1);

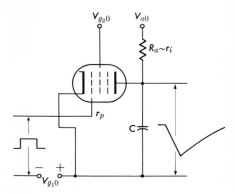

FIG. 9.9.   Linear discharge of a condenser through a pentode.   For good
linearity R_a must be large (of the order of
r_p for the pentode).

hence, the response can be fairly linear without requiring extraordinarily high voltages.

Still better linearity can be achieved by use of feedback amplifiers to keep the condenser current constant.   Two frequently used circuits are the *Miller* integrator, shown in Fig. 9.10, and the *bootstrap* integrator of Fig. 9.11. (These are actually simple versions of the general operational integrator discussed in Sec. 5.9.)

In the Miller circuit, the integrator itself consists of R, C, and the pentode T_2; the tube T_1 serves only to gate the integrator on or off.   Let us assume that the voltage gain, $A_0 \approx -g_m R_a$, of the amplifier circuit of T_2 is a constant.   The cycle starts when T_1 is cut off by a negative signal on its control grid, and C starts to charge through R.   An increase in voltage by an amount v_i at point P produces a decrease in voltage of amount $-|A_0|v_i$ at point Q; thus, the voltage at Q drops $|A_0|$ times as fast as it rises at P.   For example, if $|A_0| = 100$, the anode of T_2 drops by 100 V when the grid voltage has risen only 1 V.   Since

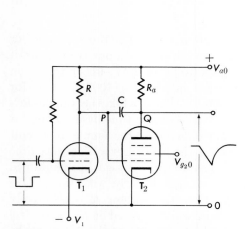

FIG. 9.10.   Gated "Miller" integrator circuit.

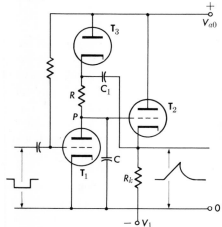

FIG. 9.11.   Gated "bootstrap" integrator circuit.

the original voltage drop across R may be 200 V or more, the output can be made extremely linear. If we look at the circuit at the point P, it is apparent that the condenser C charges slowly, as though it had an effective capacity $C_{\text{eff}} = C(1 + |A_0|)$. This circuit takes advantage of the same *Miller effect* which proved a limitation to the use of triodes at high frequency (see Section 4.3.5).

In the bootstrap-integrator circuit of Fig. 9.11, the integrator proper consists of R, C, and the cathode follower T_2. When T_1 is cut off, the voltage across C starts to increase as C charges through R. This increase in voltage appears almost unattenuated at the cathode of the cathode-follower T_2 and is applied to the top of R through the large condenser C_1. This voltage increase cuts off the diode T_3, so that the top of the resistor R can rise freely. The voltage across R thus remains nearly constant as C charges, and the charging current is almost constant. Therefore, the output voltage rises as $v_o = I_1 t / C$, where I_1 is the quiescent current of the gate-tube T_1.

9.3 DELAY LINES

In many applications involving pulse circuits, pulses from one output must be delayed in order to bring them in time coincidence with pulses from another output. Such timing differences may occur even if the pulses at the various outputs originate from one and the same initiating event, since amplifiers, trigger circuits, or flip-flops produce different amounts of delay.

Time-coincidence procedures are also often required in nuclear physics. Here pulses may be produced by several nuclear detectors as a result of nuclear events, between which time correlations exist. In order to investigate these correlations, variable delays are used in one or more channels. Naturally, the fastest pulses must always be delayed to bring them into coincidence with slower pulses, since the latter cannot be speeded up. For this purpose we may use *delay lines* which, ideally, merely transform a function $f(t)$ to $f(t - \tau_d)$ without changing the shape or amplitude of a signal. The simplest form of delay line, shown in Fig. 9.12, is merely a length, l, of transmission line with a signal velocity v, which is terminated in its characteristic impedance. The output signal will then be delayed by $\tau_d = l/v$. For normal coaxial cables with a

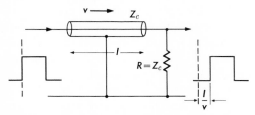

FIG. 9.12. Delay cable terminated in a resistor equal to the characteristic impedance of the cable, to avoid reflection.

straight inner conductor, $1/v$ ranges from 4 to 8 nsecs per meter of cable length. Generally, such cables are used only for delays smaller than about $0.1\ \mu\text{sec}$; for longer delays the volume of cable required becomes excessive. Considerably longer delays can be achieved with special delay cables, in which the inner conductor is wound as a helix, sometimes on a ferromagnetic core. Such cables may provide delays of up to a few microseconds per meter. For longer delays, lumped-constant artificial delay lines, like those shown in Fig. 9.13, may be used. These are essentially low-pass filters comprised of a series of inductances and condensers. For still longer delays, of up to several milliseconds, we may employ acoustic delay lines, using mercury or quartz blocks in which the signal is converted to an acoustic pulse by a piezoelectric transducer.

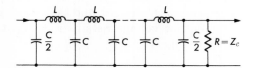

FIG. 9.13. Lumped-constant artificial delay line.

The ideal delay line only delays a signal, but any real line inevitably produces some distortion and attenuation. For straight coaxial cables, the distortion is usually small but the attenuation may be large, and additional amplifiers may be required at the output. The distortion is more serious with helical delay cables and even worse with artificial lines. In artificial lines the distortion is minimized by use of the largest possible number, n, of LC-sections for a given total delay time, $\tau_d = n\sqrt{LC}$, since the rise time of the line, $\tau_r \approx 1.1\tau_d/n^{2/3}$, decreases for increasing n.

Unless a delay line is terminated in its characteristic impedance, a signal fed to the line will be reflected. If the end of the line is open, the sign of the reflected signal is the same as that of the incident signal; if the end is short-circuited, the sign is reversed. For the artificial line, as shown in Fig. 9.13, the characteristic impedance is $Z_c = \sqrt{L/C}$, where L and C are the inductance and capacitance per section. Delay lines are usually correctly terminated to avoid reflections. However, in some cases, they may be unterminated.

If, for instance, the rise time of a pulse is long compared with the delay introduced by the cable, the cable acts mainly as a capacitance, loading the output of the pulse-producing device, and reflections will hardly be noticed. If a delay line is properly matched at its input but not at its output, pulses will be reflected at the output but they will be absorbed entirely at the other end, so that no unwanted reflections will be seen at the output.

Since delay lines consist entirely of linear circuit elements (i.e. elements in which the current depends only on the first power of the applied voltage), there will be a linear relation between the amplitude of the input signal and the output signal even though, as we have seen, the output signal may be distorted.

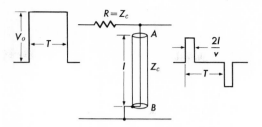

FIG. 9.14. "Differentiator" circuit using a short-circuited delay line.

If this linearity need not be maintained, electronic circuits may be used to provide variable delays of many seconds, or even hours, if necessary. Simple examples of such circuits will be discussed in Section 9.7.2.

Delay lines may be used also as differentiator circuits. As shown in Fig. 9.14, the input pulse is applied to a short-circuited delay line through a resistor R equal to the characteristic impedance of the line. The signal reflected out of phase by the short-circuited end of the line will cancel the input signal after a time $2l/v$; hence, the output will consist of short rectangular positive and negative pulses of width $T_c = 2l/v$. So long as T_c is large compared with the rise time τ_s of the input pulse, the peak value of the output pulses will be simply $\frac{1}{2}V_0$. For T_c comparable to τ_s, the peak value of the output pulse will be

$$v_{op} = \tfrac{1}{2}V_0(1 - \epsilon^{-2.2T_c/\tau_s}).\qquad(9.11)$$

9.4 CLAMPING CIRCUITS

As we have noted earlier, whenever a signal is passed through a series condenser, the average value of the voltage must be zero. In pulse circuits we frequently measure the peak-to-peak height of a pulse relative to a particular fixed base line, but the circuit requirements may dictate the use of a series condenser to isolate the anode supply voltage of a vacuum tube from the grid of the following stage, for example. The difficulty is illustrated in Fig. 9.15. Since the average value of the voltage across R must be zero, the integrated areas of the signal above and below the zero-voltage axis must be equal for all the cases shown. Thus, while all of the signals have the same peak-to-peak amplitude V_0, only for case (a), where the pulse is narrow and far from another pulse, will the peak positive value of the pulse be above the threshold voltage. In order for the threshold discrimination to be valid for all the cases, we must restore the zero base line of the signal, which has been removed by the condenser. Circuits to accomplish this function are called *clamps* or *dc-restorers*.

Clamping circuits utilize the nonlinear characteristics of rectifiers, either tubes or semiconductor devices, to provide a different effective value for the resistance R for positive-going and negative-going signals. Figure 9.16(a) shows a typical arrangement in which a diode is placed in parallel with R. Then, as shown in

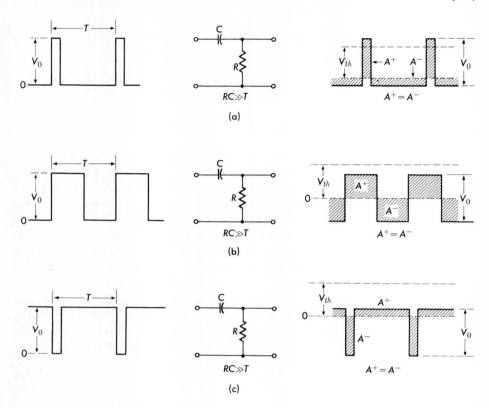

FIG. 9.15. Rectangular pulses passed through an RC-coupling network. The average voltage across the output must be zero, therefore the area above the zero axis must equal that below the zero axis for all cases. Only for the widely spaced narrow positive pulses in (a) does the peak of the output voltage come above the fixed positive threshold V_{th}. For all cases the RC-time constant is much greater than the period T.

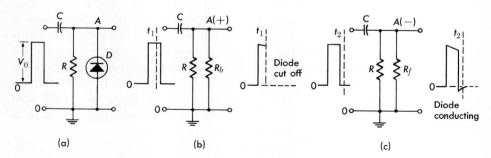

FIG. 9.16. Diode clamping circuit. (a) Circuit arrangement for clamping positive pulses, (b) equivalent circuit and output during positive portion of pulse, (c) equivalent circuit and output during negative portion of pulse.

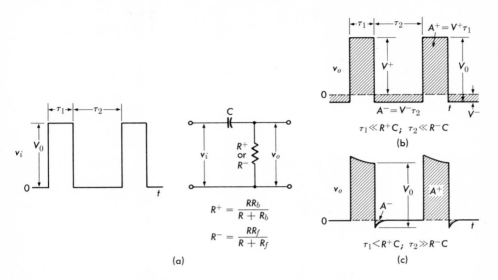

FIG. 9.17. Detailed response of diode clamping circuit of Fig. 9.16. (a) Definitions
of parameters, (b) idealized response, (c) actual response showing negative overshoot
when diode conducts.

Fig. 9.16(b), when the point A is positive with respect to ground, the diode is
cut off, and the equivalent resistance in the circuit is the parallel combination
of R and R_b, the back resistance of the diode. When point A is negative as in
Fig. 9.16(c), the diode conducts, and the equivalent resistance is the parallel
combination of R and R_f, the forward resistance of the diode. If the voltage
swing is more than a few tenths of a volt for a semiconductor diode or more than
a few volts for a tube, R_f will be much smaller than R_b, by several orders of
magnitude. Suppose that we choose $R \gg R_f$. Then, as shown in Fig. 9.17,
during the positive pulse of duration τ_1, a total charge, $Q^+ = I^+\tau_1 =
V^+\tau_1/R^+$, must flow onto the condenser. During the interval τ_2 between the
pulses, a total charge, $Q^- = I^-\tau_2 = V^-\tau_2/R^-$, must flow out of the condenser. Because the condenser cannot accumulate charge, $Q^+ = Q^-$, so that

$$V^-\tau_2/V^+\tau_1 = R^-/R^+. \qquad (9.12)$$

The left-hand side of (9.12) is just the ratio of the areas of $V(t)$ below and above
the zero axis. Since $R^- \approx R_f \ll R^+ = RR_b/(R + R_b)$, the area below the
line is much less than that above; therefore, $V^+ \approx V_0$, the full peak-to-peak
value of the input voltage, so long as τ_2 is not much smaller than τ_1. In most
circuits, R_f is so small that the RC-circuit acts like a differentiator on the
negative half-cycle, so that the diode actually conducts only for a short period
instead of during all of the time τ_2, and the signal resembles that shown in
Fig. 9.17(c). Equation (9.12) is still valid, however, if we interpret the left-hand
side as the ratio of the areas for positive and negative signals.

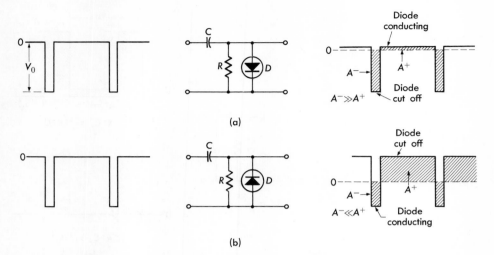

FIG. 9.18. (a) Diode clamping circuit for narrow negative pulses, (b) improper clamping obtained with diode reversed.

By reversing the diode, as in Fig. 9.18(a), we may clamp the most positive portion of the signal to the baseline. However, note the case shown in Fig. 9.18(b), where we are using the circuit of Fig. 9.16 to clamp the narrow peaks of the negative pulses to the base line, so that the diode conducts during the narrow negative peaks. From Eq. (9.12), we see that R^- is still much less than R^+, but now τ_2 is much less than τ_1; hence V^- is not much smaller than V^+. Therefore V^+ is considerably less than V_0. From this example it is apparent that for proper clamping, the circuit should always clamp on the *broad base between pulses*, not on the narrow pulses themselves.

Some other typical clamping circuits are shown in Fig. 9.19. We may utilize, instead of a diode, the rectifying property of a vacuum-tube grid at zero bias.

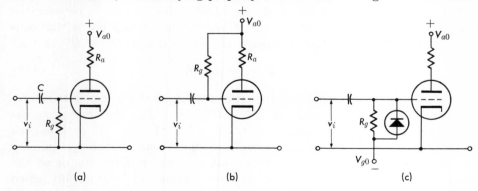

FIG. 9.19. Clamping at a triode grid. (a) Grid resistor returned to cathode, (b) grid resistor returned to anode supply voltage, (c) with external diode returned to negative bias supply for clamping positive input pulses.

Note particularly the circuit of Fig. 9.19(b). Here we have returned the grid resistor R_g to the anode supply rather than to the cathode! This circuit, strange from the viewpoint of linear circuits, is actually a much better clamp than the circuit shown in Fig. 9.19(a). If the grid is returned to the cathode, the quiescent value of the grid voltage will be slightly less than zero by a few tenths of a volt, because of grid current flowing through R_g. Thus, when a series of negative pulses is fed to the input, clamping action will not start on the positive-going signal until this initial negative bias has been overcome. However, if R_g is returned to the anode supply, the grid-cathode "diode" is initially conducting, and *any* value of positive-going signal will be clamped. For case (b) in the figure, the actual zero-signal grid-cathode voltage will be positive, not negative, but can be closer to zero than for case (a). The circuits of Fig. 9.19(a, b) are useful only for clamping negative pulses, for we have no way of reversing the grid-cathode "diode" of the tube. To clamp positive pulses, we must use an external diode across R_g, as in Fig. 9.19(c), clamping the negative base to the negative grid-bias voltage.

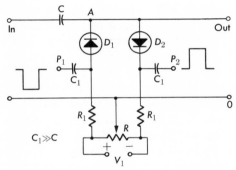

FIG. 9.20. Gated clamping circuit.

Since the forward resistance is usually smaller for semiconductor diodes than for vacuum diodes at the same forward voltage, semiconductor devices provide better clamping if the back resistance is sufficiently high and the peak inverse voltage rating larger than the maximum pulse height. Point-contact diodes are preferable to junction diodes, for the minority-carrier storage effects in junction diodes (see Section 3.3.3) cause the back resistance to be low immediately after a forward current is passed through the junction.

For some applications, we wish to vary the clamping action of the circuit in accordance with other signals which may or may not be present. Figure 9.20 shows a gated clamping circuit. Here both diodes, D_1 and D_2, are normally conducting; point A is thus maintained at a fixed dc-level between $-\frac{1}{2}V_1$ and $+\frac{1}{2}V_1$, which can be adjusted by the voltage divider R. Thus if a signal is applied across the input, no signal will appear at the output. However, if gating pulses P_1 and P_2 of opposite sign are applied to the clamp diodes as shown, both diodes will be cut off, and an input signal of either sign will be transmitted to the output. If only the negative gate P_1 is applied, so that D_2 is still conducting, only a negative signal at the input will be transmitted to the output. In most applications of such circuits, the gate pulses are applied synchronously with the signal pulses to be passed, and these are called *synchronous clamping* circuits; actually, from the function of the circuit, *synchronous declamping* would be a more appropriate description. With such circuits we can eliminate a great deal of low-frequency interference, such as hum and microphonics, which might be present in a train of pulses, since we transmit signals through the circuit only during the brief gate period.

9.5 PULSE-HEIGHT CLIPPING CIRCUITS

Clipping circuits are used when it is desired to transmit only a portion of a pulse above or below a certain fixed level (one-sided clipping). By combining two one-sided clipping circuits, one of which clips the portion of the signal above one given level and the other the portion below another, only the part of the signal between the two levels will be transmitted (double clipping).

Clipping circuits, like clamps, use the nonlinear properties of rectifiers for their operation. Two examples of one-sided clipping circuits for positive pulses are shown in Fig. 9.21; similar circuits for negative pulses are obtained simply by reversing the diodes. A clipping circuit is frequently preceded by a clamping circuit (Fig. 9.16), to provide a fixed reference level for all pulses to be clipped. Figure 9.21(a) shows a series clipping circuit; only the portion of the signal with an amplitude greater than V_1 is transmitted. For proper operation of the series clipping circuit, the resistance R must be chosen much greater than the forward resistance, R_f, of the diode; R must also be much less than the diode back-resistance R_b, or else a signal below the clipping level will not be attenuated sufficiently. Sudden transients in the input below the clipping level may be coupled to the output through the effective parallel capacity of the diode. This effect can be minimized by reducing the value of R. We also require that $R_1 \gg R$, to minimize shifts of the clipping level by charging of the coupling condenser C. It is clear that a compromise value of R must be determined, optimal to the particular application.

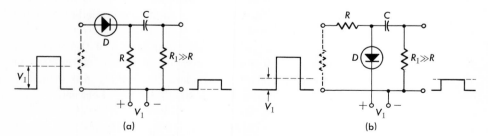

FIG. 9.21. Clipping circuits for positive pulses. (a) Series diode, (b) shunt diode. A dc return path (dotted resistor) must be provided for proper operation.

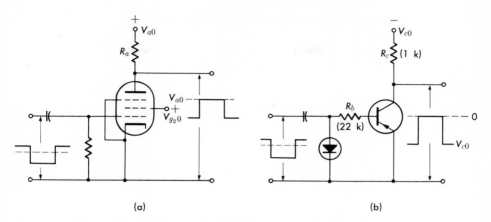

FIG. 9.22. (a) Pentode clipping circuit, (b) transistor clipping circuit.

In the shunt clipping circuit of Fig. 9.21(b) the positions of the diode and resistor are reversed; hence, this circuit transmits only that portion of the signal that is smaller than V_1. We again require that $R_f \ll R \ll R_b$ and $R_1 \gg R$ for proper operation of the circuit; a compromise value of R must therefore be determined for optimization. In the shunt clipping circuit, the effect of the diode capacity is to cause a rise-time distortion of fast input pulses; thus R should be kept small to minimize the integration time.

We may also make clipping circuits which use the cutoff or saturation characteristics of vacuum tubes or transistors, as shown in Fig. 9.22. In the pentode circuit of Fig. 9.22(a), the signal is clamped to zero by the grid-cathode "diode" of the tube. The clipping action is determined by the cutoff bias of the tube, V_{g_1c}. The magnitude of this bias, in turn, is determined by the value of the screen voltage, $V_{g_1c} \approx -V_{g_20}/\mu_{g_2g_1}$. An amplified and reversed clipped signal appears across the anode resistor R_a. This circuit can also be used for double clipping if R_a, V_{a0} and V_{g_20} are so chosen that the anode voltage drops to the knee in the I_a vs. V_a characteristic for $V_{g_1} = 0$. The top part of the input signal will then be strongly compressed.

In the transistor clipping circuit of Fig. 9.22(b), clipping action is achieved by the saturation characteristics of the transistor. The negative input pulses are clamped to zero level by the diode in the base circuit. The negative pulse, of amplitude V_0, causes a current, $I_b \approx -V_0/R_b$, to flow in the base, since R_b is much greater than h_{ie}. The base current saturates and the collector voltage rises to zero, producing a positive output pulse of magnitude $\approx V_{c0}$. Because $I_c \approx h_{FE}I_b$ and the output voltage is I_cR_c, the input pulse is effectively clipped below the level $-V_{c0}R_b/h_{FE}R_c$. For the circuit shown, $R_b/R_c \approx 10$ and, for $h_{FE} \approx 50$, the clipping level is about -0.6 V. Transistor circuits are particularly suitable for clipping small signals. The maximum input amplitude is limited by the maximum permissible base-emitter voltage.

9.6   PULSE GENERATORS: GENERAL CLASSIFICATION

Circuits for generation of fast voltage pulses bear a generic relationship to linear oscillator circuits for generating sinusoidal waveforms in that they both employ regenerative networks, derived either from positive-feedback amplifiers or negative-resistance elements such as tunnel diodes. However, in most pulse generators the circuit parameters chosen ensure that the operating points of the active elements involved in the circuit do not remain fixed but vary over wide ranges, so that the loop gain of the circuit does not remain constant over the whole cycle. We may distinguish three types of states of the circuit: stable states (s), metastable states (m), and unstable states (u). In a stable state, the biases of the amplifying circuit elements are such that the loop gain of the circuit is less than 1, and regeneration does not occur. In a metastable state, the loop gain is less than 1, but the biases are changing with time in such a way that the loop gain will eventually become greater than 1 without intervention of an external signal. In an unstable state, which usually persists for only a very brief time, the loop gain is greater than 1, and regeneration occurs, driving the circuit to another metastable or stable state.

We can distinguish between three general modes of operation:

1. *Astable* or *free-running* operation. Such circuits are self-exciting and have no stable states. They switch continuously between two metastable states, passing through intermediate unstable states, in a sequence m-u-m-u-m. The operation of most astable circuits can, however, be synchronized by the injection of external pulses, which can influence the duration of one or both of the metastable states.

2. *Monostable* or *one-shot* operation. In such circuits, there is an initial (stable) state and a second (metastable) state. The circuit must be triggered by an external signal to be made unstable, and then it is driven to the metastable state, from which it eventually reverts to the initial stable state in a sequence s-u-m-u-s. In some cases external triggering is also used to affect the duration of the metastable state.

3. *Bistable* or *flip-flop* operation. In such circuits there are two stable states, and the circuit must be triggered by external signals to cause it to switch between the stable states in a sequence s-u-s-u-s.

9.7   MULTIVIBRATOR CIRCUITS

The most common type of pulse-generator circuit is one which contains two vacuum tubes or transistors, only one of which is conducting during each stable or metastable state while both conduct during the unstable transition state. Through analogy with mechanical vibrators, the circuits are termed *multivibrators*. Multivibrator circuits may provide astable, monostable, or bistable operation, depending on the choice of biases and on the values of the interconnecting elements. The circuit is always arranged so that part of the output

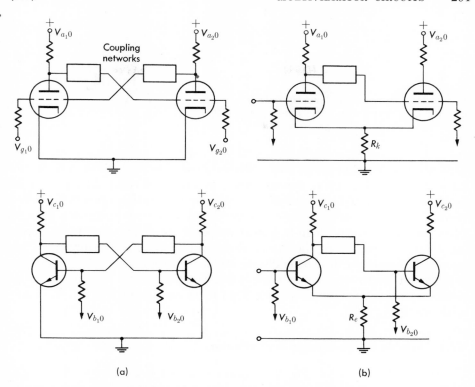

FIG. 9.23. Coupling in multivibrator circuits. (a) Symmetrical anode coupling (tube) or collector coupling (transistor), (b) unsymmetrical cathode coupling (tube) or emitter coupling (transistor).

of each stage is fed to the input of the other stage, in the manner indicated in Fig. 9.23. The two amplifiers are interconnected either symmetrically, that is, from each anode or collector to the opposite grid or base (called *anode-coupled* or *collector-coupled*), or unsymmetrically, that is, one connection from one anode or collector to the opposite grid or base and a second connection through a common cathode or common emitter resistor (called *cathode-coupled* or *emitter-coupled*). The actual interconnecting networks may be resistors, condensers, or a combination of both, depending on the type of circuit operation desired. Several examples of different types of multivibrator circuits will now be discussed. The basic principles of operation are analogous for tube and transistor circuits; therefore, we shall not show all possible variations of each circuit type.

One important phenomenon that is often found in transistor switching circuits but does not occur in tube circuits is *saturation*. A transistor saturates when the base-collector voltage difference falls to zero. Under this condition, a further rise of base current cannot produce a further rise of collector current; it can only cause the emitter-base diode to conduct more heavily. This leads to carrier storage in the base and, for some types of transistors, also in the collector because

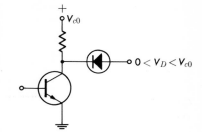

FIG. 9.24. Use of clamp diode to prevent
saturation of transistor. The diode prevents the collector voltage from falling
below V_D.

of forward conduction of the base-collector diode. As we have seen in Section
3.3.3 and Fig. 3.11, carrier storage causes reverse conduction during a certain
period of time after bias reversal. In transistor switching circuits this effect
results in a turnoff delay which may be considerable (up to 1 μsec), even for
transistors with a good high-frequency response for small signals. In special
fast-switching transistors, the turnoff delay can be made reasonably small, but
for very fast operation it is generally preferable to use circuits in which saturation
is prevented under all circumstances. One way to prevent it is to clamp the
collector with a biased diode (which itself must have negligible turnoff delay),
as shown in Fig. 9.24.

9.7.1 Astable anode-coupled multivibrator

The triodes T_1 and T_2 in Fig. 9.25(a) are arranged essentially as RC-coupled
amplifiers, with the anode of each tube connected by coupling condensers C_1
and C_2 to the grid of the other tube. The circuit will be astable, provided that
both grid biases, V_{g_10} and V_{g_20}, are above the cutoff biases of the respective
tubes. To simplify the expressions, we shall assume that $R_{a_1} \ll R_{g_2}$ and $R_{a_2} \ll$

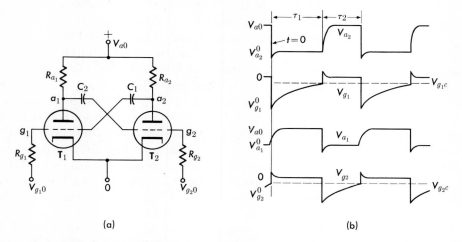

(a)   (b)

FIG. 9.25. Astable multivibrator. (a) Circuit arrangement, (b) voltage waveforms
at anodes and grids.

R_{g_1} and also that the coupling condensers C_1 and C_2 are much larger than the spurious circuit capacities. In practice, these conditions are ordinarily well satisfied.

Suppose that a transition has just occurred, so that at the time $t = 0$ (Fig. 9.25b) T_2 has just started conducting. Then the anode current of T_2 has suddenly increased from zero to its maximum value, and the voltage across the anode resistor R_{a_2} has fallen from V_{a0} to $V_{a_2}^0 = V_{a0} - I_{a_2}^0 R_{a_2}$. This negative-voltage step, $-I_{a_2}^0 R_{a_2}$, will be transmitted essentially unattenuated through the condenser C_1 to the control grid of T_1. If this step is sufficiently large, $V_{g_1}^0$ will then be much less than the cutoff bias of T_1, and T_1 will be cut off, so that V_{a_1} (which had been previously $< V_{a0}$) rises toward V_{a0}. Because the control grid of T_2 is going into clamp, $V_{g_2} \rightarrow 0$. During the metastable state, all of the voltages except for V_{g_1} remain at essentially the same values as at $t = 0$, but V_{g_1} gradually increases toward V_{g_10} as C_1 charges through R_{g_1} with a time constant $\approx C_1 R_{g_1}$. Before V_{g_1} reaches the voltage V_{g_10}, T_1 will come out of cutoff at $V_{g_1} = V_{g_1c}$ and will start conducting at time $t = \tau_1$. The circuit is then in an unstable state; both tubes are conducting. As T_1 starts to draw current, V_{a_1} will decrease from V_{a0}, and the negative change in voltage will be transmitted through C_2 to the grid of T_2, tending to reduce the current I_{a_2}. Thus V_{a_2} will increase, causing a positive signal to be transmitted through C_1 to g_1; the current in T_1 will increase further; V_{a_1} will become more negative, driving T_2 further toward cutoff, etc. This regenerative process will continue until V_{g_1} becomes positive; then T_1 will go into clamp, T_2 will be cut off, and the loop gain will become less than 1. The intermediate unstable state will be short-lived, and the transition will occur very rapidly, as fast as permitted by the resistances and the spurious distributed capacities of the circuit. Thus, shortly after the time $t = \tau_1$, the circuit is in its second metastable state, with T_1 on and T_2 off. The second state will persist for a period τ_2 until C_2 has charged through R_{g_2} sufficiently to bring T_2 out of cutoff; then the circuit will again revert to the initial state. We shall now analyze the process quantitatively.

A. Duration of metastable states. During the period $0 < t < \tau_1$ the voltage at the control grid of the cutoff tube T_1 is

$$V_{g_1} = V_{g_10} - (V_{g_10} - V_{g_1}^0)\epsilon^{-t/R_{g_1}C_1}. \tag{9.13}$$

At $t = \tau_1$, we have $V_{g_1} = V_{g_1c}$. Substituting and solving for τ_1, we obtain

$$\tau_1 = R_{g_1}C_1 \log \frac{(V_{g_10} - V_{g_1}^0)}{(V_{g_10} - V_{g_1c})}. \tag{9.14}$$

An analogous expression can, of course, be found for τ_2 if we simply replace all subscripts 1 with 2. If the circuit is symmetrical, so that all resistors, condensers, and biases are the same for each triode, then $\tau_1 = \tau_2$.

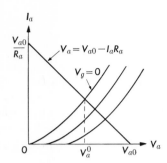

FIG. 9.26. Load-line construction to determine quiescent anode voltage at tube with clamped grid ($V_g = 0$).

To solve for τ_1, we need the values of $V_{g_1}^0$ and V_{g_1c} besides the known resistance, capacity, and bias voltage. We may, to good approximation, take $V_{g_1c} \approx -V_{a0}/\mu_1$, where μ_1 is the amplification factor of T_1. The voltage $V_{g_1}^0$ can be determined from the load line of T_2, as shown in Fig. 9.26, since $V_{g_1}^0 = V_{a_2}^0 - V_{a_20}$.

For example, let T_1 and T_2 be two halves of a 12AU7 double triode, with $V_{a0} = 300$ V; $R_{a_1} = R_{a_2} = 10$ kΩ; $R_{g_1} = R_{g_2} = R_g$; $C_1 = C_2 = C$; $V_{g_10} = V_{g_20} = V_{g0} = 0$ (grid resistors returned to ground) or 300 V (grid resistors returned to the anode supply). From a 10-kΩ load line, we find that $V_a^0 = 130$ V for $V_g = 0$, so that $V_{g_1}^0 = -170$ V. Since $\mu \approx 20$, $V_{g_1c} \approx -300/20 = -15$ V. Then, from (9.14), we obtain

$$\text{for} \quad V_{g0} = 0 \text{ V}, \qquad \tau_1 = \tau_2 \approx 2.45\, R_g C,$$
$$\text{for} \quad V_{g0} = 300 \text{ V}, \qquad \tau_1 = \tau_2 \approx 0.4\, R_g C. \qquad (9.15)$$

From this result we see that we can change the period of the multivibrator by about a factor of six by varying V_{g0} between 0 and V_{a0}; this control is convenient but not linear. Linear control of the period can be obtained if we vary both grid resistors or condensers simultaneously.

B. The unstable state. We shall now consider in more detail the voltage changes occurring at the anodes and grids during and immediately after the transition state. The parameters that determine the rapidity of the transition for this circuit are typical of those that limit the speed of other multivibrator circuits. The unstable state may be subdivided into three different parts, which we shall call a, b, and c, as in Fig. 9.27. For time $t = 0$ we take the moment when the control-grid voltage of T_1 is just passing the cutoff bias, V_{g_1c}, from the negative side while T_2 is still conducting at its full saturation value. Let us look first at V_{a_2}, the anode voltage of T_2, as shown in Fig. 9.27(a). During the brief period a, both T_1 and T_2 are conducting and, as the g_m of T_1 rises with increasing anode current, the loop gain rapidly becomes greater than 1. Both V_{a_1} and V_{g_2} decrease rapidly at a rate determined by the RC time constant at the anode of T_1; the effective resistance is the parallel combination of R_{a_1} and $1/g_{m_1}$, and the effective capacity is the sum of the capacity at the plate of T_1 and the input capacity

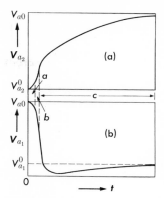

FIG. 9.27. Detailed wave shapes of the anode voltages of the two tubes in a multivibrator, during and just after switching. (a) Tube initially conducting approaching cutoff, (b) tube initially cut off going into conduction.

of T_2, which includes the Miller effect since T_2 is conducting. After a very short time t_1, T_2 is cutoff. In practical cases t_1 is of the order of 10–100 nsec. During this period, V_{a_2} has increased only slightly. During the second interval b, T_2 is cut off; therefore, the loop gain falls to zero, and the input capacity of T_2 drops to a smaller value. Now, V_{a_2} continues to rise at a rate determined by the time constant $R_{a_2}C_p$, where C_p is the parallel combination of the anode capacity of T_2 and the input capacity of T_1, which includes the Miller effect. The change in V_{a_2} is coupled to g_1 by C_1, so that V_{g_1} follows the rise until $V_{g_1} = 0$. At that moment, V_{a_2} has increased only by an amount $-V_{g_1c} \approx V_{a_0}/\mu$. During the third interval c, $V_{g_1} > 0$, and T_1 will draw grid current, which charges C_1 through R_{a_2} and prevents any further rise of V_{g_1}. If the effective forward resistance of the grid-cathode diode of T_1 is small compared with R_{a_2}, the anode voltage V_{a_2} rises exponentially toward V_{a_0} with a time constant $R_{a_2}C_1$. Since $C_1 \gg C_p$, this final stage of the switching process requires most of the time.

To keep the rise time of the anode voltage as small as possible, a small value of the coupling condenser C_1 is required. The minimum value of C_1 is subject to the following limitations.

1. For proper operation of the circuit, C_1 must be at least comparable to the spurious capacity C_p.

2. If C_1 is decreased by a certain factor, R_{g_1} must be increased by the same factor to keep τ_1 fixed. The maximum usable value of R_{g_1} depends on leakage currents between g_1 and the other electrodes of the tube. Since these currents may vary irregularly, the current through R_{g_1} must be kept large compared with the leakage current. For this reason, R_{g_1} is seldom made larger than about 10 MΩ.

During the interval a of the transition, the anode voltage V_{a_1} of T_1 first falls with a time constant RC_p, where R is the parallel combination of R_{a_1} and $1/g_{m_1}$ (because of the feedback, the anode of T_1 presents a low impedance, like a cathode follower). During the second interval b, V_{a_1} continues to fall, for the grid is still rising. The time constant for this portion is determined by that at

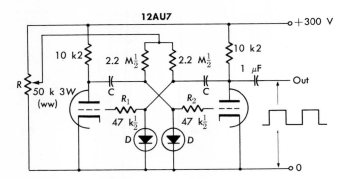

FIG. 9.28. Astable multivibrator modified with diodes to produce square waves. (Any small silicon diode with low reverse conduction and peak-inverse voltage > 150 V may be used for D, such as the 1N215.)

the grid, since C_p has decreased as a result of the cutoff of T_2. During the third interval c, V_{a_1} will *overshoot*, first falling below its equilibrium value $V_{a_1}^0$ (see Fig. 9.27(b)) because V_{g_1} is slightly greater than 0 while C_1 is charging. Note that the anode voltage of T_1 falls much more rapidly than the anode voltage of T_2 rises; in practice the whole switching time of T_1 may be ≈ 100 nsec.

C. Improvement of the wave shape. For some purposes, it is desirable to derive a square wave without the negative peaks shown in Figs. 9.25 and 9.27. We can achieve this simply by passing the output of the astable multivibrator through a clipping circuit, which clips off the bottom portion of the wave. Another method for improving the waveshape is shown in Fig. 9.28. In this circuit, small silicon-junction diodes D with small carrier-storage time are placed between the grids and ground. These diodes carry the great bulk of the current, charging the coupling condenser C while the control grid current is kept small by the series resistors R_1 and R_2; thus overshoot is minimized, and the circuit generates a relatively square waveshape. The period 2τ of the wave can be adjusted with the potentiometer R over a range of a factor of 6, from about $0.9C$ to $5.4C$ seconds (C in microfarads; compare with Eq. 9.15); C should not be made smaller than about 100 pF, to maintain an output signal of reasonably square shape.

D. Transistorized astable multivibrator. A simple symmetrical astable multivibrator circuit, with germanium pnp-transistors in place of tubes, is shown in Fig. 9.29. This circuit produces reasonably good square waves free from overshoot peaks, since the base current of a transistor is always finite when the transistor is conducting and does not suddenly start at a critical bias, as in a tube. The period of this multivibrator, for large values of C, is about $2\tau \approx 0.3C$ sec (C in microfarads). Unless high-frequency transistors with small turnoff delay are used, this circuit is not adaptable to very short periods. In addition, since the circuit does not include a stabilized-bias circuit, the output amplitude and frequency are rather strongly temperature dependent.

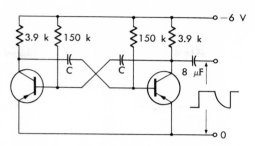

FIG. 9.29. Astable multivibrator employing low-frequency pnp-transistors.

9.7.2 Monostable multivibrator

A typical transistor monostable multivibrator circuit is shown in Fig. 9.30. The stable state of the circuit is with Q_1 cut off and Q_2 saturated, whereas the opposite holds for the metastable state. In the stable state, the current through Q_2 is determined by the external resistors R_{c_2} and R_e. If we assume that the voltage drop across the saturated transistor is essentially zero, then in the stable state, we have

$$I_{c_2}^0 \approx V_{c0}/(R_{c_2} + R_e). \tag{9.16}$$

In order for Q_2 to be in saturation, the base current, $I_{b_2} \gtrsim I_{c_2}/h_{fe}$, must be sufficiently large for (9.16) to be valid. Since $V_{be_2} \approx 0$ and $I_{c_2} \approx I_{e_2}$, we note from the circuit that

$$I_{b_2} \approx (V_T - I_{c_2}^0 R_e)/R_T. \tag{9.17}$$

Combining (9.16) and (9.17) and solving for R_T, we obtain

$$R_T \lesssim \frac{h_{fe}R_{c_2}(V_T - I_{c_2}^0 R_e)}{V_{c0} - I_{c_2}^0 R_e} = h_{fe}(R_{c_2} + R_e)\left[\frac{V_T}{V_{c0}} - \frac{R_e}{R_{c_2} + R_e}\right]; \tag{9.18}$$

if R_T is greater than the value specified by (9.18), Q_2 will not saturate.

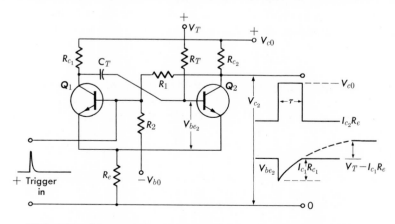

FIG. 9.30. Monostable multivibrator. General form of circuit.

The circuit can be triggered to the metastable state by a positive pulse applied to the base of Q_1, which turns Q_1 on. The negative signal coupled through C_T turns Q_2 off. The metastable state will persist until C_T charges sufficiently through R_T to bring Q_2 out of cutoff, when V_{be_2} becomes about 0.

The analysis of the duration of this metastable state is identical to that for the astable multivibrator.*

After Q_1 has fired, the base of Q_2 drops by an amount $I_{c_1}^0 R_{c_1}$, where, if Q_1 is in saturation,

$$I_{c_1}^0 \approx V_{c0}/(R_{c_1} + R_e). \tag{9.19}$$

The base-emitter voltage of Q_2 will then rise exponentially toward $V_T - I_{c_1}^0 R_e$ as

$$V_{be_2} = -I_{c_1}^0 R_{c_1} + [V_T + I_{c_1}^0(R_{c_1} - R_e)](1 - \epsilon^{-t/R_T C_T}). \tag{9.20}$$

The metastable state will end after a time τ, when $V_{be_2} \approx 0$. Substituting for $I_{c_1}^0$ from (9.19), and solving for τ, we obtain

$$\tau = R_T C_T \log\left\{\frac{V_T + V_{c0}[(R_{c_1} - R_e)/(R_{c_1} + R_e)]}{V_T - V_{c0}[R_e/(R_{c_1} + R_e)]}\right\}. \tag{9.21}$$

In most typical circuits, the emitter stabilization resistor R_e is much less than R_c, and R_T is simply connected to V_{c0}, so that $V_T = V_{c0}$. Then

$$\tau \approx 0.5\, R_T C_T. \tag{9.22}$$

In the circuit discussed, both Q_1 and Q_2 are saturated when conducting. As noted in Section 9.7, this may cause a rather long turnoff delay, lengthening τ. After the circuit has switched back to the state where Q_2 conducts and Q_1 is cut off, it has not yet returned to its original stable state since C_T must still be recharged to its equilibrium value. During this time, which is called the *recovery time*, the circuit is less sensitive to a following trigger pulse. The recovery time depends mainly on the time constant $(R_{c_1} + R_e)C_T$. The ratio, γ, of this recovery time to the period of the metastable state, τ, is independent of C_T and, in the approximation of (9.22), is

$$\gamma \approx 2(R_{c_1} + R_e)/R_T \approx 2R_{c_1}/R_T. \tag{9.23}$$

But, in the same approximation, from (9.18) we obtain

$$R_T \lesssim h_{fe}R_{c_2}; \tag{9.24}$$

hence

$$\gamma \gtrsim 2R_{c_1}/h_{fe}R_{c_2}, \tag{9.25}$$

---

* Care should be taken, however, to choose such a value for R_T that the current through it is large compared with the reverse conduction of the base-emitter and base-collector junctions of Q_2, for this conduction is very sensitive to temperature changes.

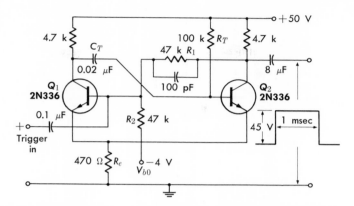

FIG. 9.31. Practical transistor monostable circuit of type shown in Fig. 9.30, for producing relatively large (45-V) output pulses.

and if $R_{c_1} = R_{c_2}$, as is usually the case, the minimum value of γ depends only on the transistors!

As a typical example, we may consider the circuit shown in Fig. 9.31. Here $V_T = V_{c0} = 50$ V; $Q_1 = Q_2 = 2N336$, $R_e = 470\ \Omega$ for stabilization; $R_{c_1} = R_{c_2} = 4.7$ kΩ; $h_{fe} = 75$. In order that Q_2 be in saturation during the stable state, R_T must be less than about 76×4.7 k$\Omega = 350$ kΩ. We choose $R_T = 100$ kΩ, and $C_T = 0.02\ \mu$F; thus the duration of the metastable state will be about $\tau \approx 1$ msec. We must choose R_1 and R_2 large so that they do not load the collector of Q_2, and V_{b0} sufficiently negative so that Q_1 is cut off when Q_2 is saturated. We choose $R_1 = R_2 = 47$ kΩ and, since $I_{c_2}^0 \approx 50$ V/4.7 k$\Omega \approx 10$ mA, the voltage drop across R_e will be about $0.01 \times 470 \approx 0.5$ V. In the stable state $V_{be_1}^0$ will be

$$V_{be_1}^0 = (V_{b0} - I_{c_2}^0 R_e)R_1/(R_1 + R_2). \qquad (9.26)$$

For $R_1 = R_2$,

$$V_{be_1}^0 = \tfrac{1}{2}(V_{b0} - I_{c_2}^0 R_e). \qquad (9.27)$$

Therefore $V_{be_1}^0$ would be less than 0 and Q_1 would be cut off even for $V_{b0} = 0$ V. However, to be doubly safe and to avoid accidental triggering, we would probably choose V_{b0} slightly negative, perhaps at -4 V, so that $V_{be_1}^0 \approx -2.25$ V. The positive trigger pulse applied at the base of Q_1, necessary to flip the circuit to the metatable state, must then be at least $+2.25$ V. The output voltage from the collector of Q_2 would be about $V_{c0} - I_{c_2}^0 R_e = 49.5$ V in amplitude, except for the current drain in R_1 when Q_2 is cut off. This will drop the output swing about 10%, to ≈ 45 V.

A vacuum-tube monostable multivibrator, using a 12AU7 double triode, is shown in Fig. 9.32. In the stable state, T_2 is conducting and T_1 is cut off. The circuit is triggered to the metastable state by a negative pulse applied at the

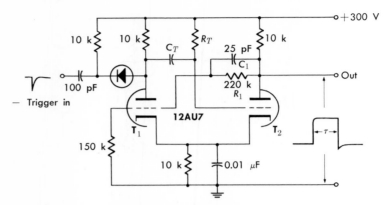

FIG. 9.32. Practical vacuum-tube monostable circuit with diode triggering circuit. (For $R_T = 1\ \text{M}\Omega$ and $C_T = 100\ \text{pF}$, $\tau \approx 30\ \mu\text{sec}$.)

anode of T_1, which couples to the grid of T_2 through C_T and starts the regenerative transition. The circuit could also be triggered, analogously to the transistor circuit, by a positive pulse on the grid of T_1. The small condenser C_1 in parallel with R_1 increases the loop gain during the fast transition; for this reason it is often called a *speedup* condenser.

Use of a diode in the trigger input, as shown, has the advantage that the diode cuts off as soon as the circuit reaches the metastable state, so that any residual trigger voltage or any other changes occurring in the trigger circuit have no effect on the duration of the metastable state.

Monostable multivibrators are frequently used to produce delayed pulses. If the output signal is passed through a differentiator and a clipper which transmits only negative pulses, then the circuit will produce, in response to the input negative trigger pulse, a delayed negative trigger at a time τ after the initial trigger.

9.7.3   Bistable multivibrator

A typical bistable multivibrator circuit, or *flip-flop*, using a double triode, is shown in Fig. 9.33. This circuit has two stable states, one with T_1 cut off and T_2 conducting, the second with T_1 conducting and T_2 cut off. The circuit is triggered from one stable state to the other by means of negative pulses applied through the halves of the 6AL5 double-diode trigger tube, which couple through the speedup condensers C_1 and C_2 to the grid of the conducting tube. The anode of each tube is direct-coupled to the grid of the other tube through a resistance divider; hence, the drop in anode voltage of the conducting tube drives the other tube past cutoff. Bias for the grids is furnished by the drop across the common cathode resistor R_k, which is bypassed by a small condenser so that the bias voltage will not change during the transition and the cathode will remain at a constant voltage of about $+80$ V.

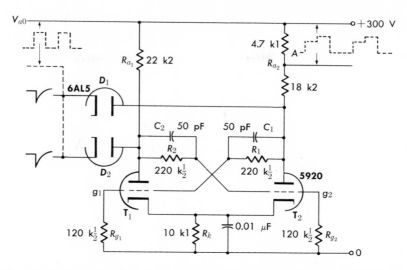

FIG. 9.33. Bistable multivibrator circuit ("flip-flop") using diode triggering network.
These circuits may be connected in cascade to make binary scalers.

It should be noted that a negative trigger pulse will cause a transition only if
applied to the grid of the *conducting tube*. If applied to the grid of the other tube,
it will only increase the cutoff bias; it will not flip the state. Therefore, if we
apply trigger pulses simultaneously to *both* tubes, by connecting the cathodes
of the trigger diodes, the circuit will flip one way on the first trigger, then the
opposite way on the second, etc. The output waveform at either anode will
therefore go through a complete cycle for each *two* input triggers, so that the
circuit divides by two. Therefore, flip-flops find an important use in counting
or *scaling* circuits; if the output on one flip-flop is connected to the input of the
next, then after n stages, the input will have been divided by exactly 2^n.

Frequently such dividers or scaling circuits are operated not by short trigger
pulses on the trigger diodes but by a voltage that jumps between V_{a0} and a
value of about 50 V below V_{a0}. This voltage may be applied directly to the
cathodes of D_1 and D_2, as shown in Fig. 9.33. Each negative step initiates a
switching process; the positive steps have no effect since the diodes cut off and
no signal is fed to the grid of the cutoff tube. For example, if T_1 is conducting,
the anode of D_2 is about 150 V lower than V_{a0}; if the cathode of D_2 jumps
from $V_{a0} - 50$ V to V_{a0}, then D_2 remains cut off and no signal is transmitted
to g_2. Because the anode was previously clamped to $V_{a0} - 50$ V by D_2, the
only change is an increase in the anode voltage of T_1 by about 50 V. Therefore,
if the input voltage jumps up and down twice, the voltage at A jumps up and
down only once. Point A can then be connected through another double diode
to the next stage of the scaler.

Notice that only a fraction of the anode voltage of T_2, $\beta = 4.7\,\mathrm{k}/(4.7\,\mathrm{k} + 18\,\mathrm{k})$,
is coupled to the input of the next stage of the scaler. This is necessary so

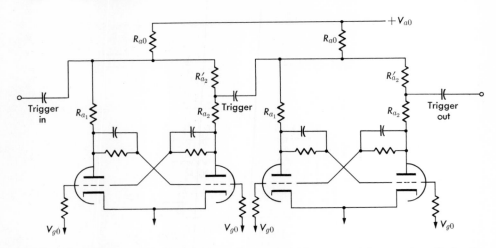

FIG. 9.34. Method for cascading bistable multivibrators without using diodes for coupling between stages, used in inexpensive scaling circuits. A portion of the output from each stage is applied through a small coupling condenser across the common anode resistor R_{a0}. Because of loading by the plate of the conducting tube, negative trigger pulses will appear only at the plate of the cutoff tube and will be coupled to the opposite grid through the speed-up condenser. To avoid improper triggering on positive pulses the ratio of R_{a2} and R_{a2}' ($R_{a2} + R_{a2}' = R_{a1}$) must be carefully adjusted.

that the output of our circuit, *and not the pulses which trigger it*, shall trigger the following circuit. If we interconnected the binaries by connecting the full output from one stage to the next, then each trigger into the first stage would trigger every following stage. The split resistor in the anode of T_2 effectively attenuates any interstage coupling of triggers.

Another method for triggering a sequence of flip-flops is shown in Fig. 9.34. This is less expensive than diode-triggering networks, for it employs only resistors and condensers. However, since it must convert the square signal to alternate positive and negative pulses, and can transmit positive pulses, there is a chance of mistriggering a circuit on a positive pulse unless the pulse amplitude is kept within close limits, and the inexpensive triggering network is less reliable than that employing diodes.

The speedup condensers C_1 and C_2 are required for fast switching action. If they are omitted, the loop gain for rapid voltage changes may become too small because of the effect of spurious input capacities, and it will become difficult to trigger the circuit with short pulses. The speedup condensers should be chosen somewhat larger than the spurious input capacities, including the Miller effect $(1 + |A|)C_{ga}$, to slightly overcompensate the effective attenuator circuit between one anode and the opposite grid. Whenever the circuit is switched, C_1 and C_2 must charge and discharge through the anode, grid, and coupling resistors to the new equilibrium voltage before the circuit is fully sensitive to the next input pulse. Therefore, C_1 and C_2 should not be made excessively large.

The resolution time of a flip-flop is defined as the minimum time between two adjacent trigger pulses in which the circuit will flip reliably. The resolution time is determined not only by the time constants associated with C_1 and C_2, but also by the amplitude and shape of the trigger pulse. For example, for the circuit shown in Fig. 9.33, the resolution time is about 5 μsec. This period can be reduced by a number of devices, such as the following.

1. *Reduction of all the resistances through which currents charging C_1 and C_2 must flow.* To maintain sufficiently high amplification with small resistances, tubes with high g_m should be used, and these should be operated at high anode current.

2. *Use of pentodes instead of triodes,* to reduce C_{ga} and the required value for the speedup condensers.

3. *Limiting the amplitudes of the voltage transients with diode clamping circuits,* and using diodes to charge and discharge the speedup condensers.

With such techniques, vacuum-tube flip-flops with a resolution time of less than 0.1 μsec can be constructed. Faster bistable multivibrators can be made by use of transistors. For example, the circuit shown in Fig. 9.35 has a resolution time of only 0.025 μsec. This particular non-saturating transistor circuit forms part of a 40-Mcps scaler used for fast counting of pulses from nuclear detectors. The high speed of the circuit is achieved by the following.

1. *The use of fast switching diffused-base micro-alloy transistors, Q_1 and Q_2, and diodes with a very short recovery time (especially D_1 and D_2).* The availability of such fast components has greatly simplified the construction of high-resolution pulse circuits. Only a few years ago, many special refinements were needed to obtain speeds comparable to those of the relatively simple circuit shown here.

2. *The collector-current clamping diodes, D_1 and D_2, which prevent saturation of the transistors.* The operation of the diodes can be explained as follows: Suppose that the flip-flop is in the state with Q_1 conducting and Q_2 cut off. The base voltage of Q_1 is then close to zero. With D_1 disconnected, the tap A on the feedback resistor from the collector of Q_2 to the base of Q_1 would show a voltage of about $470/(1800 + 470) \times -4.8$ V ≈ -1 V and, for the component values used, Q_1 would certainly saturate. With D_1 connected, however, this diode will conduct, diverting base current into the collector and thus preventing a further increase of collector current as soon as the collector voltage of Q_1 rises above -1 V. We can also say that under this condition there is a large amount of negative dc-feedback stabilizing the dc collector current of Q_1.

3. *The compensating inductances L_1 and L_2, used in series with the collector resistors of Q_1 and Q_2.* These increase the gain/rise-time ratio and therefore the switching speed in the manner explained in Section 6.2.1.

The circuit is triggered by positive pulses applied to the transistors through D_1' or D_2'. If Q_1 conducts and Q_2 is cut off, diode D_1' is cut off while D_2' conducts slightly. A positive pulse therefore is transmitted through D_2', C_1, and C_1' to the

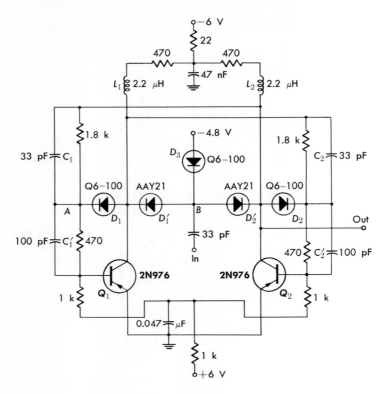

FIG. 9.35. Transistor flip-flop with 25-nsec resolution (used in Borer type 403 40-Mcps scaler). Requires fast 1- to 5-V positive trigger pulses at input.

base of Q_1, causing the circuit to switch to the other stable state. The next positive pulse goes through D_1', C_2, and C_2', switching the flip-flop back again. Acting as a clamp, D_3 prevents negative excursions of point B below -4.8 V, which would otherwise influence the trigger sensitivity for pulses applied in rapid succession.

The signal from the output of the flip-flop can be applied directly to the input of a following flip-flop of identical design.

9.7.4 Cathode-coupled multivibrator

A cathode-coupled multivibrator circuit employing a double triode is shown in Fig. 9.36. This circuit is monostable if the voltage V_1 at the control grid of T_1 is kept below cutoff, that is, $V_1 < V_{k_2} + V_{g_1 c}$ (V_{k_2} is the voltage developed across R_k if T_2 is conducting). For $V_1 > V_{k_2} + V_{g_1 c}$, the circuit becomes astable.

This circuit has some interesting properties when used as a monostable multivibrator. Since the anode of T_2 is not capacitively loaded, this point can be used to provide output pulses with steep leading and trailing edges. Another interesting feature is that a linear relation exists between the voltage V_1 and the duration τ of the metastable state (T_1 conducting). It can be shown that optimal linearity is obtained if the following relationship is satisfied:

$$\frac{R_{a_1}}{R_k} = \frac{V_{a0} - V_{k_2}}{V_{a0} - V_{g_2c}}, \tag{9.28}$$

where V_{g_2c} is the cutoff voltage of T_2 (T_1 conducting).

The linear relation between voltage and pulse width suggests several applications for this type of circuit. For instance, it may provide a delay proportional to a given voltage, or it can be used in a pulse-width modulator when a signal voltage is applied to the grid of T_1.

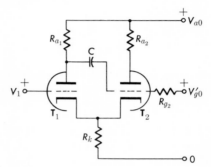

FIG. 9.36. Cathode-coupled multivibrator.

The cathode-coupled multivibrator has a smaller loop gain than its anode-coupled counterpart, because T_2 serves only as a cathode follower and therefore has a voltage gain smaller than 1. For the loop amplification to be larger than 1, we must take care that $R_{a_1}g_m > 2$ (assuming that $R_k g_m \gg 1$).

Trigger pulses may again be applied through a diode to the anode of T_1, in the same way as shown in Fig. 9.32. Since T_2 does not produce a voltage gain, they will have to be larger than for an anode-coupled circuit. The recovery time of the cathode-coupled univibrator is longer than that of the anode-coupled circuit, because the cathode resistor R_k limits the grid current of T_2, which recharges C after the circuit has switched back to its stable state (in practice R_{g_2} is usually connected to the supply voltage: $V'_{g0} = V_{a0}$).

EXAMPLE. With a 12AU7 for the double triode in Fig. 9.36, $V_{a0} = V'_{g0} = 250$ V, $R_{a_2} = R_k = 10$ kΩ, $R_{a_1} = 6$ kΩ, $R_{g_2} = 1$ MΩ, and $C = 2000$ pF. The duration of the metastable state can now be varied from 0–200 μsec if V_1 changes from about 60–85 V. The deviation from linearity is 1% at most.

9.7.5 Schmitt trigger

A useful circuit, resembling the cathode-coupled multivibrator, is the Schmitt trigger circuit shown in Fig. 9.37(a). This circuit has two stable states because here T_1 is dc-coupled to T_2. The control-grid voltage of T_1 determines which of these two states occurs. We can understand the operation of the circuit by

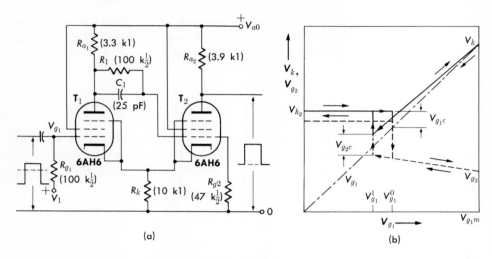

FIG. 9.37. Schmitt trigger circuit. (a) Circuit arrangement, (b) behavior of V_{g_2} and V_k for a control grid voltage on T_1 that increases for 0 to V_{g_1m} and then decreases to zero, showing hysteresis.

following the curves of Fig. 9.37(b), starting at a low value of V_{g_1}. Then the circuit will be in the state $- +$ (T_2 conducting). If V_{g_1} rises, the cathode voltage, $V_k = R_k I_{k_2}$, will remain constant ($= V_{k_2}$) until the difference $V_{k_2} - V_{g_1}$ becomes smaller than the cutoff voltage V_{g_1c} of T_1. At that moment, the anode voltage of T_1 starts falling. This decrease is fed back to the cathode of T_1 through T_2, acting as a cathode follower in the same way as discussed for the cathode-coupled multivibrator.

For a very small further rise of V_{g_1}, to $V_{g_1}^0$, the loop gain rises above 1, and the circuit rapidly switches to the other stable state $+ -$. After switching, the cathode voltage V_k has decreased a little, while V_{g_2} has decreased much more. If V_{g_1} increases further, T_1 acts as a cathode follower: the rise of V_k is almost proportional to V_{g_1}, whereas V_{a_1} and, therefore, V_{g_2} decrease further. Finally, at a very high value of V_{g_1} ($= V_{g_1m}$), T_1 draws grid current. This stage should never be reached because the input capacitor would then be charged, leading to a shift of the threshold. If V_{g_1} decreases again, V_{g_2} will rise and V_k will fall; V_{g_1} will now pass the value $V_{g_1}^0$, for which the circuit has switched to the state $+ -$, without anything happening, because T_2 is still cut off. Only at a lower value, $V_{g_1} = V_{g_1}^1$, will the difference between V_k and V_{g_2} become sufficiently less than the cutoff voltage of T_2 for the loop amplification to become larger than 1 and the circuit to switch back to its original state $- +$. This characteristic of the circuit is called *hysteresis*. A quantitative measure of this hysteresis is the voltage difference $V_{g_1}^0 - V_{g_1}^1$, which should be as small as possible for many applications. An inspection of Fig. 9.37(b) shows that we may achieve this by making the change of V_{g_2}, when the circuit switches, as small as possible. Since this jump is equal to that occurring at the anode of T_1, we must choose a small value for R_{a_1} and be sure that the loop gain remains larger than 1. For loop gains smaller than 1, the hysteresis is zero, but then the circuit behaves like a positive feedback amplifier without trigger properties.

The Schmitt-trigger circuit is widely used as a *discriminator*, i.e. a circuit that reacts only when the amplitude of a signal exceeds a predetermined voltage level. If, for instance, positive pulses of duration τ are applied to the grid of T_1 through the coupling capacitor, positive pulses of the same width but with a constant amplitude $I_{a_2}R_{a_2}$ will appear at the anode of T_2 as soon as the amplitude of the input pulses becomes larger than $V_{g_1}^0 - V_1$. The circuit can discriminate only pulses with an amplitude larger than its hysteresis; V_1 must be kept below $V_{g_1}^1$ because, otherwise, the circuit will not switch back. The trigger level $V_{g_1}^0$ will show some drift, caused among other things by changes of heater voltage and by variations in the tube characteristics. Since T_1 and T_2 compensate each other's influence on the trigger level in the same way as discussed for difference amplifiers in Section 6.6.2, the drift of a Schmitt trigger in practice is less than 0.1 V.

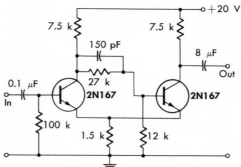

FIG. 9.38. Transistorized Schmitt trigger circuit.

A practical Schmitt-trigger circuit, using transistors, is shown in Fig. 9.38. This circuit will produce a 12-V output pulse for a positive input signal greater than 6 V. The output pulse starts within 0.1 μsec after the input signal has exceeded the threshold, and has a duration dependent on the time the input signal is above threshold, with a minimum width of about 5 μsec.

9.8 BLOCKING OSCILLATORS

Blocking oscillators utilize only one tube (or transistor) with positive feedback. To obtain positive feedback with a normal tube or transistor, some phase-reversing circuit is needed between the output and the input of the active circuit element. In blocking oscillators, transformers are often used for this purpose. Very simple blocking oscillators can also be constructed with *secondary-emission tubes* (see Section 2.13). For such tubes, signals at the control grid and the dynode have the same sign; therefore, simple capacitive coupling between the control grid and dynode suffices to obtain the desired operation. Blocking oscillators that use tubes are monostable when the dc grid-bias V_{g0} is below cutoff; they are astable when it is above cutoff.

It is desirable in a monostable blocking oscillator that the tube draw current only during the metastable state. Then a high-peak power may be delivered at a small average input power. Blocking oscillators are capable of generating voltage pulses of short duration and with very short rise times.

9.8.1   Blocking oscillator with pulse transformer

The quantitative analysis of this circuit is quite complicated;* we shall give only a general description of its operation here. The basic blocking-oscillator circuit is shown in Fig. 9.39. We assume here that V_{g0} is more negative than the cutoff voltage of the tube. If by some trigger pulse (e.g. a negative pulse at the anode), current starts to flow in the tube, an unstable state occurs; any decrease of the anode voltage results in an increase of the control-grid voltage due to the transformer action. Since an important part of the input power at the anode becomes available at the grid, this grid can be driven far positive and a high anode current will flow.

The switching action is terminated when the anode voltage falls so far below the control-grid voltage that the loop gain becomes smaller than 1. Now a

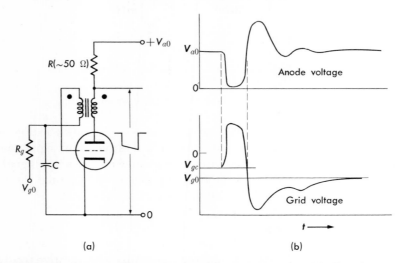

(a)   (b)

FIG. 9.39.   Blocking oscillator circuit with transformer.   (a) Circuit arrangement (dots indicate in-phase transformer terminals; secondary terminals are reversed to provide positive feedback), (b) wave shapes at control grid and anode.

---

* See, for instance, W. H. Bostick, *Pulse Generators*, Radiation Laboratory Series, McGraw-Hill, 1948, Chapters 12–15.

metastable state has been reached, during which the magnetizing current I_{am} in the transformer primary increases proportionately with time. The rate of increase is inversely proportional to the inductance L_p of the transformer primary: $I_{am} \approx E_p t / L_p$ (E_p is the voltage across the primary). The anode voltage will increase a little during the metastable state, and therefore the positive control-grid voltage will decrease a little. Yet, the anode current will increase because the ratio of the anode-to-control-grid current increases. Finally, the anode current does not rise any further; then the metastable state ends. The anode voltage now starts increasing rapidly while the grid voltage is falling at the same rate; the circuit switches back and the tube current is cut off within a very short time. The sudden cutoff of the magnetizing current gives rise to a large, positive, induced emf at the anode, followed by a damped oscillation of the circuit consisting of the transformer and tube in parallel with it. The initial state is restored after the charge accumulated on C during the metastable state has equalized through R_g. The shape of the grid and anode voltages during a pulse is shown in Fig. 9.39(b). To simplify the explanation of the operation of the circuit, the voltage change across C during the metastable state has been neglected. Since in reality the width τ of the pulse is affected by this change, it also depends on the value of C. By using commercially available pulse transformers, we can easily obtain values of τ which range from approximately 0.1 to 25 μsec.

Even small tubes, like the 12AT7 for instance, may deliver anode currents of up to a few hundred milliamperes in blocking oscillators. Thus, voltage pulses of many volts can be developed across a resistor R of less than 100 Ω in series with the anode circuit.

The switching time of the circuit is determined mainly by the total stray inductance L_s of the transformer and the spurious capacitance C_s between the primary and secondary windings ($\tau_s \sim L_s C_s$). The requirements for making both L_s and C_s small are conflicting: for a small stray inductance there must be a high degree of coupling between the windings, which results in an increase of the stray capacitance between these windings. Rise times of only a few nanoseconds have been obtained with small pulse transformers made with very thin permalloy foil cores.

9.8.2   Blocking oscillator with secondary emission tube

With this type of circuit, pulses with rise times of only a few nanoseconds and amplitudes of more than 100 V may be generated. No transformer is needed in this circuit; further, the secondary-emission amplification makes it possible to obtain even higher peak anode currents than with blocking oscillators that use transformers (currents of up to 1 A have been obtained). Let us suppose that we adjust the circuit of Fig. 9.40 in its monostable range by making V_{g0} more negative than the cutoff voltage of the tube. The operation of the circuit

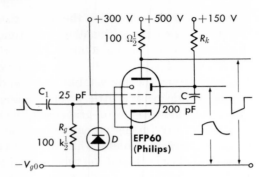

FIG. 9.40.   Blocking oscillator circuit with secondary emission tube (for values of R_k, see text).

is as follows: a positive trigger pulse at the control grid initiates an unstable state, during which the dynode pulls up the control grid, to which it is coupled by C. The dynode voltage rises very rapidly until the voltage difference between the dynode and the anode becomes so small that the secondary-emission current from dynode to anode is limited by the space charge forming in front of the dynode.   As a result of this, the effective secondary-emission gain becomes smaller than 1, that is, the sign of the dynode current is reversed.   For any further rise of the control grid, the dynode voltage would now decrease, which implies that a (meta-) stable state has been reached.   During the very fast switching process, the voltage across C has hardly changed, but during the metastable state that now follows, C is charged by the grid current.   This change causes the grid voltage to decrease (and the dynode voltage to increase) until the primary electron current to the dynode has decreased to such an extent that the space-charge density in front of the dynode becomes so small that for any further decrease of the grid voltage, the dynode voltage also starts decreasing again.   This means that another unstable state has been initiated, causing the tube current to be cut off in a very short time.   Finally, C discharges through R_k and the diode D until the quiescent state has been reestablished.   The diode D is used to shorten the recovery time.   The duration τ of the metastable state is directly proportional to C.   Its dependence on R_k, however, does not follow a simple law.   For the values of the voltages and the components given in Fig. 9.40, $\tau = 0.14\,\mu\text{sec}$ for $R_k = 100\,\Omega$; $\tau = 1.0\,\mu\text{sec}$ for $R_k = 1\,\text{k}\Omega$; and $\tau = 3.2\,\mu\text{sec}$ for $R_k = 10\,\text{k}\Omega$.

A trigger circuit with analogous properties may be obtained by feedback from the anode to the cathode of a secondary-emission tube.   Unlike normal tubes, these tubes can achieve a loop amplification larger than 1 in this way because the secondary-emission effect gives rise to a current amplification.   In the last circuit, the control grid is not capacitively connected to any other electrode, so that trigger pulses from a high-impedance source can be used.

PROBLEMS

9.1   A narrow rectangular pulse of width 2 μsec is applied to the circuit shown in Fig. 9.41. The pulse is repeated every 2 msec. Find the output voltage, in the steady state, with the diode D connected as shown and with it reversed. Assume that the forward resistance of the diode is 500 Ω and the back resistance 1 MΩ.

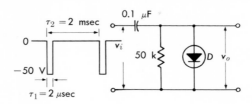

FIGURE 9.41

9.2   Determine v_o, given that v_i is a sinusoidal signal of amplitude 100 V and frequency 100 cps, for the circuit of Fig. 9.42. Assume that Q and D are typical audio-frequency devices. Repeat for a sawtooth input voltage of the same peak-to-peak amplitude.

9.3   A simple "sweep" circuit can be made by connecting a thyratron in the circuit shown in Fig. 9.43. Suppose that with the grid bias V_{g0}, the thyratron fires when $V_a = 150$ V, the discharge stops when $V_a = 25$ V, and the resistor R_a serves to limit the maximum current through the tube. Discuss the operation of the circuit, and sketch the output-wave shape for $C = 0.1$ μF, $R = 500$ kΩ. Find a value for R_a which will limit the peak tube current to 250 mA. What is the maximum deviation of the output sweep voltage from an ideal linear-time base?

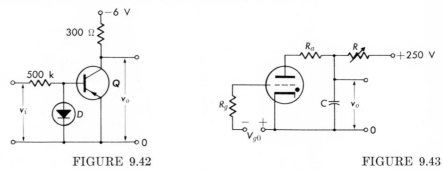

FIGURE 9.42   FIGURE 9.43

9.4   Two halves of a 12AU7 double triode are connected in the unsymmetrical astable multivibrator circuit shown in Fig. 9.44. Find the output signal v_o as a function of time.

9.5   The circuit shown in Fig. 9.45 is a so-called AND logical circuit, which should produce an output voltage only if both switches, A and B, are closed. Describe the operation of the circuit, and find the value of v_o when

   (a) both A and B are open,
   (b) A is closed but B is open,
   (c) both A and B are closed.

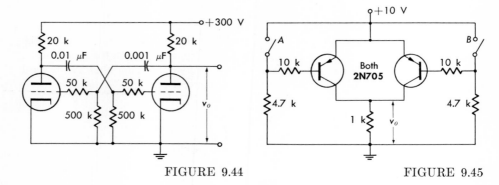

FIGURE 9.44   FIGURE 9.45

9.6   In some transistor pulse circuits the base may be overdriven to the point where the roles of the emitter and collector are essentially reversed. We may denote by α_n the normal forward current gain for a common-base circuit of the transistor (for a pnp, when the emitter is positive and the collector negative with respect to the base) and by α_i the common-base current gain, with the roles of collector and emitter inverted. The emitter-follower circuit shown in Fig. 9.46 is overdriven when a square wave of amplitude considerably greater than V_{c0} is applied to the base. Show that the output voltage v_o will be a square wave with amplitude exactly equal to V_{c0} if the base current

$$I_b = (V_{c0}/R_e)\,[1 + \alpha_n(1 - \alpha_i)/\alpha_i(1 - \alpha_n)].$$

This circuit is useful in voltage comparators for precise setting of the amplitude of pulses.

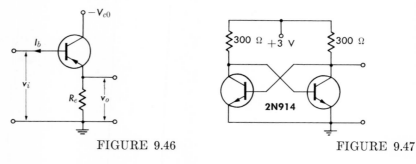

FIGURE 9.46   FIGURE 9.47

9.7   In most transistor circuits, efforts are made to avoid letting transistors reach a condition of collector saturation. However, by making use of this phenomenon, a special class of *direct-coupled transistor logic* (DCTL) circuits can be derived. An example is the diagram shown in Fig. 9.47. Show that this circuit will be bistable, and determine the quiescent base and collector voltages of both transistors.

9.8   The diagram in Fig. 9.48 shows a Schmitt trigger circuit. Find the values of the input voltage for which the circuit triggers as v_i is raised from -10 V to 0 V and then reversed. Find the amplitude of the output voltage for a 100 cps sinusoidal input signal of 10-V peak, centered at -3 V.

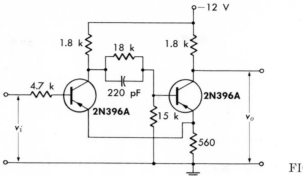

FIGURE 9.48

9.9   Figure 9.49 shows a *complementary* transistor flip-flop with a pnp- and an npn-transistor in combination. Find the quiescent voltages in both stable states at the collector, base, and emitter of each transistor. Find appropriate values of R_{c_1}, R_{c_2}, and R_e for operation of the circuit.

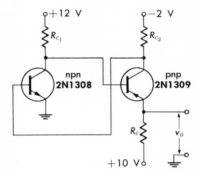

FIGURE 9.49

9.10   The diagram in Fig. 9.50 shows a triggered monostable multivibrator circuit. Describe the operation of the circuit and determine v_o as a function of time, following an input trigger.

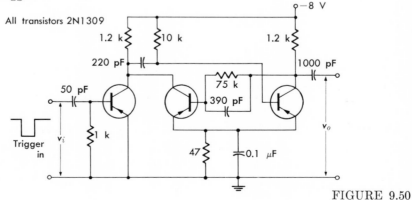

FIGURE 9.50

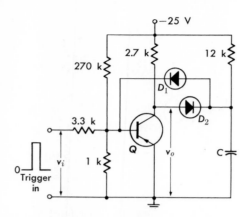

FIGURE 9.51

9.11   In Fig. 9.51, which is the circuit of a simple rectangular pulse generator, D_1 is a Zener diode, D_2 is a simple point-contact diode, such as a 1N34A, and Q is a special avalanche transistor (TA1832) with a well-defined conduction point, called a *thyristor* (by analogy to a thyratron). In the common-emitter configuration, when α_{ce} becomes greater than unity, I_c increases while V_{ce} drops to a low value. Once it switches on, by drawing base current, the thyristor will stay in the high-conductance state independent of the base current, unless the base is driven far into cutoff. Switching times are small, about 0.1 µsec. Describe the operation of the circuit and find the dependence of the output-pulse width on the value of the condenser C. (Note that the input trigger pulse turns the transistor *off*.)

REFERENCES

Lewis, I. A. D., and F. H. Wells, *Millimicrosecond Pulse Techniques*, Pergamon, 1959.
Littauer, R., *Pulse Electronics*, McGraw-Hill, 1965.
Millman, J., and H. Taub, *Pulse, Digital and Switching Waveforms*, McGraw-Hill, 1965.
Strauss, L., *Wave Generation and Shaping*, McGraw-Hill, 1960.

10.1 LIMITATIONS ON SIGNAL DETECTABILITY

We have seen earlier how to construct amplifiers of arbitrarily high gain by cascading individual stages. It would thus appear that we can amplify any signal voltage, no matter how small, to any desired level at the cost of a certain number of tubes or transistors necessary to provide the required gain. Actually, nature is not so generous, for we always encounter, in addition to the desired signal, some unwanted voltages, which are amplified together with it. If these are larger than the desired signal, it may be difficult or impossible to extract the useful information content from the signal, regardless of the amplitude. As a general classification, we may categorize all unwanted voltages as *noise* and may distinguish three different classes as follows.

1. *Avoidable external noise.* Unwanted voltages may appear at the input to an amplifier because of pickup from external sources such as radio stations, fluorescent lights, automobile-ignition systems, electrical generators, sunspots, and the like. In principle all of these can be minimized by proper electric and magnetic shielding of leads and components, by selection of frequency bands at which the interfering signals are small, or by the use of highly directional antennas.

2. *Avoidable internal noise.* Interfering voltages may be produced internally to the amplifier, from pickup of power-line or power-supply ripple voltages (called *hum*) or by mechanical vibration of circuit components (called *microphonics*). Hum may be caused by improper grounding of shields or leads so that two points nominally connected to a common "ground" on the chassis may actually have an appreciable ac signal voltage between them, by pickup from ac-operated heaters (in tubes) to grids or ungrounded cathodes, or by pickup between unshielded adjacent leads or components. All these effects can be minimized, at least in principle, by power-supply filtering, proper shielding and placement of leads, decoupling of ac heater voltages, use of dc on the heaters, or by deliberate injection into the amplifier of a signal of the same frequency but of opposite phase to cancel the hum pickup. Microphonics can be minimized by proper

shock-mounting of critical components and by use of tubes with rugged construction, such as the *frame-grid* tubes described in Chapter 2. Use of transistors
to a large extent avoids both of these difficulties, since there are no heaters and
the small size and potted construction of transistors makes them much less
susceptible to shock and vibration.

3. *Unavoidable noise.* In addition to the above undesired signals, which may be
reduced to an arbitrarily small value by optimal circuit construction, the active
and passive components essential to the amplifier—the tubes, transistors, resistors, etc.—also all produce a certain characteristic amount of noise, arising
from the discrete nature of the electrical charge and the random motion of these
charges in various parts of the circuit. Such effects cause an irreducible minimum
noise background, which is amplified along with any desired signal and which
sets a minimum threshold on detectability of signals. In this chapter we shall
be concerned only with such natural sources of noise and with means for opti-
mizing the performance of amplifiers to provide the best possible ratio of desired
signal to noise at the output. An amplifier can never, of course, produce an
output signal which has relatively less noise than that present at the input. As
a measure of the relative merit of the circuit, we define the noise figure:

$$F = \frac{(\text{signal power/noise power}) \text{ at input}}{(\text{signal power/noise power}) \text{ at output}}.$$ (10.1)

For an ideal noiseless amplifier, $F = 1$; for any real amplifier, $F > 1$.

10.2   RESISTANCE NOISE

Nyquist showed in 1928 that as a consequence of the Second Law of Thermo-
dynamics, a random, fluctuating noise voltage must be present across the
terminals of any impedance Z at any finite absolute temperature T, with a mean-
square value of

$$\overline{v_n^2} = \left| 4kT \int_{f_1}^{f_2} \text{Re}\,(Z)\,df \right|,$$ (10.2)

where k is Boltzmann's constant $(1.37 \times 10^{-23} \text{ J/°K})$, f_2 and f_1 are, respectively,
the maximum and minimum frequency in cycles per second accepted by the
measuring apparatus, and $\text{Re}\,(Z)$ is the real part of the (complex) impedance.
For a pure resistance, $\text{Re}\,(Z) = R$, independent of the frequency, and

$$\overline{v_n^2} = 4kTR(f_2 - f_1) = 4kTRB,$$ (10.3)

where $B = (f_2 - f_1)$ is defined as the *noise bandwidth*. Thus a resistor may
be represented as in Fig. 10.1(a), as a noiseless resistance R in series with a
voltage generator of mean-square noise voltage $\overline{v_n^2}$. Alternatively, we can represent the resistor as in Fig. 10.1(b), as a conductance, $G = 1/R$, in parallel

with a current generator of mean-square value

$$\overline{i_n^2} = 4kTGB. \tag{10.4}$$

From either (10.3) or (10.4), it is clear that the average noise *power* generated is

$$P_n = kTB \tag{10.5}$$

and is independent of the value of the resistance.

According to these equations, the noise depends only on the bandwidth B, and is *independent of the frequency;* noise with such a completely uniform frequency spectrum is called *white noise.* Since the total noise energy must be finite, these relations cannot hold to infinite frequency. Because of quantum effects, the noise decreases for $f > kT/h \approx 10^{13}$ cps and approaches zero as $f \to \infty$. Such extremely high frequencies are of little interest in the present discussion. The actual noise voltages produced by resistors at room temperature are by no means negligible. For example, for $R = 10$ kΩ, $B = 10$ kcps, and $T = 300°$K, the root-mean-square noise voltage is 1.27 μV.

The noise bandwidth B is not necessarily identical with the usual 3-db bandwidth defined in Chapter 4. If the 3-db bandwidth Δf is defined by a single RC- or LC-filter, then $B = (\pi/2) \Delta f$; for a multistage circuit the response falls off rapidly with frequency after the 3-db points, and $B \to \Delta f$. If a high-impedance signal source, represented by a noise-producing resistance R, is connected to the input of an amplifier, the noise bandwidth is frequently that of the RC-filter, consisting of R and the input capacity C_i of the amplifier, rather than that measured with a signal generator. The noise bandwidth in such cases is $\Delta f = 1/4RC_i$, and Eq. (10.3) can be replaced by

$$\overline{v_n^2} = kT/C_i. \tag{10.6}$$

For example, for $R = 1$ MΩ, $C_i = 50$ pF, we have $\Delta f = 5$ kcps and $\sqrt{\overline{v_n^2}} = 9 \,\mu$V.

Because of their construction, the actual resistors used in amplifier circuits may produce more noise than that given by (10.3) and (10.4), when we use the

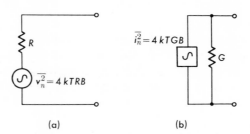

(a)   (b)

FIG. 10.1. Equivalent circuits for thermal noise. (a) Voltage source and noiseless resistance, (b) current source and noiseless conductance.

measured value of R. Wire-wound resistors follow these relations quite precisely at low frequencies but, because of their inductance and distributed capacity as well as the familiar skin effect, Re (Z) tends to increase at high frequencies and the noise output increases. The reactive components also give rise to undesirable resonances which can change the frequency response of the amplifier. The less expensive "carbon" or "composition" resistors have excellent high-frequency characteristics but, because of their granular nature, produce a considerable excess noise at low frequencies when they carry a dc-current. The rms value of this excess noise voltage varies approximately in direct proportion with the voltage across the resistor and inversely as the square root of the frequency. Such resistors should therefore never be used in the anode or collector circuits of low-frequency amplifiers, if optimal noise-free operation is important. Resistors made by deposition of thin films of metals or carbon on insulating substrates most closely approximate ideal performance from dc to very high frequencies, but these are frequently available only in a limited range of resistance values and are expensive and somewhat fragile.

10.3   TUBE NOISE*

The total noise power W at the output of an n-stage amplifier is a sum of contributions of all stages:

$$W = W_1 A_{p_1} \cdots A_{p_n} + W_2 A_{p_2} \cdots A_{p_n} + \cdots + W_n A_{p_n},$$

where $W_1, W_2, \ldots$ are the noise powers and $A_{p_1}, A_{p_2}, \ldots$ are the power gains of the individual stages. According to the definition given in Eq. (10.1) we may write, for the noise figure of the whole amplifier,

$$F = F_1 + F_2/A_{p_1} + F_3/A_{p_1}A_{p_2} + \cdots, \tag{10.7}$$

where $F_1, F_2, \ldots$ are the noise figures of the individual stages. Clearly, if A_{p_1} is sufficiently large, the noise figure of the amplifier is largely determined by that of the first stage only, and we need only try to optimize the performance of this stage.

There are three principal contributions to the noise developed by vacuum tubes.

1. *Shot noise.* This is caused by statistical fluctuations in time of the electron emission from the cathode; these produce an ac-noise component in the anode current which is frequency-independent up to frequencies of the order of the reciprocal of the transit time of electrons across the tube. For a temperature-limited diode, the mean-square noise current, as shown by Schottky in 1918, is

$$\overline{i_n^2} = 2eI_aB, \tag{10.8}$$

---

* For a detailed treatment, see A. Van der Ziel, *Noise*, Prentice Hall, New York, 1954.

TABLE 10.1

Equivalent Noise Resistance of Typical Vacuum Tubes

Tube type	g_m, mA/V	R_{eq}, ohms
6BQ7A (triode)	6.4	430
6AN4 (triode)	10	250
416A (triode)	50	100
6AK5 (pentode)	5.1	1820
6AK5 (triode)*	6.7	370
6CB6 (pentode)	6.5	1390
6CB6 (triode)*	8.4	290

* The pentodes are usually connected as triodes by joining the screen grid to the anode and the supressor to the cathode.

where e is the electronic charge (1.6×10^{-19} C) and I_a is the dc anode current. Under space-charge-limited operation, which is of much more practical interest, the noise is far less than that given by (10.8), by a factor of 5 to 20. For tubes under this operation, the mean-square noise current at the anode is usually expressed in terms of an equivalent noise resistance, R_{eq}, as

$$\overline{i_n^2} = 4kTBR_{eq}g_m^2 . \tag{10.9}$$

This is equivalent to a mean-square noise voltage at the *grid* of

$$\overline{v_n^2} = \overline{i_n^2}/g_m^2 = 4kTBR_{eq}. \tag{10.10}$$

For a triode, the equivalent noise resistance is approximately

$$R_{eq} \approx 2500/g_m. \tag{10.11}$$

Some representative values of the equivalent noise resistance of triodes and of pentodes connected as a triode are given in Table 10.1.

2. *Partition noise.* In screen-grid tubes, the fluctuations in the division of the electron current between the screen grid and the anode constitute an extra source of noise called *partition noise.* This type, like shot noise, is frequency independent over a large frequency range. It considerably increases the total noise current in the anode circuit. For a pentode, the total equivalent noise resistance is approximately

$$R_{eq} \approx \frac{I_a}{I_a + I_{g2}} \left[\frac{2500}{g_m} + \frac{2 \times 10^4}{g_m^2} I_{g2} \right] \Omega. \tag{10.12}$$

Specific values are given for some tube types in Table 10.1.

3. *Flicker noise.* Effected by irregular changes in the emitting power of the cathode, this noise causes R_{eq} to rise as $1/f$ at very low frequencies. This source

of noise exceeds shot and partition noise at low frequencies but falls off to negligible values at frequencies above 1–10 kcps. Flicker noise is particularly troublesome in sensitive dc-amplifiers. Very-low-frequency components of the flicker noise appear as drift. Unlike shot noise, flicker noise does not appear to be a basic property of the thermionic-emission process, because it can be reduced by careful construction of the cathode or by use of other than oxide cathodes.

4. *Grid-current noise.* At negative control-grid voltages smaller than about one volt, a fraction of the electron current still reaches the grid and causes some grid current. At higher negative grid voltages, the electron current rapidly becomes negligible, but positive ions formed in the residual gas by electron impact will still reach the grid.

Both sources of grid current exhibit the same noise characteristics as the shot effect, for their mean-square value is given by a formula similar to Eq. (10.8). The residual grid current of a good tube, operated at a negative grid bias of more than, say, -1.5 V is quite small, usually less than 10^{-10} A. Even this small current, however, may give the predominant contribution to the total noise when the impedance in the grid circuit is high, since the noise voltage at the grid due to grid-current fluctuations is proportional to the absolute value of this impedance. Grid-current noise can be minimized if we select the tubes carefully and run them at reduced anode and heater voltages and at a not-too-small negative grid bias.

5. *Induced grid noise.* This is caused by random currents in the grid circuit due to fluctuations in the number of electrons passing the grid wires per unit time. It can be visualized as follows: an electron approaching the grid induces a pulse of current in the grid circuit in one direction; as it moves away again a current pulse flows in the other direction. The net total induced charge, and thus the average grid current, is of course zero, but a noise current is set up due to the final transit time τ of the electrons. It can be shown that the mean square of this noise current increases as the square of the frequency (so long as $f \ll 1/\tau$).

Induced grid noise contributes significantly only at high frequencies ($\gtrsim 100$ Mcps). As for grid-current noise, its contribution is determined by the total impedance in the grid circuit. The electron transit time, which causes induced grid noise to appear, is important also in another respect. It produces an ohmic conductance G_t between grid and cathode proportional to f^2, which must be taken into account when tube noise at high frequencies is discussed. The mean-square current due to induced grid noise is related to this conductance by

$$\overline{i_n^2} \approx 5(4kTB)G_t. \tag{10.13}$$

An equivalent circuit for tube noise, in which the noise sources just discussed have been incorporated, is shown in Fig. 10.2. The total conductance of the grid circuit, consisting of the external conductance G_e and the tube conductance G_t in parallel, is acted upon by two current sources, $\overline{i_{n_1}^2}$ and $\overline{i_{n_2}^2}$, which represent

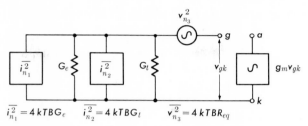

FIG. 10.2. Equivalent circuit for tube noise: G_e = ohmic conductance in external grid circuit; G_t = input conductance of tube; R_{eq} = equivalent shot noise resistance of tube.

the mean squares of grid-current noise and induced grid noise, respectively. The shot noise—and for pentodes, the partition noise—is represented by a voltage source in series with the parallel combination of G_t and G_e, delivering a mean-square noise voltage $\overline{v_{n_s}^2} = 4\,kTBR_{eq}$. A complication in applying this diagram arises from the fact that $\overline{i_{n_2}^2}$ and $\overline{v_{n_s}^2}$ are partly correlated and, therefore, their contributions cannot always be simply added together.

10.4 TRANSISTOR NOISE

The random motion of free electrons and holes in a transistor also gives rise to current fluctuations. If no dc-current is passed through a transistor, the mean-square noise voltages are of the same order of magnitude as those of any resistor with the same value of resistance. The noise output, however, increases strongly when the transistor is operated at normal voltages and currents, much as in a composition resistor. This can be ascribed to *shot* and *flicker* noise at the junctions. The mean-square noise voltage is much higher at low frequencies, due partly to surface-leakage effects, increasing approximately as $1/f$ for frequencies below 100 kcps. Above that frequency, the noise is approximately constant (but still much higher than the simple resistor noise); it increases again at high frequencies as α decreases, with a factor of $1 - \alpha^2/\alpha_0$, where α_0 is the common-base current gain at zero frequency.

The actual magnitude of the noise output from transistors depends sensitively on the detailed construction of the transistor, the leakage conductance, the type and amount of doping used, the relative homogeneity of the junctions, etc. Therefore, it is not possible to give quantitative formulas for transistor noise that correspond to those for vacuum tubes. Manufacturers' data frequently include noise figures for special low-noise transistors. Many transistors are noisier than tubes, for general use, and are infrequently employed where a minimum noise figure is a major requirement. Transistor noise is partly due to current fluctuations in the base-emitter circuit; therefore, the best noise figures are often obtained for low-impedance signal sources. Field-effect transistors, which have a very low input current, can be used with good results also in combination with high-impedance signal sources.

10.5 LOW-NOISE AMPLIFIERS; GENERAL CONSIDERATIONS

In the design of practical amplifiers to provide an optimum noise figure, there are three major constituents which may be optimized: (1) components, (2) bandwidth, (3) circuit. These three criteria are somewhat interrelated, and the detailed design of low-noise amplifiers is a complex procedure, beyond the scope of the present book. Here we shall simply indicate the general considerations which govern the practical choices and, in the next section, we will show how these can be implemented in some typical circuits.

Choice of optimal components. Vacuum-tube circuits are still preferred to transistor circuits for most applications, and triodes are preferable to pentodes for the input stage. The input tube should have a high value of g_m to minimize R_{eq}, and must be biased to maintain g_m at a high value but never so close to zero bias that grid current can flow, since this would give rise to a large increase in the noise figure. Manufacturers' data should, of course, be consulted to determine an optimal low-noise tube. Some special tubes employ gold plating on the grids to reduce secondary emission, and provide lower noise figures than others with a comparable transconductance. The actual value of the ohmic resistance employed in the input stage should be kept to a minimum consistent with proper matching of the input, as will be discussed later. All resistors used in the input stage should have low noise figures over the range of operating frequencies. Metal film resistors, if available, provide low noise figures over the widest bandwidth; otherwise, wire-wound resistors should be used for low-frequency amplifiers and composition resistors for high-frequency amplifiers. Electrolytic condensers may also introduce noise, and should be avoided in the first amplifier stages.

Choice of optimal bandwidth. The ultimate bandwidth of the amplifier should not be larger than that required to provide adequate response to the widest band signal which must be amplified, since the noise power, whatever the source, increases in direct proportion to the bandwidth. If the input resistance of the signal source is low, the value of B is determined by that of the whole amplifier, not simply by the input circuit. Bandwidth restrictions can often be most conveniently set if we incorporate a narrow-band filter into one of the stages. However, if the circuit involves a detector at one or more stages, as in a communications receiver, it is important to take account of the nature of the detector. For example, if the detector is an ordinary "linear" detector such as a diode rectifier, the rectification process blocks both noise and signal voltages of one sign, so that random positive and negative contributions to the noise voltage cannot cancel one another at the detector output. Rectifier detectors thus greatly reduce the effectiveness of a filter placed *after* the detector. If the bandwidth of the circuit preceding a rectifier detector is B_1 and that following the detector is B_2, the effective noise bandwidth of the whole circuit is $\sqrt{B_1 B_2}$. So for low noise, *both* B_1 and B_2 must be small. However, if the circuit employs a *phase-sensitive detector*, in which the signal is actually coherently centered about zero frequency without rectification (see Problem 7.13), the noise band-width will be independent of B_1 and will simply be $2B_2$; here a narrow-band post-detection filter can provide minimum noise figure.

The choice of signal frequency should also, if possible, be optimized for low-noise performance. As noted earlier, very low frequencies and very high frequencies introduce additional sources of noise, due to flicker and induced grid noise, and should be avoided. If the amplifier must be operated at these extremes, special care must be taken in tube selection for optimal performance in these ranges. Since flicker noise increases with cathode current, low-frequency amplifiers are often operated with very low anode voltage and reduced heater voltage on the first stage, in so-called *starved current* operation. The consequent increase in shot noise can be more than offset by the reduction in flicker and grid-current noise.

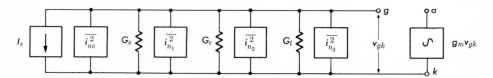

FIG. 10.3. Equivalent circuit for calculation of noise figure: I_s = signal current; $\overline{i_{ns}^2} = 4kTBG_s$ = mean-square noise current from signal source; G_s = effective conductance of signal source transformed to grid circuit; $\overline{i_{n3}^2}$ = mean-square tube shot noise current; other terms defined in Fig. 10.2.

Choice of optimal circuit. One of the chief requirements in the design of low-noise amplifiers for high frequencies is matching the input circuit so as to provide a minimum over-all noise figure. This is critical since, as is shown in Eq. (10.7), the noise figure of the first stage largely determines the performance of the whole amplifier. The complete equivalent input circuit is shown in Fig. 10.3. The actual signal source has an effective noise conductance G_{in}, which by definition produces a mean-square noise current $\overline{i_{in}^2} = 4kTBG_{in}$. This is transformed by the input-matching circuit to an effective conductance G_s with a mean-square-noise current $\overline{i_{ns}^2} = 4kTBG_s$. The signal-to-noise ratio at the input is

$$\left(\frac{S}{N}\right)_{in} = \frac{\overline{I_{in}^2}}{\overline{i_{in}^2}} = \frac{\overline{I_s^2}}{\overline{i_{ns}^2}} = \frac{\overline{I_s^2}}{4kTBG_s}, \tag{10.14}$$

where $\overline{I_{in}^2}$ is the mean-square input-signal current and $\overline{I_s^2}$ the mean-square signal current at the grid. From the equivalent circuit, the output signal-to-noise ratio is

$$\left(\frac{S}{N}\right)_{out} = \frac{\overline{I_s^2}}{\overline{i_{ns}^2} + \overline{i_{n_1}^2} + \overline{i_{n_2}^2} + \overline{i_{n_3}^2}}. \tag{10.15}$$

For convenience, the voltage source, $\overline{v_{n_3}^2} = 4kTBR_{eq}$, that represents tube shot and partition noise, has been transformed to an equivalent mean-square current source $\overline{i_{n_3}^2} = \overline{v_{n_3}^2}(G_s + G_1 + G_t)^2$.

The noise figure of the stage, from (10.1) and (10.13)–(10.15), is then

$$F = 1 + \frac{G_1}{G_s} + \frac{5G_t}{G_s} + \frac{R_{eq}}{G_s}(G_s + G_1 + G_t)^2. \tag{10.16}$$

To find the minimum value of F as a function of the only adjustable parameter, G_s, we set $dF/dG_s = 0$. Solving, we obtain

$$G_{s_{opt}} = \sqrt{(G_1 + 5G_t)/R_{eq} + (G_1 + G_t)^2}, \tag{10.17}$$

or, since $G_s = G_{in}/m^2$, with m the transformation ratio of the input transformer, we have

$$m_{opt} = \left(\frac{G_{in}^2 R_{eq}}{G_1 + 5G_t + R_{eq}(G_1 + G_t)^2}\right)^{1/4}. \tag{10.18}$$

It should be noted that this value of m is different from that required for optimum signal transfer, which would be $m = \sqrt{G_{in}/(G_e + G_t)}$. The term G_1 includes the losses in the input transformer as well as any other actual conductances in the grid circuit. Since G_t increases with the square of the frequency, it can be ignored for low-frequency amplifiers, but it tends to dominate the noise figure at very high frequencies. In high-frequency amplifiers, care must be taken so that G_t does not increase because of parasitic feedback through the grid-anode capacity of the first stage. One solution is to use a grounded-grid amplifier at the input, although this has a very low input impedance. Another is to use the cascode amplifier described in Section 6.3.4, which provides high gain and high input impedance with very little undesirable feedback.

10.6   PRACTICAL LOW-NOISE AMPLIFIERS

We shall consider two quite different examples of low-noise amplifiers to illustrate some of the practical techniques for the design of such circuits for special requirements.

The first circuit, shown schematically in Fig. 10.4, is of a broad-band, very-high-frequency (VHF) preamplifier, such as might be used for a communications receiver. The amplifier is tuned to a center frequency of 45 Mcps, with a bandwidth of 2.8 Mcps. The input two stages comprise a cascode amplifier circuit, which uses special low-noise VHF triodes, with a high g_m of 15 mA/V and a μ of 60, and operates at an anode current of about 16 mA. The third stage is a tuned pentode amplifier, which serves chiefly to transform the high impedance at the output of the cascode to a low impedance for driving the next stage. This circuit also employs a low-noise tube, although the requirements for this stage are far less critical than for the input. The amplifier provides an over-all power

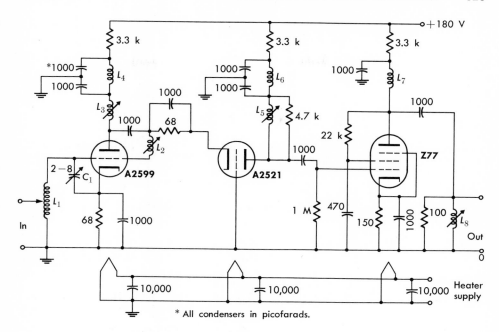

FIG. 10.4. Schematic diagram of a tuned low-noise VHF preamplifier.

gain of 35 db with a noise figure of only 1.4, extremely small for this frequency range.

The tap on the input autotransformer L_1 is adjusted to provide optimal matching of the source conductance to the input. Circuit L_1C_1 and the inductors L_3, L_5, and L_8 are all tuned to the center frequency. Inductor L_2 is adjusted to neutralize the first stage. The other inductors and condensers in the anode circuits are simply to provide for decoupling of the anode leads and prevent feedback through the common power supply. The heater leads are also decoupled by feed-through condensers. The bandwidth of the amplifier is largely determined by the tuned circuit of L_5, since the output impedance of the grounded-grid stage is very high. A 4.7-kΩ resistor is connected in parallel with L_5 to decrease the Q of this circuit to a value consistent with the required bandwidth.

The second circuit, shown in Fig. 10.5(a), is a broad-band transistor differential preamplifier, which operates over a frequency range of 1 cps to 1 Mcps, providing a voltage gain of about 20. The input impedance is raised to about 50 kΩ by the bootstrapping condensers C_1 and C_2, which provide feedback from the emitter to the base of the transistors, as in an emitter follower. The input transistors Q_1 and Q_2 are silicon pnp-transistors especially selected for low noise. The second stage formed by the npn-transistors Q_3 and Q_4, is a conventional difference amplifier. The gain is set by the value of R_1 relative to the 1.5-kΩ resistors in the collectors of Q_3 and Q_4, which determines the amount

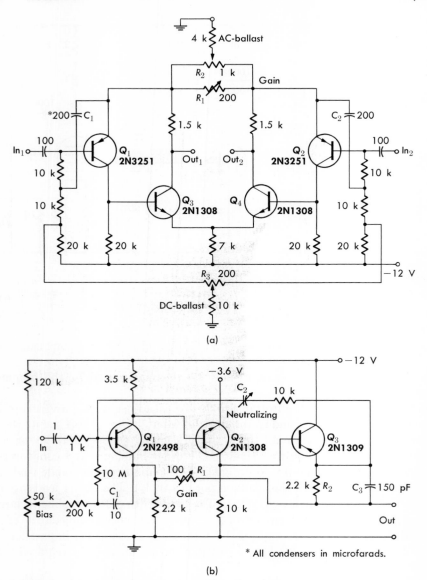

FIG. 10.5.   (a) Schematic diagram of a low-noise transistor differential preamplifier, (b) special unity-gain high-impedance input circuit for use with source resistances greater than 20 kΩ (Courtesy Princeton Applied Research Corporation).

of negative feedback to the emitters of the input transistors. We may balance the circuit for alternating current and direct current by setting the potentiometers R_2 and R_3. All resistors are of the metal-film variety, to minimize noise.

The noise figure of the circuit, measured with a narrow-band amplifier at a frequency of 10 kcps, depends markedly on the source resistance, R_s, of the circuit providing the input signal. The noise figure is below 3 db for 500 Ω <

$R_s < 10$ kΩ, below 6 db for 200 Ω $< R_s < 20$ kΩ, and below 10 db for 80 Ω $<$ $R_s < 100$ kΩ, rising to 20 db for R_s of 10 Ω or 10 MΩ. An input transformer must be used for impedance matching of source resistances of 100 Ω or less if a reasonable noise figure is to be achieved.

For operation with values of R_s greater than 20 kΩ, a high-impedance unity-gain circuit with a field-effect transistor like that shown in Fig. 10.5(b) can be used for matching the source to the amplifier. With this circuit connected, the noise figure is below 3 db for 30 kΩ $< R_s < 3$ MΩ. The high-impedance matching circuit employs a field-effect transistor Q_1 with a bootstrap condenser C_1 to raise the effective input resistance to about 50 MΩ. Adjustment of the neutralizing trimmer C_2 lowers the input capacity to a few picofarads. The gain is adjusted by the value of the feedback resistor R_1. The network R_2C_3 at the output of the emitter-follower stage of Q_3 forms a compensated attenuator of relatively high impedance for optimal matching to the amplifier input.

Because of flicker noise in the semiconductor components, the noise figure of the preamplifier, measured over a narrow bandwidth with a constant source resistance, deteriorates at low frequencies. For a source resistance of 2 kΩ, about the optimal value, the noise figure is below 3 db for frequencies greater than about 1 kcps but rises to 6 db at 100 cps and finally to about 20 db at 1 cps. With the high-impedance input stage and an optimal source resistance of 200 kΩ, the low-frequency noise figure is worse below 1 kcps, rising to 20 db at about 50 cps. Because of the input conductance, the noise figure also increases at very high frequencies with the high-impedance input stage, rising to about 10 db at 1 Mcps.

PROBLEMS

10.1 (a) Show that the mean-square noise voltage across the parallel RC-network shown in Fig. 10.6(a) is kT/C, independent of R.

(b) Find the mean-square noise voltage across the parallel RLC-network shown in Fig. 10.6(b).

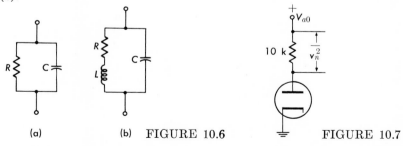

(a)   (b)   FIGURE 10.6   FIGURE 10.7

10.2 Calculate the rms noise voltage in a 100-kcps bandwidth across the 10-kΩ anode resistor in Fig. 10.7 when the diode is operating under temperature-limited conditions at an average anode current of 5 mA. Compare this result with the voltage across the resistor with the diode turned off.

10.3   According to Eqs. (10.9) and (10.11), the mean-square shot noise voltage from a triode depends on the transconductance of the tube. The transconductance, however, depends on the average anode current (Eq. 2.20), which in turn is a function of the grid-bias voltage.   Calculate the variation in the rms noise component of v_o for the circuit shown in Fig. 10.8 as V_{g0} is varied from zero to cutoff, for $\frac{1}{2}$ 12AU7, assuming that all the noise is given by Eq. (10.9).

10.4   A broad-band amplifier has a bandwidth of 2 Mcps and a noise figure of 10 (or 10 db).   Given that the amplifier has a voltage gain of 10^5, what is the actual rms noise voltage across a 1-kΩ resistor at the amplifier output?

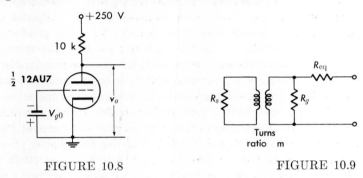

FIGURE 10.8   FIGURE 10.9

10.5   A signal generator with a source resistance $R_s = 300\,\Omega$ is coupled by an ideal transformer with a ratio of secondary-to-primary turns m to a triode amplifier with $R_{eq} = 500\,\Omega$, with an equivalent parallel grid resistance $R_g = 1\,\mathrm{M}\Omega$.   Find the value for the turns ratio m for the lowest noise figure in a low-frequency amplifier with negligible input conductance.   (See Fig. 10.9.)

REFERENCES

Valley, G.E., and H. Wallman, *Vacuum Tube Amplifiers*, Radiation Laboratory Series **18,** McGraw-Hill, 1948.
van der Ziel, A., *Noise*, Prentice-Hall, 1954.

COMPLEX NOTATION FOR AC-CIRCUITS

Let us consider a network consisting only of passive linear circuit elements such as resistors, inductances, and condensers, connected to a current or voltage source which provides a sinusoidal signal of frequency $f = \omega/2\pi$. The currents flowing in the branches of the network and the voltages between various branch points can in principle be found from Kirchhoff's relations if we write down expressions for the sums of the currents at the branch points and for the sums of the voltages and emf's around closed loops in the network. In this manner a set of differential equations can be derived for the network, containing terms such as iR, $L(di/dt)$, $C(dV/dt)$, etc. It is clear that such a set is a system of linear differential equations, which can be solved, after suitable manipulation, for the currents and voltages.

Only in a few very simple cases can the relation between the branch current, $i = i_o \cos \omega t$, and the resulting voltage V be written down directly. For a network consisting of only one coil of inductance L, the voltage is

$$V = L(di/dt) = -\omega L i_o \sin \omega t = \omega L i_o \cos (\omega t + 90°). \qquad (A.1)$$

From this expression it is apparent that the phase of the voltage leads that of the current by 90° and that the amplitude of the voltage is $V_o = \omega L i_o$. If the network consists of only one condenser with capacity C, the voltage is

$$V = \frac{\int i \, dt}{C} = \frac{1}{\omega C} i_o \sin \omega t = \frac{1}{\omega C} i_o \cos (\omega t - 90°) \qquad (A.2)$$

for a current $i = i_o \cos \omega t$ through the condenser. Now the phase of the voltage lags 90° behind that of the current, and the voltage has an amplitude $V_o = (1/\omega C)i_o$. For a network consisting of only an ohmic resistor R, of course we have

$$V = R i_o \cos \omega t; \qquad (A.3)$$

now the voltage and current are in phase, and the voltage amplitude is $V_o = R i_o$.

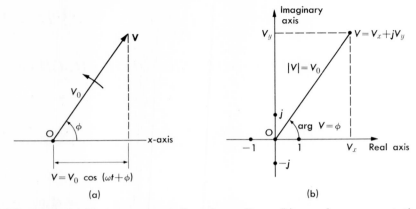

FIG. A–1.   (a) Vector representation of ac-voltage, (b) complex representation of ac-voltage.

Circuits comprising two or more elements lead to differential equations which are frequently not particularly simple. In complicated cases, a solution may generally be derived more expediently if we reformulate the problem by using complex quantities to represent the currents and voltages. Mathematically, this representation can be rigorously derived from the form of the differential equations, but it may be easily visualized by analogy with the familiar vector representation of ac-quantities. In the usual vector representation, ac voltages or currents are represented by vectors **V** or **i** with a fixed origin O (Fig. A.1a). The length V_o of a vector **V** gives the amplitude of the quantity, while the angle ϕ with the horizontal axis (x-axis) is the phase angle with respect to some voltage or current for which the phase angle has been *a priori* defined as zero. We may imagine that the vector rotates counterclockwise with a constant angular velocity, in such a way that the tip of the arrow describes a complete circle with radius V_o at a rate f times per second, and passing the position shown in Fig. A.1(a) at the instant $t = 0$. Then the projection of the tip of the arrow on the x-axis is given by the equation $V = V_o \cos (\omega t + \phi)$, which is precisely the expression for a sinusoidal voltage of amplitude V_o and phase angle ϕ.

The algebraic sum of two ac-voltages, $V_1 = V_{1o} \cos (\omega t + \phi_1)$ and $V_2 = V_{2o} \cos (\omega t + \phi_2)$, is readily derived from the vector representation as shown in Fig. A.2, by forming the vector sum **V** = **V₁** + **V₂**. The projection of **V** on the x-axis has a length corresponding to the amplitude of the voltage $V = V_1 + V_2$, whereas **V** makes an angle with the x-axis corresponding to the phase angle of the resultant voltage.

The vectors **V** can be decomposed into two perpendicular components, one along the x-axis and one along the y-axis, in the usual manner. The two components, V_x and V_y, of course provide a complete representation of the vector **V**, just as do its length and angle with the x-axis. In the complex representation of ac voltages and currents, the real number $+1$ is used as the unit along the

x-axis and the imaginary number $j = \sqrt{-1}$ as the unit along the y-axis. With this choice, the xy-plane has become the complex plane; a point with coordinates x and jy in that plane is called a complex number, denoted by $x + jy$. The length of the line connecting a point $z = x + jy$ in the complex plane with the origin has a length $|z| = \sqrt{x^2 + y^2}$. This quantity is called the *modulus* or *absolute value* of the complex quantity z. The angle between the line connecting z with the origin and the x-axis is $\phi = \tan^{-1}(y/x)$; this angle is called the *argument* of z. We may now apply these definitions to the vector $\mathbf{V}$ with components V_x and V_y along the real and imaginary axes, respectively. It is clear that $\mathbf{V}$ can be represented by the complex quantity

$$V = V_x + jV_y. \qquad (A.4)$$

The absolute value of this quantity is

$$|V| = \sqrt{V_x^2 + V_y^2}. \qquad (A.5)$$

This expression is just the magnitude of the ac-voltage. The argument

$$\arg V = \tan^{-1}(V_y/V_x) \qquad (A.6)$$

is simply the phase angle (see Fig. A.1b). Both amplitude and phase are thus contained in Eq. (A.4).

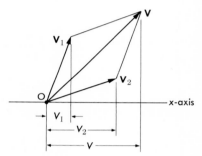

FIG. A–2.   Resultant of two vector voltages.

Why has the imaginary number $j = \sqrt{-1}$ been chosen as the unit along the positive y-axis? Because algebraic multiplication by j corresponds to a rotation by $+90°$ in the complex plane. This is easily shown by multiplying a voltage, $V = V_x + jV_y$, by j; we then have a voltage

$$jV = jV_x + j^2V_y = jV_x - V_y$$

(since $j^2 = -1$), representing a voltage with phase angle

$$\phi = \tan^{-1}(-V_x/V_y) = \tan^{-1}(V_y/V_x) + 90°$$

and the same amplitude $|V| = \sqrt{V_x^2 + V_y^2}$.

Therefore, the advantage of the imaginary unit is that it describes a phase rotation through $90°$ in a very simple way. For instance, we may write the relation between the current and voltage in an inductance, originally represented by Eq. (A.1), as

$$V = j\omega Li. \qquad (A.7)$$

We must bear in mind that both V and i are now complex numbers. We can define an imaginary resistance $V/i = j\omega L$, for the inductance.

Similarly, for a condenser of capacity C (see Eq. A.2),

$$V = \frac{-j}{\omega C} i; \tag{A.8}$$

the condenser therefore has an imaginary resistance $V/i = -j/\omega C$.

In general, any linear two-terminal network has a complex resistance or impedance, $V/i = Z$. If we have two impedances Z_1 and Z_2 in series, through which the same current i will flow, the total voltage across the terminals of this circuit is $V = Z_1 i + Z_2 i$, and therefore the total impedance is

$$V/i = Z = Z_1 + Z_2. \tag{A.9}$$

If two impedances, Z_1 and Z_2, are connected in parallel, the same voltage V is present across both, and the total current is given by

$$i = i_1 + i_2 = (V/Z_1) + (V/Z_2),$$

so that the equivalent impedance is

$$\frac{V}{i} = Z = \frac{Z_1 Z_2}{Z_1 + Z_2}. \tag{A.10}$$

Equations (A.9) and (A.10) demonstrate that calculations involving complex impedances can be carried out the same way as those with ohmic resistances. When we make such calculations, the basic rules of algebra can be used, but we must keep in mind the identities $j \cdot j = -1$, $-j \cdot j = 1$, $-j(-j) = -1$, $1/j = -j$. For example, if $Z_1 = R_1 + jX_1$, and $Z_2 = R_2 + jX_2$, we have

$$Z_1 + Z_2 = (R_1 + R_2) + j(X_1 + X_2), \tag{A.11}$$

$$Z_1 Z_2 = (R_1 R_2 - X_1 X_2) + j(X_1 R_2 + X_2 R_1), \tag{A.12}$$

$$\frac{Z_1}{Z_2} = \frac{1}{R_2^2 + X_2^2} [(R_1 R_2 + X_1 X_2) + j(X_1 R_2 - X_2 R_1)]. \tag{A.13}$$

The calculations can often be simplified a great deal by use of the following rules:

$$|Z_1 Z_2| = |Z_1| |Z_2|, \quad \arg(Z_1 Z_2) = \arg Z_1 + \arg Z_2; \tag{A.14}$$

$$\left|\frac{Z_1}{Z_2}\right| = \frac{|Z_1|}{|Z_2|}, \quad \arg\left(\frac{Z_1}{Z_2}\right) = \arg Z_1 - \arg Z_2. \tag{A.15}$$

These rules can easily be derived from (A.11) through (A.13).

EXAMPLE. The impedance of a circuit consisting of an inductance L, a condenser C, and a resistance R in series is

$$Z = R + j(\omega L - 1/\omega C). \tag{A.16}$$

If an ac-current with amplitude i_o and phase $\phi = 0$ is sent through the circuit in Fig. A.1, a voltage with amplitude

$$V_o = |V| = |Z_i| = |Z|i_o = i_o\sqrt{R^2 + (\omega L - 1/\omega C)^2}$$

results between the terminals, making a phase angle

$$\arg V = \arg Z + \arg i_o = \arg Z = \tan^{-1}\frac{\omega L - (1/\omega C)}{R} \qquad \text{(A.17)}$$

with the current.

TYPICAL TUBE AND TRANSISTOR CHARACTERISTICS

Since it is clearly impossible to attempt any complete listing of the enormous variety of tubes and transistors currently available, we present here only a small cross section of commonly used types that are typical of current components.

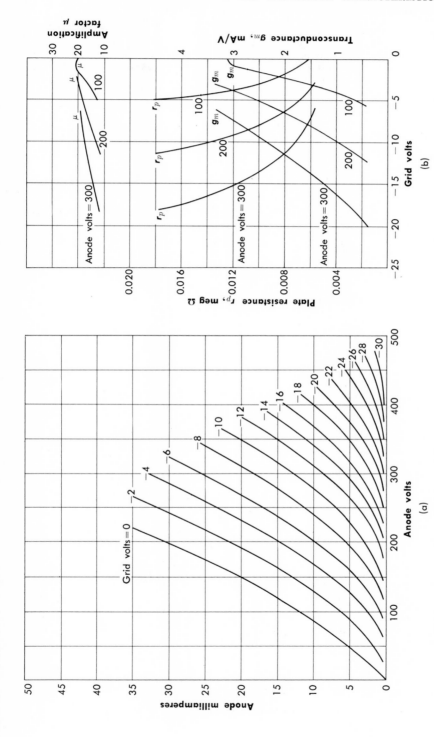

FIG. B.1. 12AU7A double triode. This is a medium-gain tube ($\mu \approx 17$) of rugged construction, excellent for general-purpose use in a wide variety of applications. (a) Typical anode characteristics (each unit), (b) variation of tube parameters with grid and anode voltages. (Courtesy RCA.)

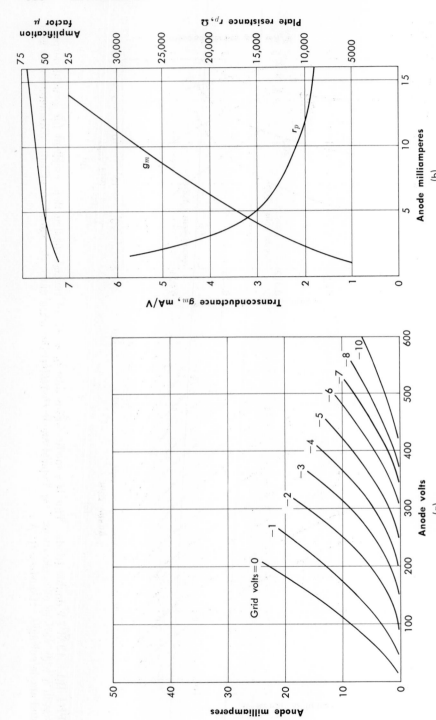

FIG. B.2. 12AT7 double triode. This is a high-gain tube ($\mu \approx 62$), less linear than the 12AU7 but useful in both small-signal amplifiers and bistable circuits. (a) Anode characteristics (each unit), (b) variation of tube parameters with anode current. (Courtesy RCA.)

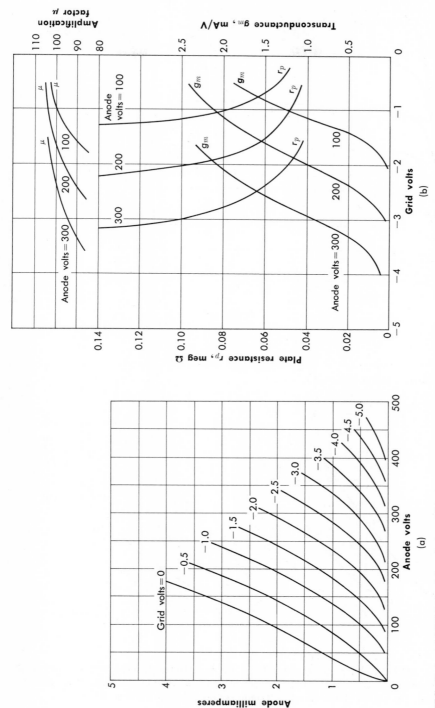

FIG. B.3. 12AX7A double triode. This is an extremely high-gain tube ($\mu \approx 100$) with low equivalent noise and hum, particularly suited for small-signal amplifiers. (a) Anode characteristics (each unit), (b) variation of tube parameters with grid and anode voltages. (Courtesy RCA.)

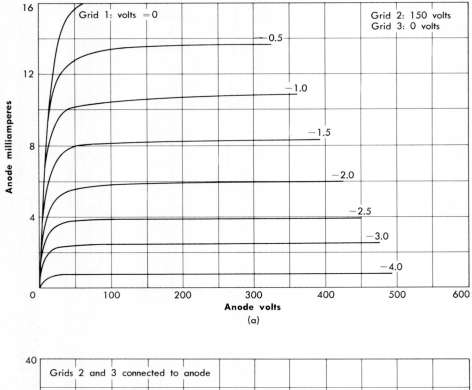

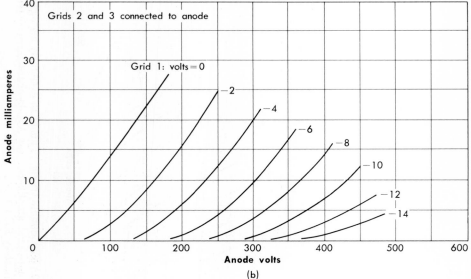

FIG. B.4. 6AU6A sharp-cutoff pentode. This is a useful general-purpose tube, particularly intended for high-frequency applications. (a) Anode characteristics, pentode connection, (b) anode characteristics, triode connection. (Courtesy RCA.)

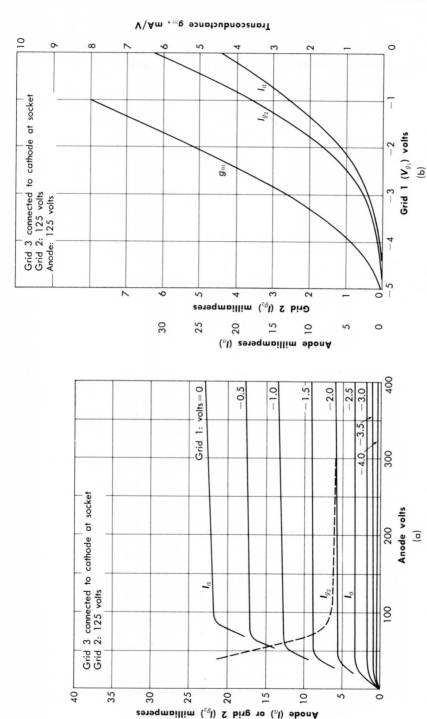

FIG. B.5. 6CB6A sharp-cutoff pentode. This is a pentode of exceptionally high transconductance combined with low capacitance for high-frequency applications. (a) Anode characteristics, (b) variation of transconductance, anode and screen current, with control-grid voltage. (Courtesy RCA.)

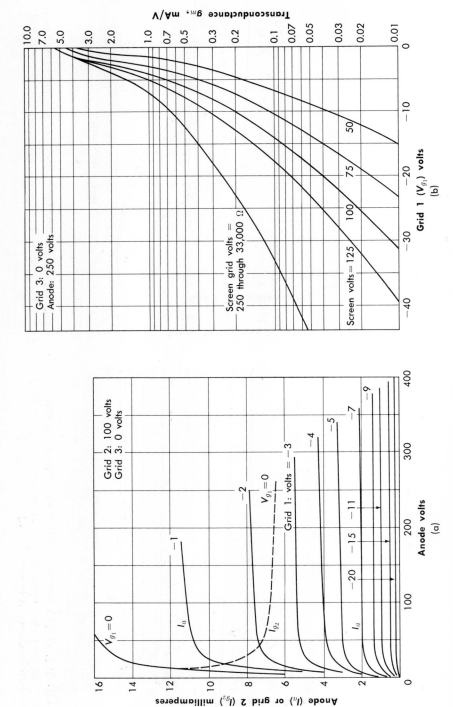

FIG. B.6. 6BA6 remote-cutoff pentode. This tube is extremely useful in variable-gain control circuits. (a) Anode characteristics, (b) variation of transconductance with control-grid voltage. (Courtesy RCA.)

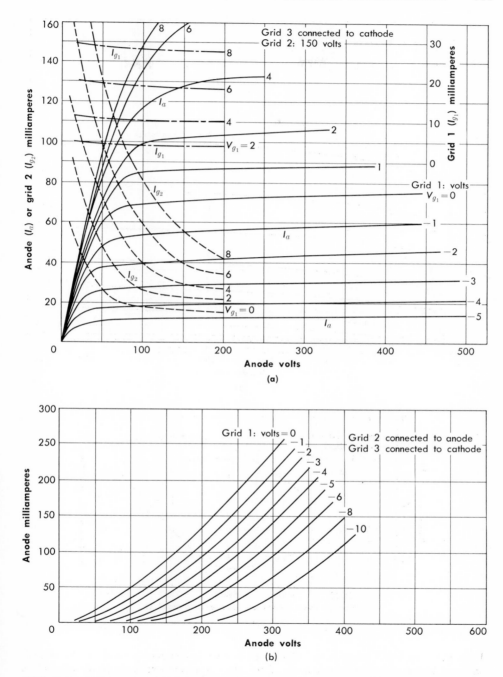

FIG. B.7. 6CL6 power pentode. This is a miniature tube, providing a 2.8-W output, often used in video-amplifier circuits. (a) Anode characteristics, pentode connection, (b) anode characteristics, triode connection. (Courtesy RCA.)

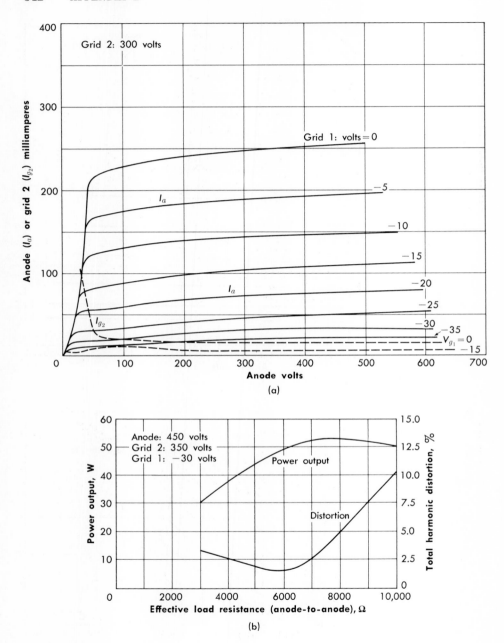

FIG. B.8. 6L6-GC beam-power tube. This tube is frequently used in the output stage of high-power audio amplifiers. Two tubes in a push-pull circuit operated class AB₁ can deliver 55 W of signal-output power with only 1.8% total harmonic distortion. (a) Anode characteristics, (b) power output and distortion as a function of load for push-pull class AB₁ connection, with 42.5 V (rms) audio input signal between the two control grids. (Courtesy RCA.)

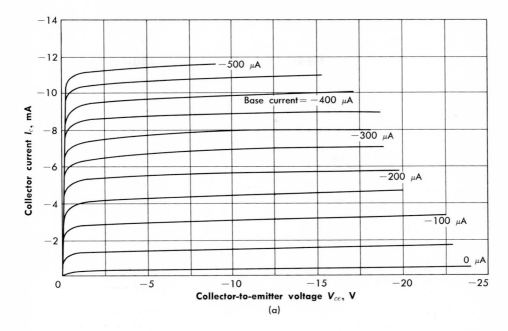

(a)

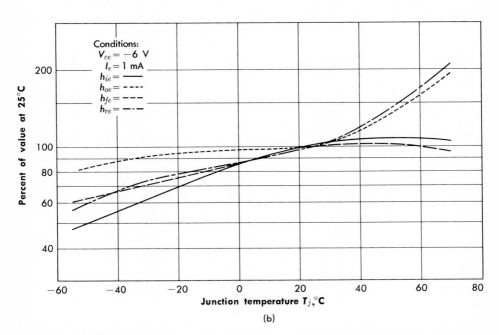

(b)

FIG. B.9. 2N464 transistor. This is a germanium pnp-alloy junction transistor intended for audio-frequency applications. (a) Collector characteristics, (b) variation of common emitter h-parameters with junction temperature.   (Courtesy Raytheon Company.)

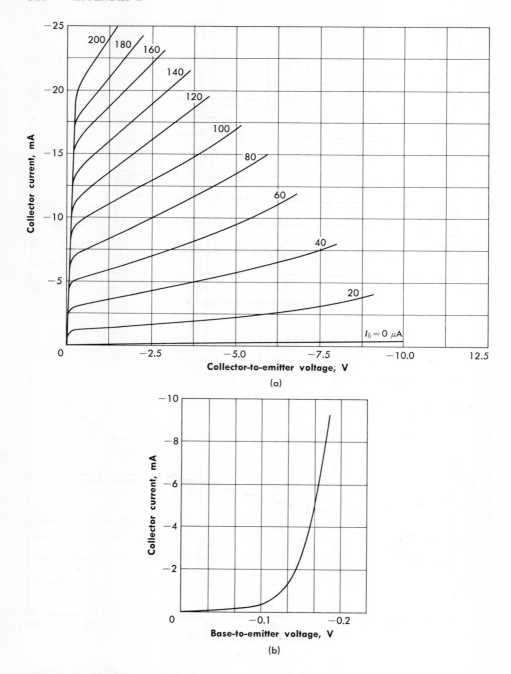

FIG. B.10.   2N417 transistor.   This germanium pnp-alloy-junction transistor is particularly intended for high-frequency use, up to 15 Mcps.   (a) Collector characteristics, (b) transfer characteristics (Courtesy Raytheon Company).

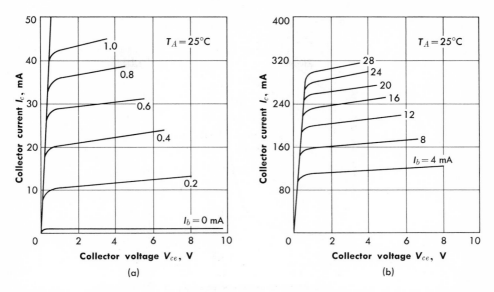

FIG. B.11. 2N438A transistor. This germanium npn-alloy junction transistor is intended for computer and switching applications. (a) Low-current collector characteristics, (b) high-current collector characteristics. (Courtesy Raytheon Company.)

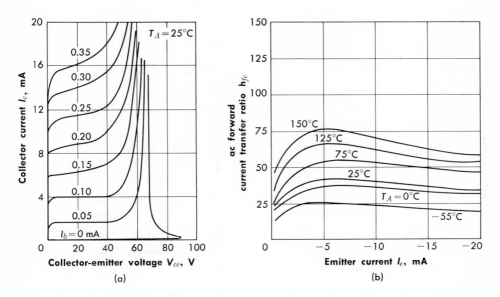

FIG. B.12. 2N1564 transistor. This is a diffused-silicon mesa transistor for general-purpose use with 600-mW dissipation and a maximum operating temperature of 175°C. (a) Collector characteristics, (b) forward-current transfer ratio as a function of emitter current and ambient temperature (T_A). (Courtesy Texas Instruments, Inc.)

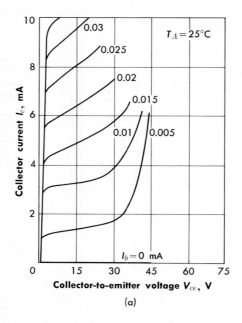

(a)

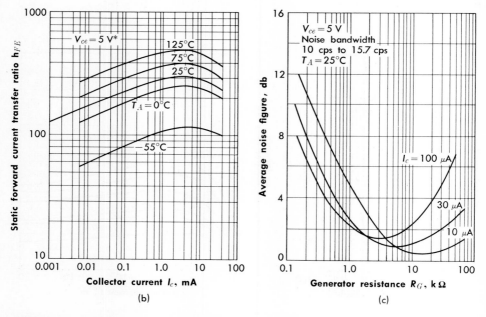

(b)   (c)

FIG. B.13. 2N930 transistor. This is a planar silicon transistor of exceptionally high gain and low noise figure for use in small-signal amplifier circuits. (a) Collector characteristics, (b) forward-current transfer ratio as a function of collector current and ambient temperature, (c) average noise figure as a function of generator resistance. (Courtesy Texas Instruments, Inc.)

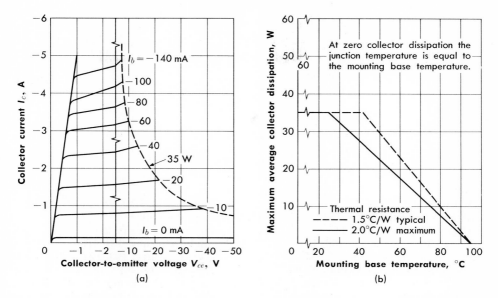

FIG. B.14. 2N297A transistor. This is a germanium pnp-alloy junction power transistor with 35 W maximum dissipation. (a) Collector characteristics, (b) power derating as a function of temperature. (Courtesy Bendix Corporation.)

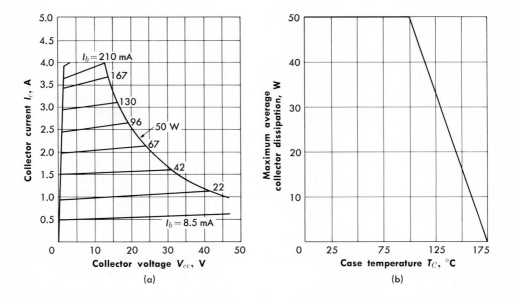

FIG. B.15. 2N1070 transistor. This is a silicon-diffused mesa npn-power transistor, useful in a wide variety of amplifier and switching applications. (a) Collector characteristics, (b) power derating as a function of temperature. (Courtesy Bendix Corporation.)

ABCDE69876